REGIONS OF THE BRITISH ISLES

EDITED BY W. G. EAST M.A.

NORTH ENGLAND

LIST OF TITLES

REGIONS OF THE BRITISH ISLES

EDITED BY W. G. EAST M.A.

NORTH ENGLAND

by

A. E. SMAILES M.A.

Professor of Geography
in the University of London

THOMAS NELSON AND SONS LTD

LONDON AND EDINBURGH

THOMAS NELSON AND SONS LTD
Parkside Works Edinburgh 9
36 Park Street London W1
312 Flinders Street Melbourne C1

302–304 Barclays Bank Building
Commissioner and Kruis Streets
Johannesburg

THOMAS NELSON AND SONS (CANADA) LTD
91–93 Wellington Street West   Toronto 1

THOMAS NELSON AND SONS
19 East 47th Street New York 17

SOCIÉTÉ FRANÇAISE D'ÉDITIONS NELSON
97 rue Monge Paris 5

———

First published 1960

Printed in Great Britain by Thomas Nelson and Sons Ltd, Edinburgh

TO MY WIFE
who has shared so much of the experience
of the North Country
from which this book springs
and who has contributed in so many ways
to make possible its preparation

ACKNOWLEDGMENTS

The author especially wishes to record his gratitude for the invaluable assistance rendered by Miss Eileen Harvey in the task of drafting the maps that illustrate this book. Her patience and skilled judgment have contributed greatly to ease the author's task.

Dr J. B. Sissons has kindly made available an unpublished map to illustrate his views on the origin of the river system of North England, and the author is obliged to his friends Dr A. Raistrick and Dr H. Thorpe for allowing him to use the photographs that appear as Plates 6 and 24, and to the Corporation of the City of Newcastle for permission to reproduce the old print of Newcastle as it was in the late-sixteenth century.

The author wishes to acknowledge the kindness of the following in giving permission for the reproduction of illustrations : Aerofilms Ltd. (Plates 12, 19, 20, 25, 26, 27, 28, 34, 40) ; Aero Pictorial Ltd. (Plate 14) ; Air Ministry (Plates 37, 38) ; British Travel and Holidays Association (Plates 1, 3, 29) ; Central Office of Information (Plates 9, 17) ; the Curator in Aerial Photography, University of Cambridge (Plates 21, 22) ; Fairey Air Surveys (Plate 39) ; The Forestry Commission (Plate 4) ; *The Guardian* (Plate 36) ; Mr J. Hardman, Kendal (Plates 15, 16) ; Pictorial Press (Plate 42) ; *The Times* (Plates 2, 7, 10, 11, 13, 30, 33, 41).

Figure 43 is reproduced from the Ordnance Survey Six Inches to One Mile Map of Durham (Sheet NZ 23 S.E.) ; Figure 18 is based upon the Ordnance Survey Map of Roman Britain. This is with the sanction of the Controller of H.M. Stationery Office. Crown Copyright reserved.

CONTENTS

vii

LIST OF ILLUSTRATIONS

FIGURES

PLATES

The Plates will be found between pages 316 *and* 317

Plates 44, 45, and 46 are reproduced from the invaluable collection of town plans included in Ellis' *British Atlas* (1810)

COLOUR MAP

A full-colour map of North England will be found at the end of the book, arranged to open out so that it can be consulted simultaneously with the text

CHAPTER 1

INTRODUCTION

To a Northumbrian or Cumbrian it often seems that his southern compatriots tend to ignore or forget the presence of that part of England lying between Scotland and the counties of Yorkshire and Lancashire, which so many southerners identify with the north of England. Yet the traveller journeying north on leaving Yorkshire must still traverse nearly one hundred miles before he crosses the Border into Scotland. It is the distinctiveness of this tract of country, covering considerably more than five thousand square miles, that this book sets out to portray and analyse. North England, as here considered, is roughly co-extensive with the four northernmost counties of England, but more satisfactory geographical limits than the county boundaries have been adopted.

The main lowland tract of England narrows northwards in the vale of York, and it becomes constricted around Northallerton into a narrow gateway between the North York Moors and the Pennines (see folded map within back cover). Farther north is a lowland annexe along the northeast coast. The main south–north route on the east side of Britain passes through the Northallerton gate and approaches the Tees to traverse this coastal lowland. The northernmost parts of Yorkshire, in Cleveland and Teesdale, must be considered, especially in their modern context, along with those parts of Teesdale and the vale of Tees that lie north of the river in Durham, as essentially part of northeast England. On the other hand, beyond the narrowing of the coastal lowland that takes place in north Northumberland, where the hills come close to the sea by Lindisfarne, the extreme north of the county towards the Tweed, and the bounds of Berwick beyond that river, are inseparable from the rest of the Merse, or lower Tweed basin. A relic of the failure of the Scots to oust English lordship completely from the soil of Scotland during the Middle Ages, Berwick, as part of England, is an anachronism. It is so intimately associated, as urban centre, with the appropriately named Scottish county of Berwickshire that even a Northumbrian author has no hesitation in assigning it to a Scottish volume of the series. For geographical treatment it properly belongs there.

From the Cheviot westwards the Border is a satisfactory geographical boundary although, as the head of Solway is reached, its lack of definition in the fringing lowland is reflected by the long existence of debatable territory (threapland). The actual frontier there was not settled till 1552, when it was demarcated by an artificial mound, the Scots Dyke (Fig. 21).

The southern part of Westmorland, comprising the ancient Barony of Kendal, is drained south to Morecambe Bay, and is separated from the nucleus of the barony of Westmorland, at the head of the vale of Eden, by the high moorlands of Shap and Crosby Ravensworth. It is clearly oriented southwards and has closer ties with Lancashire than with North England. The same applies to the southernmost part of Cumberland, in the Millom district along the west coast adjacent to the coastal fringe of Furness. The Lake District, however, in spite of its divergent orientations and the separation of its southern and northern parts along the major transverse watershed of northern England, here parting Solway drainage from that to Morecambe Bay, is so incontestably a unit by reason of its distinctive physical characteristics, reflected in its human development and destiny, that it must be treated as such. For regional treatment in the final chapter of this volume the Lake District is included as a whole.

North England includes between two and three-quarters and three million inhabitants, about 6 per cent of the population of Great Britain on a somewhat higher proportion of its area. Within its bounds are some of the most heavily urbanised parts of the country, including on Tyneside one of the seven major conurbations, as well as some of the most extensive tracts of deserted waste (Fig. 13). The great majority of its inhabitants live in the intensely developed industrial area of the Northeast Coast, but two-fifths of its area is uninhabited moorland, and between these extremes are large areas of thinly settled rural countryside. Its coasts and hills, its farmlands and fells, its coalfields and cities exemplify a great many of the elements that compose the richly variegated surface of Britain. Naturally some features that assume major importance in certain parts of the country are missing. Their absence, no less than the presence of a particular combination of others, contributes to the unique character of the north country.

North England lies in Highland Britain, almost entirely northwest of that major physical boundary, often roughly referred to as the Tees-Exe line, which separates the northwestern, and predominantly highland, portion of the island, developed on ancient rocks, from Lowland Britain, with its younger, softer rocks, to the southeast in England. Rocks younger than Carboniferous are present only in limited areas, and both chalk and Tertiary formations are completely unrepresented. In this part of Highland Britain, however, the North Sea and the Irish Sea approach within eighty miles of each other. The isthmian nature of North England is as fundamental a fact of its geography as is the extent and prominence of its highland backbone. The coastal lowlands of the east side are a northward extension of the farmlands of lowland England, beyond the Northallerton gate ; those of the west, bordering the Solway Firth and extending up the vale of Eden, are an outlying tract, detached from the farmlands farther south. Yet areas of lowland are never very extensive between the coastline and the framing hills. Over much of North England the association of lowland and highland is intimate indeed, and the cultivated lands are closely integrated in farming organisation with extensive moorlands close by. What is locally known as ' dale ' is a major feature of the physical and human geography of North England. Outside the dales, the farmlands for the most part are essentially coastal lowlands, and the coal and iron-ore fields that have provided the foundations of the commercial and industrial development are, in a peculiar degree, seaboard in their distribution. The precocious rise of coal mining and the coal trade depended above all upon this geographical fact, and the modern seats of commerce and industry are two coastal areas— the Northeast Coast and West Cumberland. With rare exceptions the cities of North England are ports.

An appreciation of the most profound differences in the human geography of Great Britain requires recognition not only of the well-known distinction between highland and lowland theatres of action but also, hardly if any less important, of those between western and eastern fields of colonisation by the immigrants who came across the sea to these islands in successive waves during the three millennia that followed from about 1800 B.C.

North England presents a double front, along its Irish and North Sea shores, and its highland backbone emphasises the contrasts of orientation between west and east sides, as it does those of climate. From the early phases of human colonisation, before the Middle Ages, these contrasts have left abiding social differences, over and above obvious ones in place-names and dialects. The east became more Anglian, whereas the west remained more strongly British till it was infused with Norse people and culture. Because of these primary differences of peopling and the enduring significance of the dichotomy of orientation, the counties of Cumberland and Westmorland group naturally over against Northumberland and Durham.

Deep-rooted and real as are the differences between the western and eastern sides of North England, nevertheless it is easy to exaggerate them at the expense of appreciating the distinctiveness of the whole area as compared with the rest of the country. The coastal lowlands on opposite sides of North England are in close proximity, and the intervening highland country is penetrated by a lowland passage, the

3

Tyne Corridor, as well as by the easy saddle of Stainmore farther south. The importance of the close approach of the west and east coasts, at a point where a gateway through the highland barrier facilitates contact, was given signal recognition by the Romans when they established the northern frontier of their empire along the wall that Hadrian built between Tyne and Solway. It is also a key factor in the situations of both Carlisle and Newcastle. It has always fostered the movement of people across the country. Aided by the improvement of communications through the Tyne Corridor and also over Stainmore, the modern economic development of the Northeast Coast, with the concentration of more than two million people there, has greatly strengthened the association of northwest England with the northeast, creating new forms of interdependence.

The metropolitan functions of Newcastle in the northeast have been greatly enhanced by remoteness from London and other great cities. If the northwest has experienced metropolitan integration to a less degree, so that Carlisle is left to discharge more limited services in the absence of a greater city, it is also the case that the northwest looks outside its own borders east to Newcastle rather than north or south to cities in Scotland and Lancashire that are still more remote from it.

In North England the absence of a continuous front of contact with the populous areas of England to the south has combined with sheer distance from the main seat of government to preserve a high degree of provincial consciousness. Until quite modern times there was a very considerable measure of administrative independence, if not of unified control. For long the prince-bishops of Durham ruled in their palatinate as sovereign lords ; and, in order to secure the frontier of their kingdom against the Scots, the English kings delegated power to local territorial lords and in the marchlands tolerated much, such as castle building, that they would not brook among vassals in nearer and more secure parts of the realm.

The emergence of the Anglo-Scottish Border to the north of our area can easily lead us to underestimate the affinities of the people of North England with the Scots, affinities which have been emphasised by circumstances of physical geography, as well as of historical development, that are very different from those farther south. The transition zone between England and Scotland lies south of the Border ; it is North England, the marches of England towards Scotland.

The association of what is now Cumberland and Westmorland with southwest Scotland in the Celtic kingdom of Strathclyde was reinforced by the process of Norse settlement around the shores of the Irish Sea. On the east side of the country no less close ties between southeast Scotland and what became Northumberland and Durham were

4

emphasised by differences with the area south of the Tees that arose from the Danish colonisation of Yorkshire.

North of the Tees the rest of the ancient kingdom that emerged from the Anglian colonisation north of the Humber was practically unaffected by Danish settlement. The people between the Tees and Forth share a common ancestry that is still reflected in their speech and customs. Subsequent historical development severed Lothian from Bernicia, and from the eleventh century the Anglo-Scottish frontier in the east became the Tweed. There it has remained, with Berwick, which was alternately held by the English and the Scots between 1174 and 1333, the sole outpost of the English kingdom. But the Tees and not the Tweed is still the major dialect boundary.

Nor must we overlook the fact that the immigrants who have flocked into the industrial areas of North England, especially during the nineteenth century, included, in addition to those from the rural districts of North England itself, particularly large contingents from Scotland and Ireland. The modern currents of migration that have chiefly affected North England have flowed southwards and eastwards, far outbalancing northward movement from the more southerly parts of Britain. It is understandable, therefore, that the inhabitants of North England should lay claim to the virtues, if not admit to the weaknesses, of both Scots and English. Nor is it surprising that they should take advantage of their geographical position to celebrate the feasts of both Christmas and Hogmanay with a nice impartiality.

Hardly less striking than the old-established, persisting contrast between the tamed countryside of farms in the lowlands and valleys and the wilderness of the framing hills is the antithesis that has emerged in North England between the areas which have been transformed by mining and industrial activity and those which have remained more or less rural.

Long before the widespread modern industrialisation of Britain that has taken place during the last two centuries there were industrial regions in North England. Parts of it were among the first tracts to be rendered geographically distinctive by industrial activity. The early industrial landscapes have subsequently been greatly extended and the industrial imprint has been heavily intensified; but, outside the areas so affected, there remain in North England some of the most profoundly rural and intact parts of the traditional British countryside. While it cannot be denied that industry and urbanisation have defaced extensive areas, the scarred face of these parts of North England has a peculiar interest for the geographer. It is the deeply lined countenance of a country grown old in a rich experience of technological adventure.

First on Tyneside, later but still early on the Wear and the coast of west Cumberland, were some of the earliest scenes of considerable coal-mining enterprise, as well as of large-scale shipment of coal. These areas, too, were the earliest seats of coal-using industry, and as such among the archetypes of large-scale, capitalist, and geographically concentrated industrial organisation. North England was the home of railways, accessories of the coal trade that developed from the earlier wagonways. In other respects also it has played an historic rôle in the development of our modern industrial civilisation, and it abounds in sites illustrious in the annals of technology. The landscape itself is a museum rich in residual features that tell the story of the advance of mining and transport techniques. Yet North England contains much more than 'the fossil shells of nineteenth-century industry'. Now, in addition to such major manifestations of twentieth-century heavy industry as those established by Imperial Chemical Industries on both sides of the Tees estuary, the reactors that herald a new industrial age of applied nuclear power came into operation in 1956 at Calder Hall on the west coast of Cumberland (Pl. 36).

North England is rich, too, in ancient monuments, especially of a military character, which have endured when most contemporary buildings have crumbled and disappeared. Hadrian's Wall (Pl. 17), that most imposing of the relics in Britain that serve to remind us of the power and material achievement of ancient Rome, and the numerous remains of fortified buildings that sprang up during the long centuries of warfare and lawlessness in the Border country, especially have long stimulated local archaeological and antiquarian studies, and the journals of two local archaeological societies go far back into last century and provide a great wealth of recorded information.

As well as compelling the attention of the student of industrial geography, North England offers to the urban geographer illuminating examples. The grandeur of the ancient city of Durham, where noble architecture crowns a magnificent site to provide an epitome of the medieval cathedral and fortress city (Pl. 40), needs no advertisement. Carlisle also has special interest, however, as exemplifying the English county town through all the typical phases of its development, while Newcastle expresses the continuous evolution of a medieval fortress city and port, situated like London at the lowest bridge of a tidal estuary, into the nerve-centre of a great industrial agglomeration and capital of a far-flung province. In the process its nuclear area experienced a comprehensive replanning treatment that makes it unique. And if North England displays in Newcastle one of the very few old-established British cities where the heart of the city is not almost entirely chance-grown, it can also provide some of the earliest British examples of towns designed and created in conformity

with town-planning principles.   They were products of the needs of
the early coal trade—Whitehaven (Pl. 27) and later Maryport in west
Cumberland ; on the northeast coast Middlesbrough and Seaham
Harbour, which enjoy the distinction of being the first towns to owe
their existence to railways.   West Hartlepool followed, and latterly
Peterlee and Aycliffe are coming into being as two of the post-war
New Towns (Fig. 41).

If the industrial landscapes and townscapes of North England must
seem of special interest to some geographers, the fascination of this
part of the country is not by any means limited to those students of
sequent occupance whose analytical zest is not diminished by aesthetic
sensitivity.   For those who show greater enthusiasm for studying the
face of the earth as God made it and for those more romantic students
of the humanised landscape who, in their attachment to the countryside
in its traditional guise, shun the uglier or more heavily built-up areas,
North England has hardly less to offer.   Within its bounds are some
of the most extensive remaining tracts both of empty hill country and
of rural countryside, long occupied and comparatively unmodified
during the past hundred years.

North England has not altogether escaped the excrescences of the
automobile age, but its disfigurements are chiefly the old and somewhat
localised scars of Carboniferous capitalism rather than the general rash
of modern Subtopia.   Outside its industrial areas the countryside of
North England is as yet comparatively uncluttered.   Parts of its coastline rank among the finest stretches of the English coast that still
remain uncommercialised.   In the farmlands of its lowlands and dales
the traditional texture, and even fabric, of settlement, with buildings
of local stone still predominant, persist.   The need for preserving the
wild hill country as a national heritage has fortunately been recognised
before it is too late, and a large proportion of North England lies within
the areas designated as National Parks (Fig. 13).   But the destiny of
the northern hills is not seen purely in terms of maintaining their
present aspect.   Great tracts of Border fells, as well as scheduled
portions of the Lake District, are being reclothed with forest.   Here
the problems, aesthetic and social as well as economic, that are associated
in a large-scale experiment in planning land which is sub-marginal for
farming are being confronted.

Whether your main geographical interest is physical or social,
whether it lies in the past or in the present, in the countryside or in
towns, North England offers a rewarding field of study, and it is hoped
that readers will find this book both a stimulus to visit and explore the
country with which it deals and a guide to understanding the scene
presented there.

Finally, while it has seemed both logical and essential that a study in regional geography should begin with a description of the physical setting as the stage of human action, it is suggested that the reader who is quite unfamiliar with geological and geomorphological terms may prefer to begin with Chapter IV. Although every effort has been made to present clearly the facts of structure and of the development of the surface features, the scientific language proper to these disciplines cannot be avoided in a work that makes any claim upon the attention of the trained geographer. The rest of the book, it is hoped, is less difficult reading for those not equipped with a specialist vocabulary.

CHAPTER 2

THE STRUCTURAL BASIS OF NORTH ENGLAND

ROCKS of Carboniferous age outcrop over the greater part of the area
of North England, although they are extensively concealed by an
irregular cover of glacial and other superficial deposits. Younger rocks
are now restricted to three areas (Fig. 1). The most extensive of these
is in the southeast, where, beyond an irregular line running from the
mouth of the Tyne to the Tees below Barnard Castle and so into Yorkshire, the Carboniferous rocks pass under an uninterrupted succession
of Permian, Triassic, and Jurassic rocks, the youngest representatives
of which cap the plateaux of the North York Moors. Triassic rocks also
form the rock floor of the lowlands at the head of the Solway round
Carlisle, and extend southeastwards up the vale of Eden between the
Pennine and Lake District highlands to Kirkby Stephen. Finally, a
narrow fringe of Triassic rocks flanks the western margin of the Lake
District highlands along the coast south of Whitehaven.

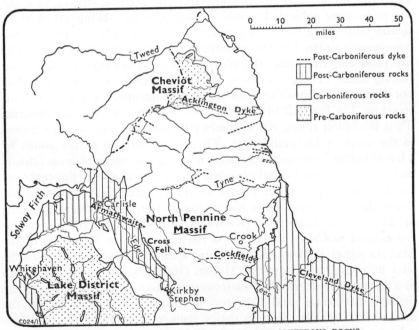

Fig. 1 NORTH ENGLAND : EXTENT OF CARBONIFEROUS ROCKS.

9

The pre-Carboniferous rocks

Rocks older than the Carboniferous age protrude on the Scottish border in north Northumberland as the Cheviot massif, and over a larger area in the Lake District. The northern Pennines are the site of another pre-Carboniferous massif that has played a profound part in the structural evolution of North England. The Carboniferous cover here is relatively thin and the pre-Carboniferous basis is exposed below Cross Fell along part of the Pennine escarpment. It reappears to the east over a small area in upper Teesdale and has been proved more than 2,000 feet below sea level in a boring at Crook in the Durham coalfield.

That pre-Carboniferous rocks are now exposed over a considerable area as the core of the Lake District (Fig. 2) is the result of the intense denudation which followed the dome-like uplift of this area. The old rocks are completely surrounded by a girdle of Carboniferous sediments except to the southwest along the coast from St Bees Head southwards. Here, still younger Triassic rocks overlap directly on the flanks of the massif. The ancient rocks of the Lake District show an ENE-WSW 'Caledonian' grain imparted to them by the intense folding of early Palaeozoic times. The violent contortion and extreme stresses to which the rocks were subjected result in their outcrops being streaked by shatter belts along which dislocations have taken place. The intense compression suffered by the constituent rocks has also been responsible for producing in some the cleavage that makes them valuable for roofing slates. The main axis of the Caledonian folding, however, does not correspond in position with the maximum uplift of the later dome structure, but lies well to the north of the centre of the Lake District. Thus the oldest rocks, chiefly slates (the Skiddaw Series) are exposed to the north of Derwentwater. They are succeeded to the south by a broad belt of heterogeneous volcanic rocks, consisting of lavas (chiefly andesitic), ashes, and conglomerates, which extend across the centre of the Lake District and are known as the Borrowdale Volcanic Series. Their thickness amounts to about 10,000 feet, and reflects the scale of the volcanic activity of Ordovician times. These rocks are also represented in Caldbeck Fells as a narrow strip that lies north of the Skiddaw Slates, while the latter in turn are again exposed farther south-west in a small area north of Millom (Black Combe). Finally, south of a great tear-fault, which runs from northeast to southwest from Shap through Ambleside and Coniston to Broughton-in-Furness at the head of Duddon Bay, Silurian shales, flags (mudstones), and grits over-ride the Ordovician volcanic rocks to form the southern part of the

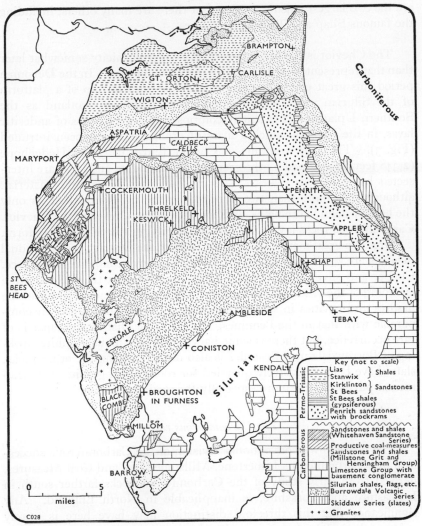

Fig. 2   NORTHWEST ENGLAND : GEOLOGY.

Lake District within its frame of Carboniferous rocks. The fault junction is marked by a narrow strip of distinctive rocks, containing calcareous beds, the Coniston and Ashgill Limestones.

The intense earth-movements that the ancient rocks of the Lake District have suffered were accompanied by igneous intrusion. Igneous injections are not only widespread and extraordinarily varied both in form and rock-type, but occupy extensive areas, especially in the west, where the Ennerdale granophyre and the Eskdale granite occur. These are the two largest igneous masses, but there are many others, including the famous Shap and Threlkeld granites.

The Cheviot is the product of a phase of vulcanicity somewhat later than that represented in the rocks of the Lake District. In the Devonian period this great pile of volcanic rocks was built on top of a platform of the Silurian rocks, which extend over southern Scotland as the Southern Uplands. It is chiefly composed of a great mass of andesitic lavas, in the heart of which a mass of granite has later been intruded (Fig. 3). The twin summits of Cheviot (2,676 feet) and Hedgehope (2,348 feet) are formed by the granite. Both granite and lavas are intersected by numerous dykes. The present mass of volcanic material, although it is more than two hundred square miles in extent, is only the heavily denuded remains, and, a few miles southwest of the Cheviot, Carboniferous rocks are found directly overlying the Silurian platform.

Ores of a great many metals occur in the Lake District, but individual deposits are small and few have ever been of any economic importance. Copper and silver-lead attracted early attention, but their exploitation is a thing of the past, and modern working of the gangue materials of the fissures and cavities in which the metals occurred has not been comparable with that in the Pennines. In the Lake District fluorspar is of rare occurrence, but there is some barytes. The famous graphite working of Borrowdale near Seatoller is also dead. Among the other rocks, slates have been extensively quarried for roofing and granites for ornamental purposes, and more especially for road material.

The Carboniferous rocks

The well-known conventional division of the Carboniferous succession into Carboniferous Limestone, Millstone Grit, and Coal Measures, derived from early study of the Carboniferous rocks farther south in Lancashire and Yorkshire, is inapplicable in North England. Any significance that this threefold distinction may have here is purely palaeontological, and so far as the terms suggest a description of the actual rock-type their use can be quite misleading. A more realistic conception is obtained by considering the Carboniferous rocks as a continuous succession of marine sediments, comprising limestones, sandstones, and shales, with deep-sea conditions, reflected by limestones, represented in some of the earlier phases but decreasingly evident later, whereas shallow water and even deltaic conditions, the latter represented by coal seams and underlying fireclays, assume increasing importance. The significant distinction is thus between the lower Carboniferous rocks, which contain important, albeit thin, limestone beds but only

12

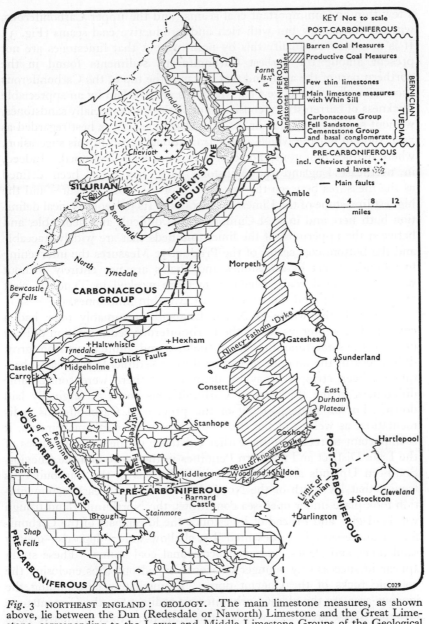

KEY Not to scale

POST-CARBONIFEROUS

Barren Coal Measures

Productive Coal Measures

Few thin limestones

Main limestone measures
with Whin Sill

Carbonaceous Group
Fell Sandstone
Cementstone Group
and basal conglomerate

PRE-CARBONIFEROUS
incl. Cheviot granite and lavas

— Main faults

0   4   8   12
miles

Fig. 3 NORTHEAST ENGLAND : GEOLOGY. The main limestone measures, as shown above, lie between the Dun (Redesdale or Naworth) Limestone and the Great Limestone, corresponding to the Lower and Middle Limestone Groups of the Geological Survey. Above the Great Limestone are only a few thin limestones. The main productive coal measures comprise about 900 feet of strata between the Brockwell and High Main (Shield Row) seams. For post-Carboniferous dykes see Figure 1.

13

a few thin and unimportant coal seams, and the upper Carboniferous, without limestones but with rich and productive coal seams (Fig. 3). It is necessary to qualify this by pointing out that limestones are not present among the earliest Carboniferous sediments found in the northern part of the area, and that towards the top of the Carboniferous succession the productive Coal Measures are overlain by an appreciable thickness of barren strata, consisting of shales and especially sandstones, without significant coal seams. The Millstone Grit is best regarded as part, though not the whole, of the transitional series in this succession, where neither limestones nor coal seams are well developed. Indeed, in northeast England the Millstone Grit has often been defined as the measures between the lowest coal of the Coal Measures and the highest limestone of the Limestone Groups. Its palaeontological defini- tion both here and in west Cumberland is difficult and debatable, and between the uppermost of the limestone beds that are widely traceable and the bottom coal seams of the Productive Measures the intervening five hundred feet of sandstones and shales are not entirely without weakly developed coals, which in fact are worked in Tynedale west of the coalfield ; and there are at least two thin limestones.

Although the whole of North England presumably once had a cover of Carboniferous rocks, the Carboniferous sedimentation did not begin at the same time throughout the area and, quite apart from great differences in the amount of Carboniferous sediments that has subse- quently been stripped away by denudation, there were considerable differences in the thickness of Carboniferous rocks as originally laid down. For an understanding of the process of Carboniferous sedi- mentation, as well as of the effects of subsequent earth-movements, it is important to recognise the earlier existence of the ancient masses of the Lake District and northern Pennines in the south and the Cheviot- Southern Uplands area to the north. Whereas in the Carboniferous trough that lay south of the North Pennine massif [1] early sedimenta- tion took place under open-sea conditions, the Northumberland trough was land-girt, and instead of limestones the lower part of the Carboni- ferous succession is represented by shallow-water deposits—mainly sandstones and shales, and even occasional coal seams. These strata appear in successively younger crescent-shaped outcrops enclosing the volcanic rocks of the Cheviot dome. Immediately surrounding the igneous area are the oldest Carboniferous sediments—the Cementstone Group. These are shales, which contain the numerous distinctive beds of muddy limestone (cementstone) as well as bands of fine-grained sandstone. Engirdling this belt in turn are the massive coarse sand- stones of the Fell Sandstone Group. The succeeding strata, com-

[1] This term is here preferred to ' Alston Block ', used by Trotter and Hollingworth.

14

prising in Northumberland the Carbonaceous or Scremerston Coal Group, consist of softer sandstones and shales, with several thin seams of coal. These strata are especially thick (more than 2,000 feet), and their outcrop is especially extensive, in the structural trough between the Cheviot dome and the minor Bewcastle dome to the southwest, that is in the Border dales of the upper North Tyne and Rede. Altogether, the lower Carboniferous succession, below the Limestone Groups, may exceed 6,000 feet of strata that are quite unrepresented south of the Tyne valley in the northern Pennines.

Throughout this early period of Carboniferous sedimentation the Lake District and North Pennine area was still a landmass, and even after its subsequent submergence much less deposition took place on it than farther north. Covering the North Pennine massif, and sweeping across Northumberland in great arcs round the outcrops of the earlier Carboniferous rocks, these later deposits of the lower Carboniferous seas show a clearly marked rhythm of deposition with repetition of the sequence, limestone, shale, sandstone, and coal. This Yoredale (Uredale) sequence is most regularly developed in the Middle Limestone Group between the Oxford and Great Limestones, where all four members of the sequence—limestone, shale, sandstone, and coal—are frequently present, and the cycle comprises from 50 to more than 100 feet of strata. The limestones in particular are massive and constant, and thin coals (seldom over 1 foot thick) are associated with them ; there are also some ironstones. The limestones, although the most constant and easily traced strata, are thin and in the aggregate amount to only a small proportion (10 to 15 per cent) of the total thickness even of the Limestone Groups. The thickest limestone, known as the Great Limestone, which can be traced without difficulty right along its outcrop from the Pennine escarpment to north Northumberland, is at most only about 100 feet thick, and thins northwards to only 25 feet.

This description of the lower Carboniferous succession is broadly applicable to Northumberland and Durham, but there is a good deal of lateral variation in the sediments which, judging from the evidence of fossil content, were laid down contemporaneously. Certainly no detailed lithological sequence can be regarded as applying throughout North England, much less for a still wider area to the north and south. The contemporary lower Carboniferous rocks in Westmorland, on the eastern flanks of the Lake District, where Professor E. J. Garwood worked out the zonal sequence,[1] are predominantly limestones, with a single important sandstone (the Ashfell sandstone) that may represent

[1] E. J. Garwood, ' The Lower Carboniferous succession in NW England ', *Quart. Journ. Geol. Soc.* 68 (1912), 449–586.

the Fell Sandstones of Northumberland.[1] The description of the Carbonaceous or Scremerston Coal Group given above also becomes less appropriate to the southwest, where in Cumberland rocks of this group show a considerably different character. The lower strata, mainly sandstones (Craighill Sandstone Group), are not significantly different from the Fell Sandstone below, while the upper strata include limestones (Birdoswald Limestone Group), and show the Yoredale sequence, a presage of conditions of rhythmic deposition which did not extend to Northumberland until later. The Great Limestone, however, is exceptional because of its extraordinary persistence throughout North England, for it is also the First Limestone of west Cumberland, where the Limestone Series consists in addition of six other limestones lower down, ranging through some 700 feet of strata, with separating shale beds and a sandstone between the Second and Third limestones. Some 50 feet above the Great Limestone in Northumberland, the next limestone bed, the Little Limestone, is accompanied by a coal seam which, although always thin, is perhaps the most continuously developed in Great Britain. There follow another 400 feet of sandstones and shales before the topmost limestone, the Fell Top, which is a thin and variable bed. The thinness and impersistence of the limestones in the Upper Limestone Group (the Hensingham Group of west Cumberland) above the Great Limestone, the development of massive grits, and the more important occurrence of workable coal, herald the more widespread deltaic conditions of upper Carboniferous times. The succeeding strata consist of massive sandstones with intercalated beds of shale and, in an important section, numerous well-developed coal seams. These last, however, are not by any means co-extensive with what are labelled Coal Measures on the Geological Survey maps.

The Carboniferous sedimentation was finally brought to an end by uplift and folding associated with the Hercynian earth-movements. After the long passage of time during which further earth-movements have contributed to the build of North England, the architecture of the Hercynian orogeny is far from clear. It seems certain, however, both that some very ancient elements of the structure acted as units and that their relative vertical displacements were very different from those of later times. Thus there is strong evidence that the North Pennine massif, already a rigid block before Carboniferous sedimentation began, continued to act as such, protecting its Carboniferous cover from much

[1] The lower Carboniferous rocks of Furness and south Cumberland are somewhat similar, the main mass consisting of limestone, which in a recent re-survey of the ironstone field has been subdivided into five groups, overlying basement beds of shale, conglomerates, sandstones, and limestone.

folding, though faulting and igneous intrusion were experienced here as elsewhere. The sediments laid down in the trough to the north, however, were buckled into anticlinal structures in central and north Northumberland and northeast Cumberland, with an intervening trough, while a synclinal area bordered the block along the site of the Tyne valley. The North Pennine block itself was a relatively depressed area compared with the uplifted areas to the north along the Border and to the south, where an axis of uplift ran through the North Riding and Westmorland from Cleveland to St Bees Head. The subsequent long period of denudation has effected the removal of a great thickness of upper Carboniferous rocks from much of the area, and it is to the denudation initiated by the Hercynian uplift that we must attribute the isolation of the coalfields. The present surface of most of North England is developed on lower Carboniferous rocks, but the Coal Measures have been preserved in basin-like structures to the east and west as the coalfields of Northumberland and Durham and west Cumberland.

In north Northumberland the presence of the Cheviot volcanic massif is clearly evident as a control that guided the alignment of the Hercynian structures. Not only is its outline reflected in the successive aureoles of Carboniferous sediments that dip away from it. The rocks between the Cheviot and the coast are also affected by a north–south anticlinal structure (the Holburn anticline), and an *en echelon* system of strike-faulting combined with this is responsible for the repetition and extension of the Fell Sandstone outcrop here. Faulting maintains its conformity with the strike, and it rings the Cheviot dome, the Holburn faulted anticline being followed southwest by the Bolton Fault and then by the important Swindon Fault. The latter, running ENE–WSW, has a downthrow to the north of nearly 2,000 feet.

Away to the southeast the rocks of southeast Northumberland are undisturbed by flexuring and show a remarkably steady southeastward dip. The chief structural complications are a few ENE–WSW faults that include the Ninety Fathom ' Dyke ', which runs inland from Cullercoats on the coast just north of the Tyne, crosses the river line above Newcastle, and so reaches the western margin of the coalfield on the borders of Durham and Northumberland. Near the southern margin of the coalfield another major fault, the Butterknowle ' Dyke ', is downthrown to the south by from 300 to 900 feet. Beyond this fault the Carboniferous rocks are more disturbed by folding and faulting as the anticlinal zone of the North Riding is approached. These faults of the eastern side, in Northumberland and Durham, trending ENE–WSW, contrast with those of the west, where the major faults, affecting for example the west Cumberland coalfield, run NW–SE.

Even more distinct is the major dislocation line of North England, along the great Pennine highland as it towers above the vale of Eden. This is a zone of post-Triassic downwarping, although it almost certainly follows a much more ancient line of dislocation that is at least pre-Permian. At Castle Carrock in the north it intersects the west–east system of faults (the Stublick Faults) that define the northern margin of the massif against the Tyne trough. Here the rocks are downthrown to the north as much as 1,500 feet, and the faulting has been responsible for the preservation of a string of Coal Measure pockets, the largest (six square miles) at Midgeholme west of the South Tyne valley. This fault zone was also emphasised at the time of the later elevation of the massif, for both the Pennine and Stublick faults affect the Triassic rocks.

The evidence points to the Hercynian period as that when the mineralisation of the Carboniferous rocks of the northern Pennines took place. It was associated with the faulting, the minerals finding their way by cracks to the surface Yoredale rocks from two main centres that lay on either side of the Burtreeford disturbance, which runs north–south through upper Weardale. The persistence of the mineralisation eastwards, together with the presence of the pre-Carboniferous platform at relatively slight depth under the Durham coalfield, point to the eastward prolongation of the rigid massif as a buried structure. It may well be that its outlines there are reflected by the horst that lies between the Ninety Fathom and Butterknowle Faults.

The minerals occupy fissures, which are best developed and most suitable for mineralisation in the limestones. The mineralised area (Figs. 61 and 62) is limited to the upper parts of the dales, except for an outlying area in the Tyne Corridor and the more recently discovered productive veins of barytes and witherite in the coalfield in west Durham. Galena is the main ore-constituent of the veins, with an appreciable admixture of silver near the surface, but there are also local occurrences of zinc-blende and spathose iron-ore in workable quantities. The gangue materials show a zonal disposition, an inner zone of fluorspar being surrounded by a zone of barytes that contains sporadic occurrences of witherite. The North Pennine ore-field, which is known to have yielded at least three million tons of lead ore, has been the most productive source of lead in the British Isles, and, since the decline in lead production towards the end of last century, it has yielded important quantities of zinc ore, fluorspar, and barytes.

The intrusion into the Yoredale rocks of a sheet of dolerite, known locally as the Whin Sill, was also connected with the Hercynian disturbances. Its age was long in doubt, but has now been definitely established as late Carboniferous. Its thickness varies from as little as

20 feet to as much as 240 feet, but along its more continuous outcrop in Northumberland it is generally from 80 to 100 feet thick. In the Carboniferous rocks of the northern Pennines it lies among the limestone measures and, with slight but sharp shifts of horizon, it extends across the belt of these rocks from the Tyne gap to the coast in north Northumberland and the Farne Islands (Fig. 3).

The Northumberland and Durham coalfield is a roughly triangular area, situated along the coast between Amble and the Hartlepools, its width increasing southwards to the southern edge, along a line from the Hartlepools to Woodland Fell (Fig. 41). Farther south, owing to the basin structure, Coal Measures are not present, and borings in southeast Durham show the Permian and other overlying strata overlapping on to a buried surface of rocks older than the Coal Measures. Although the Coal Measures as mapped by the Geological Survey show a maximum thickness of over 2,200 feet, some 750 to 900 feet of strata in the lower half of the series include the whole range of about twenty widely worked seams, the lowest and highest being the Brockwell and High Main.

In the broader part of the coalfield south of the river Tyne the outcrop section is confined to the area west of a line from Gateshead to Coxhoe. To the east the productive measures are buried under a considerable thickness of barren strata (amounting to as much as 1,200 feet under the Permian rocks at Sunderland), in which massive sandstones, including those that have long been quarried near Tyneside for grindstones, are predominant. Finally, beyond the irregular escarpment that runs from the mouth of the Tyne to Coxhoe and thence westwards in an arc to Shildon, the Coal Measures are overlain unconformably by the Permian rocks, which attain a maximum thickness of 800 to 900 feet. The principal structure within the coalfield is the synclinal trough (Fig. 35) that runs NW–SE on lower Tyneside, pitching out southwards but still traceable south of Sunderland. East of it the productive measures rise towards the coast, and the upper seams, which are buried near Wallsend and Jarrow, outcrop again near the Northumberland coast. Except in the disturbed area that lies south of the Butterknowle fault, the rocks of the coalfield elsewhere show a steady easterly dip towards this trough.

In the small west Cumberland coalfield (Fig. 4) the Productive Measures comprise about 1,000 feet of strata, but the principal seams range through 400 to 500 feet in the middle, between the Six Quarter and Bannock Band coals, and including the Yard and Main seams, the most important seams of the northern and southern parts respectively.

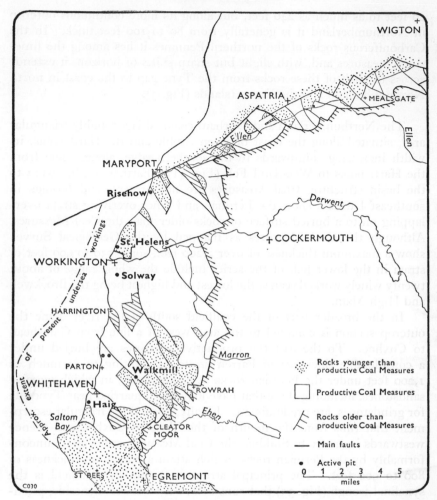

Fig. 4   THE WEST CUMBERLAND COALFIELD.

The measures in which they occur consist mainly of shales, sandstones, and mixed passage rock (caum).   Above the Productive Measures another 600 to 1,000 feet of almost barren strata are represented.   These are mainly sandstones, known as the Whitehaven Sandstone Group. The strata have been very heavily faulted, as well as folded, so that the seams are steeply inclined and severely interrupted.   Much of this faulting is post-Triassic, along NNW-SSE lines, associated with the uplift of the Lake District dome, but some Hercynian faulting along WSW-ENE lines is also represented.   The net result of the criss-cross of fault lines is that the coalfield is divided into a detailed mosaic of fault-bounded compartments, including basins where the barren White-haven Sandstones bury the coal seams and horsts where older rocks form the surface or an incomplete succession of productive measures has been left after denudation. Between Saltom Bay, south of White-haven, and Maryport, the coalfield extends right to the coast, flanking the lower Carboniferous margin of the Lake District highland. Farther northeast it extends as a narrow belt beyond Aspatria, its northern margin bounded by faulting. Whether coal exists under the Solway basin at depth has not been determined. Although the Coal Measures have been stripped away from most of the northwest since Hercynian times, it is not unlikely that a considerable tract of coal may have been preserved and buried under the Triassic infilling of the Solway basin. This is more likely in the western part than east of the position of the main railway line and road.

In both coalfields undersea workings have been pursued for a very considerable time, and the future of the west Cumberland field now depends very largely upon the undersea resources. There is no anthracite or high-quality steam-coal in either coalfield, but whereas the bitumin-ous coal of west Cumberland includes no first-class gas or coking types, the Durham coalfield is exceptionally rich in these. In any particular locality coal from different seams varies considerably, but in addition individual seams show a pronounced regional variation in character. Thus the Hutton seam of Durham (the Low Main seam in Northumber-land) produces in different districts some of the best coking- and gas-coals, and in Northumberland is mined as a steam-coal. Because of locally varying conditions of Carboniferous deposition, individual beds display a marked inconstancy of character, and, although the coal seams are more regular than the sandstones and shales, they vary in thickness and quality and not one of them can be traced throughout the extent of the Northumberland and Durham coalfield. No single seam or other stratum has been proved to be common to the two coal-fields, and attempts to correlate individual beds by their fossil content have not yielded significant results. The recurrence of names descriptive of the local thickness or importance of seams, and the fact that the same seam may be known by a variety of local names, add to the con-fusion of nomenclature.

The distribution of different types of coal that are produced is shown on Figure 41. It will be noticed that from an area in west and southwest Durham, where coking-coal of unrivalled quality occurs, the coal changes in character, becoming softer to the east and less suitable for metallurgical coke though excellent for use by gas works. North of the Tyne in Northumberland the coal loses its coking quality and has been used chiefly for household and steam-raising purposes.

Apart from the coal itself, the fireclays, which are usually present beneath as seat earths to the coal seams, are an important ancillary resource. Also, below the productive measures, on the western fringe of the Durham coalfield, important beds of ganister, sandstones of fine grain and low alkali content, have been extensively worked for refractory materials.

Neither coalfield has ever been important for clayband or blackband iron-ores, though clayband ores near the base of the Coal Measures in Durham were not without significance for the siting and development of early iron-smelting. Spathose ores that were found in some of the Pennine lead-mines, and clayband and blackband ironstones [1] occurring among the rocks of the limestone measures in Tynedale and Redesdale, were of considerable but short-lived importance about the middle of last century (Fig. 39).

Of much greater importance are the high-grade non-phosphoric haematite ores that occur as replacement deposits in the limestones of lower Carboniferous age near the coast of Cumberland and Furness. They include flats (the most famous that at Hodbarrow) filling cavities, veins that occupy faults and fissures, and, in Furness, ' sops ', which are the linings of sinks and swallowholes. The productive ores are restricted to the surface horizons and die out at relatively shallow depths of about 600 feet below sea level, a fact which suggests their later derivation in relation to a sub-Triassic surface rather than a deep-seated origin. The ore-bodies are best developed in the most massive limestone horizons, the Red Hill oolite and the Second Limestone (from the bottom) having been most important. The ore-fields are found in two areas, a northern area just inland from Whitehaven, which extends as an elongated belt through Cleator and Egremont (Fig. 5), and a southern area on each side of the Duddon estuary at Millom in Cumberland and Dalton in Furness.

The thin limestones of the Yoredale series, with their associated coal seams, were formerly worked at a great many places along their outcrops for lime-burning to provide lime both for agriculture and building. Large-scale modern workings, chiefly for roadstone and flux, have been much more restricted, especially by their need for transport facilities. They are concentrated at localities in Tynedale, Weardale, Teesdale, and Cumberland that enjoy especially favourable situations. Quarries for roadstone also work the hard igneous rocks, such as the various dykes and especially the Whin Sill, which is extensively quarried where it outcrops in places with good transport, as in the Tyne gap, in North Tynedale, and near the railhead in Teesdale.

---

[1] The lowest and therefore most northerly of these ironstones was that of lower Redesdale ; the blackband ironstone of the Tyne valley lies near the Great Limestone.

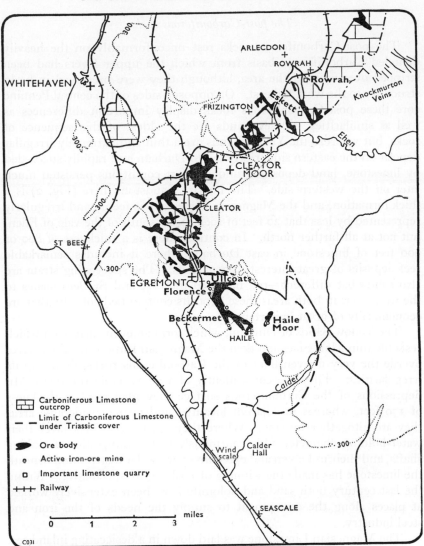

Fig. 5   THE WEST CUMBERLAND OREFIELD.

Throughout the area covered by Carboniferous rocks, stone has been extensively used in the past for building purposes. Some of the sandstones provide excellent freestones that have been used on more than a local scale for important buildings. For most of these in the north, however, good stone was available close at hand. Durham Cathedral, for example, was built of Coal Measures sandstone quarried near by at Kepier.

23

The post-Carboniferous rocks

The post-Carboniferous rocks rest unconformably on the heavily denuded Carboniferous basis from which the upper layers had been stripped over most of the area, although they were preserved in basin structures to the west and east. On opposite sides of the central Pennine core these post-Carboniferous rocks display important differences as well as similarities. Desert sands are the oldest of this sequence of rocks, but whereas the Yellow Sands are a thin and extremely irregular deposit on the eastern side, restricted to Durham and rapidly succeeded by limestone, land deposition under desert conditions persisted much later on the western side. The Penrith Sandstone here (Fig. 2) is a thick formation, and the Magnesian Limestone is feebly and irregularly represented by less that 20 feet of rock in the south of the vale of Eden, but not at all farther north. In contrast there is a thickness of 800 or 900 feet of limestone in east Durham, where it includes remarkable reef deposits of great interest to geologists. The succeeding strata are also somewhat different—red marls to the east and St Bees shales to the west—but in both areas these deposits contain beds of salts that are economically of great importance.

The Yellow Sands of Durham, which form an even surface on which rests the thin Marl Slate and then the Magnesian Limestone, themselves overlie the very uneven floor of the Carboniferous rocks, filling up its irregularities. They are consequently of very variable thickness. In depressions of the Carboniferous surface they may reach a thickness of 170 feet, whereas in adjacent localities and over considerable areas they are altogether missing. Where they occur as a thick layer their water-holding character adds enormously to the difficulties of sinking shafts, and their unknown and exceedingly irregular distribution beneath the limestone has made the winning of coal highly speculative. Within the last century both sand and dolomite have been extensively worked at places along the escarpment to supply the needs of the iron and steel industry.

The Magnesian Limestone was laid down in a desiccating inland sea, which contained salts in solution, and near the top of the limestone and in the overlying strata there are important beds of salt, anhydrite, and gypsum (Fig. 53). The main salt bed occurs about 1,000 feet below the surface of Teesmouth and the area farther southeast (Fig. 6), and over a considerable tract is more than 100 feet thick. It thins rapidly and disappears westward as it approaches the surface, but no limit to the southeast has yet been proved. Above it, separated by a thin layer of marls, is the top anhydrite, which is remarkably persistent over a more extensive area, and then 200 to 400 feet of red marls, which give way to sandstones as the succession takes on the typical character of Bunter Sandstone. Gypsum workings in the Permo-Triassic rocks of the vale of Eden date back to the pre-railway age, and within the last few years large deposits of anhydrite have been proved and worked on the Cumberland coast by Whitehaven.

In the west the counterparts of the Bunter Sandstone (800–900 ft.) and Keuper Marl (600–700 ft.) of the vale of Tees are the St Bees Sandstone, an excellent and widely used building stone, the softer Kirklinton Sandstone, and the Stanwix Shales (Fig. 2). All these formations are several hundred feet thick and represent vast accumulations under continental conditions before a renewed invasion of the sea in which the Lias shales were laid down. All that is left of the Jurassic sequence in the northwest is a small area of Lias rocks southwest of Carlisle, around Great Orton, cut short to the east by the Cummersdale Fault.

In the North Riding, however, the Lower Lias shales stretch over an extensive area in front of the great Cleveland escarpment. The Upper Lias is also a shale formation, including alum shales and also a seam of jet rock at the base, but between the Lower and Upper Lias shales the middle portion of the Lias is represented by a sandy phase with ironstone (Fig. 6). The succeeding formations, which cap the Cleveland plateau north of Eskdale, although of Inferior Oolite age, consist predominantly not of limestones, but of hard flaggy sandstones and intercalated shales of estuarine formation, and there are even some traces of coal. These rocks make their first appearance south of the Tees as the hard cappings of Eston and Upleatham hills, outliers of the main mass of the plateau from which they are separated by the Guisborough valley. The Upsall Fault, downthrown as much as 400 feet to the north but rapidly diminishing coastwards, is responsible for this duplication of the escarpment. Along it the Middle Lias sandstones, which are more resistant than the shales above and below, often form a conspicuous shelf. The rocky coast begins at Saltburn, and a few miles farther south the cliffs reach a height of more than 600 feet at Boulby, exposing a great range of Jurassic rocks, including the Middle Lias ironstones and the jet rock and alum shales of the Upper Lias (Fig. 53b). The latter were of importance before the ironstones, and were worked from the end of the sixteenth century until about 1860, at first near Guisborough but more extensively later along the cliffs both north and south of Whitby. The chief workings were about Boulby and Kettleness, where they have considerably modified the coast. The jet rock was worked along the face of the escarpment about Roseberry Topping, as well as farther southwest in Raisdale, for the Whitby jet industry, which flourished in mid-Victorian times.

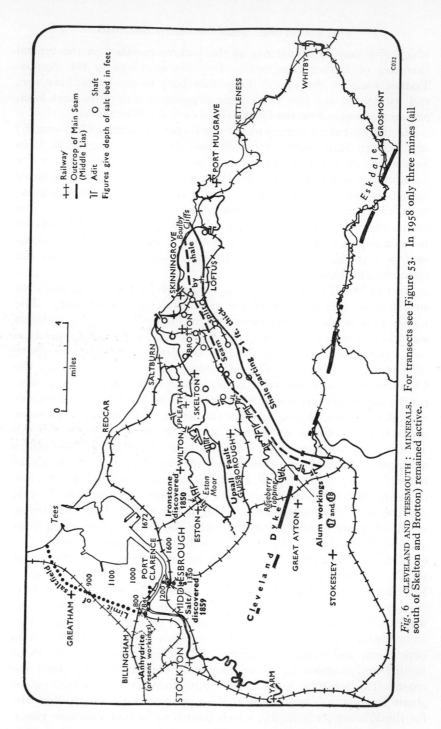

Fig. 6 CLEVELAND AND TEESMOUTH : MINERALS. For transects see Figure 53. In 1958 only three mines (all south of Skelton and Brotton) remained active.

The ironstones, although they are now almost worked out, have been exploited only during the last hundred years, following the discovery of the outcrop of the Main seam inland at Eston in 1850. Here the Main seam is over ten feet thick and directly overlies the Pecten seam, giving altogether more than 15 feet of workable ironstone, above the Middle Lias sandstones of the escarpment face. From its outcrop the ironstone dips southeast, but the great Upsall Fault, bringing up the lower strata again, is responsible for greatly lengthening the outcrop of the ironstone by bringing about its repetition along the main escarpment south of Guisborough. From here the ironstone passes south and east under an increasing cover of sandstones and shales, and in so doing thins and deteriorates in metal content. What is even more important, the seam becomes split by a shale parting, which progressively thickens southwards at the expense of the ore, and where the shale is over a foot thick the ironstone is generally regarded as unworkable. In Eskdale, and on the coast south of Whitby, the seam has faded out of recognition. What workable ore remains farther north is in a basin-like structure around Loftus and Skelton, where the ironstone lies about 700 feet below the surface (Fig. 53b).

If ironstone is a resource that is almost spent, other minerals have recently been discovered in northeast Yorkshire that may acquire considerable importance in the future. Before the War, in an unsuccessful search for oil in Eskdale behind Whitby, a boring proved the existence of natural gas (methane) in the Permian rocks about 5,000 feet below the Jurassic surface, and also a substantial thickness of potash salts, not hitherto known to occur in Britain. Since 1952 the Imperial Chemical Industries concern has been prospecting in the Grosmont district and has also tapped methane at a depth of 4,800 feet.

The absence of sedimentary rocks younger than the Jurassic and the restriction of the latter to the southeastern corner of North England in Cleveland, save for a small patch of the earliest representatives of the Jurassic sedimentaries near Carlisle, leave a great gap in the stratigraphical succession. Whereas in the English lowland the continuation and relative completeness of the stratigraphical record through the Mesozoic and well into the Tertiary eras make it possible to reconstruct with some confidence the origin and evolution of the present surface, we can only infer and surmise about the original constructional surface in northern England. The gap in the stratigraphical record means that the age of post-Hercynian folding and faulting responsible for the present disposition of the rocks is known only very imprecisely. The younger rocks present are so affected. Thus the Jurassic rocks of Cleveland have been slightly folded along west–east axes. Between the main Cleveland anticline and a more northerly one that extends

27

from Roseberry Topping to the coast between Skinningrove and Port Mulgrave, Eskdale corresponds with a synclinal trough. Again, the Triassic rocks of the west have been downwarped round the Lake District massif. The fact that they are found preserved in a wedge-like extension from the lowlands at the head of the Solway up the vale of Eden has generally been ascribed to Tertiary earth-movements uplifting the Lake District rocks into a dome and the North Pennine massif as a slab into a desk-structure tilted away from the great faults along its western margin. Here Carboniferous rocks are downthrown to the west by as much as 1,500 feet, and the Triassic rocks, themselves affected by the faulting, are preserved dipping east towards the fault zone from the Lake District dome.

Apart from these major Tertiary structures there has been much subsidiary faulting and some intrusion of igneous dykes, which run especially WNW–ESE across the country in the tract between their most notable representatives, the Acklington Dyke, which traverses the centre of Northumberland, and the Armathwaite–Cockfield–Cleveland Dyke (Fig. 1). These dykes are distinct in trend and composition from the Hercynian series and their petrology closely resembles that of the Tertiary dykes of Mull towards which they converge. (The Cleveland Dyke has been dated with some certainty as post-Eocene, and is probably Miocene.) Like other igneous rocks in the area they have been worked in places to provide roadstone.

Neither Cretaceous nor Tertiary sediments have been recorded in our area, and, although no Cretaceous deposits are represented either, it is generally assumed that the area shared the extensive marine transgression of Cenomanian times, of which there is such widespread evidence elsewhere, including the significant tract farther west in Antrim where the chalk is preserved under a capping of lava. A great thickness of Mesozoic strata would have to be removed over most of northern England before the rocks were reached in which the present surface is sculptured. Even so, Professor D. L. Linton has postulated that ancient lineaments, determined upon a Cretaceous cover, have been transferred to the exhumed undermass, so that in his view the emergence of the floor of the Cretaceous sea properly provides the starting-point for examination of the present surface features. From the consequent drainage which the emergence and tilting of the sea-floor initiated, he would trace the descent of the oldest lines of the present drainage pattern.

CHAPTER 3

THE DEVELOPMENT OF THE SURFACE

THE denudation chronology of North England awaits detailed and comprehensive investigation, and the recent extension of modern geomorphological techniques of analysis of erosion surfaces to this area is only in its early stages and as yet largely confined to the west and the extreme north. In our present state of knowledge inferences must be very tentative. Accordant summits and shelf features, however, are conspicuous and widespread features of the landscape. Their examination in the field, together with map analysis, have already begun to draw attention to the recurrence of certain levels that may be regarded as significant. The most definite indications of planation adduced by Professor S. E. Hollingworth, on the basis especially of study of the Lake District and its margins, are found at the following approximate levels—2,000 ft., 1,600–1,700 ft., 1,000–1,050 ft., 730–800 ft., 570 ft., and 400 ft.—but there are other bevellings both beyond and within this range. Altimetric frequency curves show three outstanding maxima in the Lake District, at 430 ft., 820 ft., and 1,050 ft., and these correspond with the three most prominent surfaces that may be recognised in the field. The lowest of them, at 400 ft. or 430 ft., is much in evidence in the surrounding lowlands, where it cuts across a variety of outcrops. Monadnocks of resistant Triassic sandstones rise above it to 700 ft. or 800 ft., and the 800-foot level is represented also as a shelf on the Pennine escarpment. These surfaces are well developed on the western side of the Lake District in the Eskdale granite, and elsewhere the uppermost is conspicuously developed irrespective of whether the rocks are the Skiddaw Slates or the Borrowdale Volcanics. Moreover, the Carboniferous Limestone slopes are distinctly notched at these levels, and also between 550 and 600 ft. Not only is the 570-foot surface represented in the Lake District. In the Cheviot area an altimetric frequency maximum at 560 ft. is also particularly prominent. Dr R. Common has noted the easily recognisable smooth upland surfaces in the Cheviot area at from 500 or 550 to 750 ft., as well as at 950 or 1,000 ft. to 1,200 ft. At higher levels both Hollingworth and Common agree in emphasising the importance of planation at 1,600–1,700 ft. and of accordant summit heights rising slightly above 2,000 ft., but Common points to others in the Cheviot. His 1,300–1,500-foot surface may be related to the 1,470-foot level noted by Hollingworth in the latter's analysis of altimetric frequencies in the Lake District.

To postulate that disconnected fragments of summit flats and shelf bevels at corresponding altitudes relate to unwarped surfaces, so that the altitudes at which they recur may be immediately correlated, is admittedly to make a big assumption, more especially as fairly detailed analysis is still confined to widely separated areas in north Northumberland and west of the Pennines round the Lake District. The evidence at present available, however, does suggest that at least up to the 1,000-foot level the surfaces are unwarped ; further substantiation of this evidence is required, as well as an indication of how much higher among the bevellings similar correlations may be made without admission of warping.

The upper surfaces may be presumed to have had a subaerial origin. They were possibly carved by erosion in an exhumed undermass that appeared after the removal of a chalk cover, ' stripped like wax from a sheet of glass ' (Linton). In any case they represent portions of an ancient land-surface of subdued relief, with occasional monadnocks, that has been further sculptured during later phases of subaerial erosion related to successive base-levels. But it seems more likely that surfaces up to at least 1,000 feet are remains of submarine platforms that mark the positions of stages in the recession of a shoreline. Each stage would represent a base-level to which the drainage of the land area was related, and as the sea fell back from each stillstand position, the drainage lines would be extended to a new shoreline across a bevelled platform with a veneer of marine deposits. Over this platform the adjustment to the structure through differential erosion would begin anew.

The most critical fact yet to be established for the elucidation of the morphological development is the position of the shoreline of the sea at its maximum post-Cretaceous extension. This shoreline, if its position could be established, would delimit an ancient land-surface from the staged succession of younger surfaces that have emerged from the sea. Up to the present, however, none of the bevelled surfaces recognised in North England has been linked conclusively with the Pliocene transgression and emergence known in southern England. In southeast England geomorphological analysis of the evolution of the surface from the position of the Pliocene shoreline, determined by the evidence of residual deposits as well as by physiographical evidence, has been carried out. Its significance for the recognition and interpretation of distinct facets of the present landscape, as well as the differentiation of soils in terms of maturity sequence is becoming increasingly appreciated. In comparison, the corresponding problem in northern

England has been enormously complicated by the glaciation. Rock surfaces which might have provided crucial evidence have been overlain and concealed by drift, the drainage system has been considerably modified, and a widespread mantle of drift deposits has been provided as the predominant soil materials.

The smooth, gently rolling, highland surfaces and even skylines so characteristic throughout the north country certainly bear witness to an ancient land surface (Pls. 1–16). Hollingworth discerns traces of a high-level surface rather above 2,600 feet and notes that the Cheviot summit corresponds very closely with this altitude, which is also of frequent occurrence as a summit-level in the Southern Uplands. Alternatively, it has been suggested that the summits may be monadnocks rising above the 2,000- or 2,300-foot surface, which is so widely represented and which has usually been regarded as the early Tertiary peneplane.

In north Britain generally the altitude of the highest summits falls eastwards, and Linton regards them as relict features of an inclined sub-Cenomanian surface. Accepting and developing Dr A. Bremner's conclusions about the origin of the Scottish river-system as derived from the emergence and eastward tilting of the Cretaceous sea-floor, Linton has attempted to reconstruct the smooth sub-chalk surface that would have been exposed when erosion had eaten through the sheet of chalk. As he reconstructs it the surface slopes regularly eastwards across northern England from a position more than 3,500 feet above present sea level in west Cumberland to below 1,500 feet in the North York Moors. In the lines marked by the Tweed, Solway–Tyne, and the Tees–Leven–Esk Linton would discern some of its earliest lineaments—the courses of consequent streams that drained down the slope of the emerged and tilted sea-floor that he postulates. His identification of the highest present-day summits as relics of this surface, preserved along major watersheds, has been questioned, and it has also been pointed out that large groups of presumably consequent streams do not conform to so simple an initial surface. In particular, the radial drainage of the Lake District cannot readily be fitted to the hypothesis. The later earth-movements (probably mid-Tertiary), which uplifted the surface and rejuvenated the streams to carve deeply into it, probably introduced important new features in the drainage pattern, especially in the west beyond the Pennine faults. The radial drainage of the Lake District is usually attributed to mid-Tertiary doming of that area, and the Eden has excavated its valley along a faulted syncline in which the softer rocks have been preserved west of the edge of the North Pennine block. To what extent the great Pennine escarpment is a fault escarpment and not merely a fault-line escarpment, a constructional and not simply an erosional feature, is, however, debatable.

It is noticeable that in general the present-day streams radiate from the major uplands and converge upon the major lowlands, instead of conforming to a single dominant direction. Regarding this as highly significant, Dr J. B. Sissons has recently attempted a reconstruction of the ancient surface into which the presumed consequent courses of today would fit, by drawing form-lines at right angles to these streams

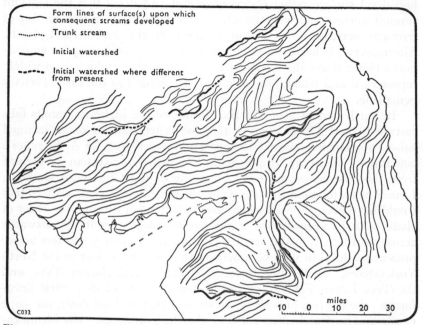

Fig. 7 SOUTH SCOTLAND AND NORTH ENGLAND. Form lines and initial watersheds (after J. B. Sissons).

(Fig. 7). The resulting major initial watersheds, which run straight or with very gentle curves over long distances, are interpreted as anticlinal axes, and the Teviot/lower Tweed as a synclinal axis, and Dr F. M. Trotter's conclusion that old fault-lines were revived along the northern and western margins of the North Pennine massif is accepted as providing other major determinants of the pattern. The Tertiary earth-movements, deduced by Sissons from study of the drainage system, are seen as the basis of the present distribution of the principal areas of high and low ground, though this may have been foreshadowed even earlier, since these earth-movements revived old-established structural lines. Whether or not the upland surface of northern England may be correlated with the Mio-Pliocene surface of southern England, and its drainage regarded as having originated on, and been superimposed from, a chalk cover, it seems clear that the land area here had been reduced, if not to a peneplane at least to a state of subdued relief with occasional monadnocks, before its margins experienced the widespread mid-Tertiary submergence, which was probably accompanied by warping and faulting. There is strong evidence that the subsequent emergence (? Pliocene) was intermittent, resulting in the development of marine abrasion platforms on which much of the present drainage pattern was initiated as extensions of rivers from the older land-surface behind.

Much laborious field work needs to be carried out before the major episodes of the earlier denudation chronology can be established with certainty and their expression in the surface delineated with precision. What is clear is that differential erosion, working upon the varied rock basis, had already modelled the salient features of the present-day landscape before the onset of the Great Ice Age. When glaciation intervened the surface of the country was in a stage of mature dissection, and the present drainage pattern, inherited largely from that of pre-glacial times, shows a high degree of adjustment to the prevailing uniclinal structure, and the rapid alternation of rocks of differing resistance. Cuesta forms are much in evidence (Fig. 8), and must have been more so before the addition of the widespread cover of glacial drift. Associated with them are strike-line valleys, etched out along the outcrops of the less resistant formations. Such, for example, is the belt of soft rocks of the Cementstone Group that surrounds the Cheviot massif. Between the igneous country and the scarped ridges of the Fell Sandstone outcrop it forms a longitudinal depression. The divergent streams from the Cheviot, entering this groove, are collected into the Breamish-Till system and drained towards the Tweed ; but farther south the Aln and Coquet, aided by transverse fracturing which has created weak zones across the Fell Sandstone belt, have maintained breaches through these uplands. Compartmentation of the sub-Cheviot depression is further emphasised by the repetition of the Fell Sandstone outcrop produced by strike-faulting. Within the main girdle of Fell Sandstone highlands a broken ridge of scarped hills runs north-south in the dales, separating the Chatton basin in Glendale from the Milfield basin, and farther south forming part of the watershed between the Aln and the Breamish (Fig. 58).

The Fell Sandstone highlands enclose Coquetdale and, sweeping west towards the Border, form the watershed between the Coquet and the Rede. Still farther south, corresponding with a slight anticline, massive grits and the numerous thin limestones of the limestone measures, reinforced by the Whin Sill, form uplands in central Northumberland

33

that are the watershed between the coastal streams (Wansbeck, Pont-Blyth) and the drainage of a large area of Border country in the west of the county in Redesdale and North Tynedale, which is collected by those rivers and finally carried southeast by the North Tyne across the grain of the outcrops as they sweep west in South Tynedale. Here the South Tyne, occupying a structural trough north of the faulted margin of the North Pennine massif, appears to be following one of the most ancient lines of the drainage pattern. It receives not only the North Tyne but also much of the drainage of the northern part of the North Pennine massif, which is tilted towards it. But the main hydrographic node of the northern Pennines, about Cross Fell, corresponds with the area of maximum uplift in the southwest, and important drainage lines follow the eastward or southeastward direction of the dip. At some stage in the evolution of the drainage system the development of subsequent streams along strike vales in the area to the east diverted these streams northwards.

Thus the Tees enters the strike vale of Triassic rocks in front of the great Cleveland escarpment, the Wear that in the Coal Measures in front of the Magnesian Limestone escarpment. Farther north, in front of the cuesta of upper Coal Measures sandstones that forms Gateshead Fell, the pre-glacial Wear flowed towards the Tyne along what is now the Team valley. A parallel valley in the Coal Measures still farther west directs the drainage of Derwentdale towards the Tyne, but at some earlier stage this drainage continued southeast into mid-Durham along the line of the Browney valley. Traces of the older valleys that prolonged the eastward or southeastward stream-courses are suggested by the contours of northeast Yorkshire where the Tees, Leven, and Esk are in line, and of east Durham in some of the ' hopes ' that groove the limestone plateau.

West of the Pennines, the Eden receives the radial drainage of an extensive sector of the Lake District. Dry gaps mark the former courses of radiating consequent streams across the Carboniferous Limestone girdle. But most of the drainage from the Lake District towards the Eden is now collected in the strike vale that runs in front of the Carboniferous Limestone escarpment. Concentrated into the Lowther, Eamont, and Caldew it is carried towards the Eden through the gaps maintained by these rivers. Except in the extreme east, where the Smardale Beck crosses the Carboniferous Limestone towards the Eden west of Ash Fell, the drainage of the Howgill Fells east of the Lake District dome, gathered in the continuation of the same strike groove south of Shap, is carried off to the south by the Lune from Tebay. Here the lower Lune, cutting back vigorously from Morecambe Bay, has captured drainage that was formerly directed towards the Eden, and the main

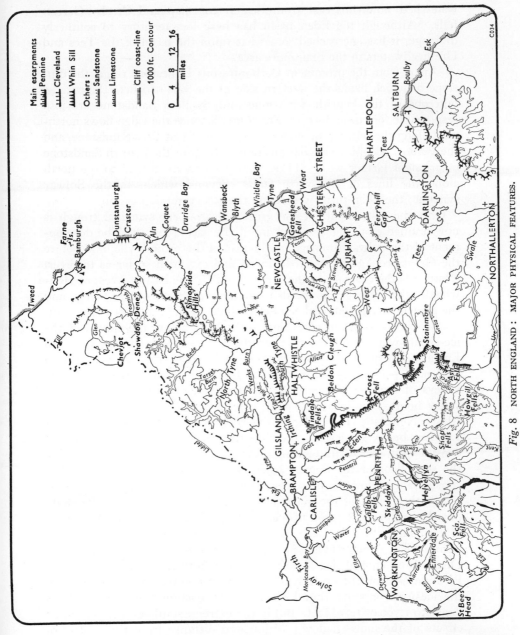

Fig. 8 NORTH ENGLAND : MAJOR PHYSICAL FEATURES.

Main escarpments
ᗢᗢᗢᗢ Pennine
ᗢᗢᗢᗢ Cleveland
ᗢᗢᗢᗢ Whin Sill
Others :
ᗢᗢᗢᗢ Sandstone
ᗢᗢᗢᗢ Limestone
ᗢᗢᗢᗢ Cliff coast-line
—— 1000 ft. Contour

0   4   8   12   16
miles

C034

35

watershed now runs east from Scafell to Shap and Crosby Garrett fells. Although the Eden basin has here lost territory to southerly drainage, it has encroached somewhat upon the basin of the Tees and Ure headwaters in the Stainmore area.

Apart from the prominent Carboniferous Limestone ridge, the dip-slope of which flanks the western side of the vale of Eden, the parallel outcrops of the Penrith Sandstone and St Bees Sandstone are also responsible for cuesta forms. For some distance the Eden flows north-west along the outcrop of shales in front of the St Bees Sandstone, and the Petteril occupies a similar position in front of the Penrith Sandstone escarpment farther west. These escarpments are cut off to the north along the lines of transverse faults, beyond which, in the Solway syncline, the Eden turns west along the structural depression.

Only the eastern part of the great Solway-Tyne synclinal trough is now drained east from the lowlying Tyne gap (450 ft.). The development of the Solway drainage has beheaded the proto-Tyne, and before the Great Ice Age the encroachment had extended so far as to divert westwards the drainage of the upper South Tyne basin. West of Halt-whistle, the Tyne gap is the drift-encumbered floor of this valley, and the present watershed has been determined by the contours of the drift.

Before the onset of glaciation, or at least before the spread of the ice-sheets which have most powerfully affected the landscape of North England, the area must have stood considerably higher above sea level than now, perhaps by as much as 200 feet. In the lower portions of the valleys of the Northumberland and Durham coalfield, the pre-glacial valley floors, now buried in drift, extend well below present sea level. Above Newcastle, for example, the rock floor of the Tyne valley lies 140 feet below sea level, indicating that the coastline must have lain considerably east of its present position. Similarly, on the west side the rock floor of the Solway basin, beneath its coating of drift, lies considerably below the present sea level.

At the height of the glaciation little of the area could have stood out above the great apron of ice. In the southwest and north only the highest summits of the Lake District, Pennines, and Cheviot protruded as nunataks. The great mass of ice that overlay the margin of the Lake District and choked the vale of Eden was so thick that it mounted the Pennine escarpment up to heights above 2,000 feet, and in the north the ice-mass lapping round the Cheviot bastion encroached up its flanks to 1,700 or 1,750 feet. But in the extreme southeast the combined effects of the snow-shadow position and distance from the centres of ice dispersal allowed much lower summits in the Cleveland hills to rise above the ice. Above about 1,000 feet they do not appear to have been glaciated.

The earliest invasion of ice was from Scandinavia across the North Sea, but it extended little farther than the line of the present east coast (Fig. 9). Evidence of its deposits is confined to the Durham coastline, and a slightly more extensive coastal fringe in the North Riding. In an early phase Scottish ice from the west was widespread over North England, but the most profound effects of glaciation derive from a later though not necessarily more extensive phase. Great streams

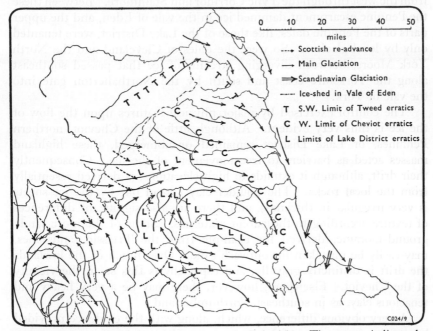

Fig. 9 NORTH ENGLAND : GLACIATION (after A. Raistrick). The arrows indicate the main directions of ice movement.

of ice then moved south from Scotland, and another centre of dispersal in the southwest of North England itself also contributed important quantities of ice, which piled up on the Lake District and vale of Eden and poured outwards. The ice-shed, as indicated by the trend of drumlins and the sources of erratics that are contained in the drift, crossed the Eden valley near Appleby towards Dufton Fell (Fig. 9). To the south the ice moved towards the great funnel-like outlet afforded by the Stainmore saddle into Teesdale and the east ; only a smaller amount escaped southwest towards Morecambe Bay. The ice moving north down the vale of Eden was confronted and split by Scottish ice, and fused with it in two streams, one sweeping east through the Tyne gap and across the flanking uplands, the other west round the northern

4

margin of the Lake District, and then south along the west coast in the Irish Sea basin.

With the North Sea basin already choked by Scandinavian ice, Scottish ice was deflected south across northeast England. The ice flow was broken into streams that skirted the flanks of the Cheviot and then reunited in mid-Northumberland. The main mass of ice passed south along the coastal belt, receiving considerable accessions from the west through the Tyne Corridor and Stainmore. Between these the Pennine escarpment dammed ice in the vale of Eden, and the upper parts of the Pennine dales, like those of the Lake District, were tenanted only by local glaciers. So were the dales of Cleveland and the North York Moors, between diverging streams of ice that passed southeast along the Yorkshire coast and south by the Northallerton gate into the vale of York.

The control exercised by major physical features upon the flow of the ice is thus very evident. Although little of the Cheviot, northern Pennines, or Lake District remained unsubmerged, these highland masses acted as barriers to free movement of the ice. Consequently their drift, although it extends to high elevations, is derived essentially from the local rocks. The boulder-clay spread out by the ice-sheets is very irregular in thickness, and there are also significant differences of texture according to the parent materials. Some of the more sandy ground-moraine, derived for example from the Triassic sandstones, may easily be mistaken for outwash sand. Over much of the lowlands the drift is distinctly gravelly, and especially is this so in the vicinity of the Cheviot. Elsewhere, however, there may be a very heavy and tenacious clay, as in southeast Northumberland.

A very obvious difference, which, along with the evidence provided by erratics, is important for reconstructing the pattern of ice movement, is that in colour between the distinctly reddish drift laid down by ice that passed over the outcrops of Triassic rocks and the bluish-grey drift characteristic of the Carboniferous rocks. The boundary between western and local ice can thus be traced without difficulty in the country south of the Tyne, and in the valleys of its right-bank tributaries, by the junction between the drifts of different colour.

Other differences relate to the form in which the drift is spread. In the open western lowlands, below about 1,000 feet, the drift surface over large areas shows pronounced striping in drumlins (Pl. 1), and these are conspicuous at the western mouth of the Tyne gap. They have been mapped by Hollingworth, and the map (Fig. 10) clearly suggests the graining which the swarms of their whale-back forms impart to the landscape in harmony with the sweep of the ice movement. The crests of some of the drumlins rise about 100 feet above the intervening

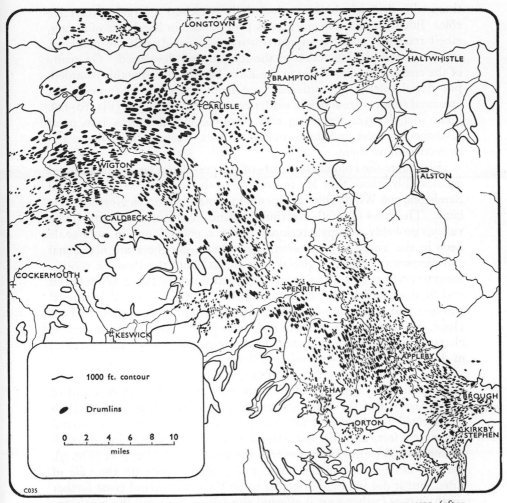

Fig. 10 THE DRUMLINS OF THE VALE OF EDEN AND THE SOLWAY LOWLANDS (after
S. E. Hollingworth).

hollows. Many are entirely composed of loose drift, but others have
rock cores and only a veneer of drift. Over most of the lowlands on
the eastern side of the country south of the drumlinised tract of the
lower Tweed basin, however, the drift occurs in the form of featureless
spreads. In the dales of the Pennines and the Lake District, too, the
drift for the most part does not show drumlin forms.

The glaciation interrupted an incompleted cycle of subaerial erosion
and the ice-sheets generally smoothed and softened the contours of the
pre-glacial surface. By blanketing them for a long period and coating

39

them with drift, glaciation undoubtedly exercised a largely protective rôle. But where ice movement was pronounced in highlands of strong, albeit rounded, relief, erosional features associated with the plucking, scooping, and planing action of the ice are well developed. On many of the crests above 2,000 feet in the Lake District the smoothly rounded, pre-glacial surface has suffered little from active ice movement, but erosional features are much in evidence in the valleys below (Pls. 10–12). They include over-deepening and straightening of valleys into great U-shaped troughs, and the formation of rock-basins in their floors and as corries above them.

Elsewhere the bold cuesta crests of the pre-glacial landscape suffered considerably where they lay transverse to the ice-flow, as did the Fell Sandstone and Whin Sill escarpments in central and north Northumberland. The lakes of south Northumberland, north of the South Tyne valley, probably occupy erosional hollows gouged out in soft shale beds in the Yoredale succession. In other areas there are occasional conspicuous examples of glacial erosion, as along the Pennine escarpment near Cross Fell. The great U-shaped trench between Whitehaven and St Bees, which has been so important in the history of local coal working and is now used by the west-coast railway to by-pass St Bees Head, the high ground of which it detaches to the west, owes its present character to glacial modification of a pre-glacial valley and diversion of drainage in its drift-encumbered floor.

The various phenomena of the retreat, as the ice receded towards the source areas, add considerably to the variety of landforms and of soil types. After the main glaciation, a renewed advance of Scottish ice affected the Solway basin but was restricted to the low ground below 400 feet, and did not extend beyond an arc running through Brampton and Cumwhitton towards the coast about Maryport (Fig. 9). Thus it did not invade the Tyne valley or penetrate up the vale of Eden, but it did impinge in places upon the Cumberland coast farther south, just as farther west it affected the Isle of Man and the northernmost parts of Ireland. Deep exposures of drift in the Carlisle area clearly show the different layers that represent the contrasting phases of the Pleistocene history. The lower boulder-clay of the main glaciation is separated from the upper boulder-clay of the Scottish re-advance by a mass of sands and gravels.

The main de-glaciation was rapid, and the phase of valley glaciation in the highlands was very restricted. In the Lake District the small amount of morainic material and the freshness of its forms indicate that the phase of valley- and corrie-glaciation was short. The special glacial features of the Lake District valleys, in particular the presence of well-marked moraines in their upper parts, are probably the product of a late revival of corrie-glaciers which may perhaps be correlated with the post-Alleröd phase in Scandinavia. The great masses of scree that are so prominent a feature of the walls of the U-shaped valleys reflect the intense frost-shattering suffered during these later stages by the great cliffs that had been left on the disappearance of the glaciers. Tarns occupy many of the corries, and in the rock-basins of the ungraded and stepped valleys are long ribbon-lakes in various stages of silting. Professor W. H. Pearsall has shown that these differences, related to variations in the rock-type and therefore the degree of erosion suffered by the surrounding country, are in turn responsible for differences in the chemical composition of the water, upon which differences in flora and fishes depend. Lakes such as Wastwater, Ennerdale Water, Buttermere, and Crummock Water have preserved their pristine rocky character, whereas others such as Coniston, Windermere, Ullswater, and especially Esthwaite have evolved further by silting. This evolution from rocky to silted lake has been accompanied by a general progression from a trout community to a perch-pike community.

As the ice fell back from the highlands the small valley-glaciers shrank rapidly, and the dales were freed from ice while it still occupied the adjacent lowlands. Much land-drainage and melt-water was thus impounded in lakes by the gradually receding or intermittently withdrawing ice. In the Carlisle plain and vale of Eden, where Hollingworth and Trotter have thoroughly investigated the glacial and post-glacial landforms and sequence of events, some two hundred former lakes have been identified. In the Solway lowlands such lakes were formed by the re-advance of Scottish ice. Other lakes were created between the receding ice-fronts as the component ice-streams fell apart—Tweed and western ice cleaving in central Northumberland, Lake District and Scottish ice in the Carlisle plain. The evacuated areas between were extensively flooded with melt-water that found difficulty in escaping. As it moved along the receding or temporarily stationary ice-margins seeking lateral escape, the water often cut trenches across emergent ridges and spurs of the underlying surface. Spillways at successive levels are exceedingly numerous and sometimes spectacular features in many parts of northern England.[1] Since Professor P. F. Kendall first drew attention to the phenomena round the margins of the high ground of northeast Yorkshire, the development of many others has been reconstructed. A remarkable series of inter-

[1] The humped, or 'up and down', nature of the longitudinal profile of many of these channels, which in other respects resemble railway cuttings, and the similar shape of many drift-plugged channels as revealed by borings in the coalfield, suggest that their evolution has been a good deal more complex than had previously been supposed. Perhaps they are not simply water-cut channels of post-glacial origin ; ice erosion may have contributed.

connected lakes in the dales along the southern margin of the Tyne ice carried drainage from the extreme northwest of the Pennines around Tindale Fells eastwards and ultimately into Lake Wear, which occupied Durham between the high ground to the west, the Magnesian Limestone plateau to the east, and the ice-front to the north. These have been successively investigated by Dr A. R. Dwerryhouse, Dr A. Raistrick, and Dr W. S. Anderson, and more recently Professor R. F. Peel has surveyed and described in detail two of the overflow channels—Beldon Cleugh and East Dipton channel. While these channels were being cut, Lake Wear discharged southwards by an outlet in the bounding rim of the Permian escarpment, cutting the great trench at Ferryhill (Fig. 8). Extensive planation at 320 feet in the Ferryhill area and the shelf in the gap, together with the accordant height of delta deposits, suggest that the glacial lake persisted for a period at this level before the Ferryhill spillway was abandoned. This happened when the northward retreat of the ice exposed a lower col in the Magnesian Limestone escarpment east of Chester-le-Street. Lake Durham was then drained eastwards by this outlet, and the downcutting of the lower Wear gorge was initiated.

Many spillway channels were left high and dry as notches in the watersheds when normal drainage was resumed, but some of the lines established by overflow drainage persisted after the evacuation of the area and brought about diversions of drainage from the pre-glacial lines. Such is the lower Wear below Chester-le-Street where it flows in a gorge across the Magnesian Limestone to Sunderland; the pre-glacial drainage of central Durham flowed north into the Tyne in front of the escarpment of upper Coal Measures sandstones that forms Gateshead Fell. In the drift-choked northern part of the deserted pre-glacial valley of the Wear, the Team, a small tributary of the Tyne, now flows high above the pre-glacial valley floor.

The lake impounded in Glendale between the Cheviot and Fell Sandstone highlands, like Lake Durham, was for a time drained south. This outlet cut the deep channel of Shawdon dene near Glanton which provides an easy railway and road route through the Breamish–Aln watershed (Fig. 8). When it was later able to escape north it adopted a new channel, east of the pre-glacial one near Crookham, which was choked with morainic material. This and other spreads of kettle-moraine, such as that south of Wooler (Fig. 58), were left by stagnant ice as it wasted away. They provide a chaotic assortment of gravelly mounds enclosing ill-drained peaty hollows.

Large delta deposits of sand and gravel, such as occur north of Durham city, were dumped in the lakes of late-glacial times. Their positions and bevelled surfaces are important clues for the reconstruction of successive stages of withdrawal of the ice and lowering of the water-level. At some of the more stable positions in the process, lakes were held up long enough for laminated clays to be deposited on their floors over extensive areas. Such are the flats of Lake Milfield in Glendale and others in Lake Carlisle and Lake Darlington. Among other phenomena of fluvio-glacial origin associated with the retreat of the ice are deposits of englacial streams in the form of kame dumps aligned along the receding ice-front and esker-trains strung out at right angles. The Bradford kame (Fig. 58) in the coastal plain of north Northumberland inland from Bamburgh, is a well-known example; but even more remarkable is the great esker-train that extends westwards through the Tyne gap. In the Brampton district an extensive kame-belt marks the phase of withdrawal of Scottish ice. Between the ridge features are basin-like hollows, without easy drainage. Talkin Tarn, for example, lies in such a hollow and others are conspicuous in the Carlisle plain. Similarly, kames on Cotherstone Moor mark the retreat of western ice across Stainmore.

Since the ice finally retreated, streams have done an enormous amount of work, both in excavating their valleys in drift and rock and in transporting and sorting the drift material. In this they have been assisted by considerable uplift of the surface. Extensive terraces (Pl. 8) of re-handled glacial sands and gravels occur along all the main valleys, but some of these conspicuous terraces are related to high, temporary and local base-levels. They are the work of late-glacial floodwater, and are not truly post-glacial in the sense of being related to the sea level of North England after the evacuation of the country by the ice had been completed. Much drift has been stripped away from the slopes of the highlands, but below about 1,200 feet it forms a fairly continuous mantle of varying thickness, with only occasional protrusions of rock. In northeast Yorkshire, however, the plateau surface above about 700 feet is free from drift.

In its main features the hydrographic pattern is the same as that of pre-glacial times, and undoubtedly the principal effect of the glaciation was to spread over most of the area a coating of drift, which softened the contours and choked or partly infilled the pre-glacial valleys. Thus, although the major outlines of the landscape are the same, the relief is much less pronounced than before the glaciation. In Durham, for example, numerous borings in the heart of the coalfield have shown that the rock-floor of the middle Wear valley often lies more than 200 feet below the drift surface. This means that the present crest of the Magnesian Limestone escarpment rises in places more than 700 feet above the pre-glacial valley-floor. In the coastal districts of Northumberland only the highest points along the broken cuestas of the pre-glacial landscape now protrude as rock outcrops, low knolls amidst the almost featureless expanse of drift. In the drumlinised tracts of the Solway basin the rock-floor is completely covered, and rock outcrops occur only where some of the deepest valleys are cut down right through the drift.

In the highlands, where the drift did not completely conceal the lines of the pre-glacial valleys, the post-glacial drainage in general has remained faithful to the pre-glacial pattern. The pre-glacial valleys emerged after the Great Ice Age with a partial infilling of drift, in which the post-glacial streams have rapidly cut down. The Tyne is a noteworthy example, and keeps within the pre-glacial valley almost throughout even its lower course. Its bed is cut in soft drift, except at the great bends below Newcastle, where the river is now attacking the sides of the pre-glacial valley.

In the lowlands, however, the pre-glacial valleys have sometimes been completely obliterated, and the post-glacial stream courses, determined by slight irregularities in the surface of the drift, may be quite unrelated to the buried pre-glacial valleys. Such streams may have had to cut through only a relatively thin cover of drift, so that they have come to entrench themselves in the solid rock below. The Blyth, Wansbeck, and Coquet all flow in their lower courses in youthful, narrow, steep-sided rock-valleys, superimposed from the drift cover. Even where post-glacial stream courses occupy pre-glacial valleys they are not necessarily in perfect alignment there with the positions of the pre-glacial channels. A striking example of such a deviation was revealed by borings in the Caldew valley in Cumberland while investigating for the construction of a reservoir. The Tyne departs little from the exact line, but the Wear in central Durham is often engaged in cutting into the rock of the pre-glacial valley side, as is the Allen in its gorge below Staward. The uneven deposition of drift in valleys across which the ice had moved transversely rather than longitudinally predisposed post-glacial stream courses to show this excentric tendency. The contour of the drift surface here forced the new stream to cut down in the comparatively driftless side of the valley, which was often the eastern side. In this way glaciation has contributed to emphasise the asymmetric profile of many valleys. In addition to the examples already cited, the tributaries of the North Tyne and Rede show these features to a pronounced degree.

The Wear is especially interesting as exemplifying contrasts in valley types. Its composite valley includes the dale section, where the river is flowing southeast in the drift-covered floor of a broad, open, pre-glacial valley (Pl. 7); its northward course in central Durham also occupies a pre-glacial valley carved in front of the Magnesian Limestone, but it is often engaged in cutting into the rock side of this valley; finally, beyond the abrupt eastward bend of the river at Chester-le-Street, the lower Wear valley is post-glacial—a deep gorge cut across the limestone plateau, which was prepared by the overflow that drained a glacial lake.

As compared with its pre-glacial ancestor, the Tyne is beheaded. The upper Irthing occupied a pre-glacial valley which turns towards the Tyne in the Tyne gap; but here deposition of drift and fluvio-glacial material has diverted its drainage towards the Eden, and at Gilsland it is now engaged in cutting a rocky gorge towards the west.

Such repeated contrasts between broad, open, pre-glacial valleys, in which an infilling of drift has further reduced the relief, and post-glacial gorges or ravines are among the most striking features of scenic diversity in North England. 'Dale' is a place-name especially associated with the former, and smaller, but open, and fairly mature, tributary valleys are often called 'hopes'. The post-glacial notches are 'denes' in the area of Anglian place-names, 'gills' in those areas where the place-names are of Scandinavian origin. Among them are such deep-cut post-glacial valleys as the denes of the east Durham plateau and the gills of northeast Yorkshire. Cleft-like gullies in dale sides, of extremely youthful character, are often called 'cleughs', and some of the more striking spillway trenches, suspended in spurs and watersheds, are known by the same name. In the Lake District, glacial over-deepening of main valleys has left the side valleys hanging above them, and the tributary streams that empty into the main valleys by gorges and waterfalls are sometimes picturesquely named 'Sourmilk Beck'.

The late-glacial or post-glacial level of the land was probably higher than today, but there has been partial recovery from the subsequent drowning, and besides submerged forests there are also traces of raised beaches at intervals along the coasts. In north Northumberland, where the limestone measures of the lower Carboniferous meet the coast, their resistant beds, including the Whin Sill, form a succession of bold promontories between small bays (Fig. 58). The Farne Islands are outlying fragments of the Whin Sill, which forms the headland of Bamburgh (Pl. 19) and again appears on the coast to the south, from Dunstanburgh to Craster. Passing south along the Northumberland coast the amplitude of the bays becomes generally greater, and between the sandstone headlands are more extensive stretches of smooth, drift-fringed coast. In some at least of the bays, e.g. Druridge Bay and Whitley Bay, are the seaward ends of drift-plugged pre-glacial valleys. The present river mouths are not in harmony with the major features of the coastal graining.

From just north of the Tyne to Hartlepool the Magnesian Limestone forms a rocky cliff coast, breached only by the estuaries of the Tyne and Wear, though notched by many post-glacial denes. Then, between Hartlepool and Saltburn, the lowlying shores of the Tees estuary mark the seaward end of the great strike-vale in the Triassic rocks. There follow the imposing cliffs of the Estuarine Series of the Inferior Oolite, reaching 660 feet at Boulby.

The lowlying shore of the Solway Firth, with extensive tidal mud-flats, is rarely in contact with the island-like mounds of drift that rise inland above extensive tracts of peat-covered and terraced marine warp —the Solway mosses or ' flows '. Associated raised-beach gravels, produced by uplift of shingle spits, form the present shoreline. A post-Roman breach in this fringe is responsible for the irregular re-entrant, Moricambe Bay. Farther south this lowlying coast is suc-ceeded by a cliff coast of Coal Measures rocks, and, from St Bees Head, of Triassic sandstone, with some stretches of raised-beach gravels that are especially well preserved near Workington.

To the major scenic contrasts between upland surfaces with drift-free slopes and the drift-covered lowlands, and between mature pre-glacial forms and young post-glacial forms both in individual valleys and between one valley and another, there are added others that arise from differences in rock-type and in the nature of the drift and the form of its deposition. These last have already been noted, and so has the fact that, because the greater part of North England is com-posed of flexured and warped, but not highly folded masses of strongly stratified rocks, the varied rock nature is expressed in the scenery chiefly by the prominent development of cuesta forms.

It remains to draw further attention to the cuesta ridges that pro-trude from the drift, and to the individuality of the two areas of pre-Carboniferous rocks in the Cheviot massif and the Lake District. The rapid alternation of inclined shales, sandstones, and occasional lime-stones that is typical not only of the Carboniferous but also of the Triassic and Jurassic succession is responsible for a great many scarp-forming outcrops, but some are only local, representing the development of lenticular masses of harder rocks. The positions of the chief scarp features are shown on Figure 8. The most prominent and extensively developed escarpments east of the Pennines are associated with the Fell Sandstone, the grits, limestones, and Whin Sill of the limestone measures, massive sandstones in the Coal Measures that occur especially above the main productive measures, the Magnesian Limestone, and the flaggy grits of the Inferior Oolite. In the coastal belt of north Northumberland, traversed obliquely by the outcrops of the limestone measures, scarped hills emerge occasionally above the drift but do not form continuous lines. In southwest Northumberland where these outcrops sweep west towards the Tyne gap they dip fairly steeply south to the synclinal trough in front of the North Pennine massif. Rapid alternations of thin and steeply tilted limestones above and below the Great Limestone, with the Whin Sill itself, here give a very pronounced cuesta relief (Pl. 17), the limestone scars appearing in rapid succession between the Roman Wall and the river Tyne.

West of the Pennines the more massively developed Carboniferous Limestone, the Penrith Sandstone, and the St Bees Sandstone, are responsible for the major cuestas in the bands of rocks that surround the Lake District. In the coalfield to the west, which is much cut up by intersecting faults, the Whitehaven Sandstone tends to form tilted horst blocks.

Contrasts between strike-line valleys and those that are cut transversely across the grain of the outcrops are noteworthy. Whereas in the former each side presents a remarkably smooth, even skyline as viewed from within the valley or from the opposite side, in the latter their outlines are notched by the craggy profiles of the intersected escarpments. The sides of the North Tyne valley below Wark, where the river cuts across the successive limestones and the Whin Sill, show this feature conspicuously, as do the valleys of the Coquet and the Aln between the sub-Cheviot lowland and the sea. In the Aln basin the separation of resistant sandstones by shale bands is responsible for a triple line of crags south of the river—Callaly, Lorbottle, and Edlingham crags.

The different orientations of the dales in relation to the trend of the geological outcrops, which themselves vary in facies, introduces many variants and imparts much of their distinctiveness to individual dales. Asymmetric cross-valley profiles are the rule and, as has already been noted, this feature has often been accentuated by the disposition of the drift infilling. In major features, such as the vale of Eden and Glendale, and in innumerable tributary valleys that enter the Northumbrian dales, asymmetry is equally characteristic.

The dales of the northern Pennines form inliers cut down into the Yoredale rocks (Fig. 61). Various limestones (eight in all), from the Tynebottom to the Fell Top, outcrop along the sides of the dales as ' feature-making ' beds that sometimes form distinct benches. But, like the dales of northeast Yorkshire cut down in the slab-like estuarine series of the Inferior Oolite, the Pennine dales show a more symmetrical character in cross-profile. As a result of the outward dip of the rocks from the Cross Fell dome, the dale streams ultimately pass from the strata that contain these limestones on to the non-calcareous rocks of the upper portion of the Carboniferous sequence. The passage across the Great Limestone, second below the Fell Top and thickest and most regular of the limestones, has considerable economic significance as marking the usual limit of the productive ore-mining area of the upper dales. It is the Great Limestone and the series below it that have yielded most of the ore.

The igneous massif of the Cheviot and the strongly folded pre-Carboniferous rocks in the heart of the Lake District give rise to quite different scenery, and the distinctiveness of the Lake District that is an expression of structure is reinforced by the rôle that glacial erosion has there played in developing the scenery. Within six or eight miles of the Cheviot itself (2,676 ft.) the radiating streams have reached lowlands below 500 feet, so that their valleys are deeply scored in the igneous rocks along crush lines. Yet in spite of the extreme vigour of the relief, craggy forms are remarkably lacking, and the steep valley-sides rise rounded and grassy (Pl. 2) to the bevelled ridges, with sur-mounting monadnocks.

In the Lake District the radial drainage pattern that has been super-imposed from a surface of younger rocks upon the folded pre-Carboni-ferous massif has lost some of its symmetry by adjustment to the shatter-belts that traverse the ancient rocks. Along these shatter-belts, valley development has been able to proceed rapidly, and modification of the original drainage pattern by successive captures has followed. As well as to the abrasive action of ice in truncating spurs, the Lake District valleys owe their straightness in some sections to their coin-cidence with shatter-belts. Some of the easy passes that interconnect valleys at their heads are likewise attributable to them. Honister, Sty Head, Wrynose, and Dunmail Raise all follow the lines of shatter-belts.

Only in the Lake District are the erosional forms of ice action really predominant, though even there the high summits above about 2,000 feet show the rounded pre-glacial surface more or less unmodified by moving ice. Even before glaciation there must have been significant differences between the scenery of the slate country and that of the volcanic or granite rocks, but ice action has greatly emphasised the contrasts (cf. Pls. 9–15). The massively jointed and heterogeneous volcanic rocks have been susceptible to the plucking action of ice and have become very craggy and rugged, with masses of harder lavas and coarse breccias standing out as cliffs and scars. In these massive rocks cirque and arête forms are better developed than in the slates to the north and south, where abrasion by smoothing and rounding, not pluck-ing, has been predominant and smoothly rounded, rather conical forms are general. The Skiddaw Slates give more uniform scenery than the more varied slates and grits to the south, but the latter, although more diverse, also generally form lower and more gently sloping country than the steep hills of the Skiddaw Slates.

In the granite areas, jointing has facilitated removal of rock by plucking, and some precipitous north and northeast facing crags are found in Ennerdale, but the granite has weathered deeply and has usually been abraded to form rounded knobs, which project through the peaty turf that fills the hollows on the higher ground—a knobbly rather than a craggy surface. Over and above these distinctive features, however, the scenery of the Lake District is unique in North England especially because of the sculpturing of its great radiating valleys by moving ice, the agent which also prepared the basins that are now occupied by the lakes.

CHAPTER 4

CLIMATE, SOILS, AND VEGETATION

Climate [1]

A CONSIDERABLE range of altitude and marked contrasts in degree of exposure to the principal air-streams that affect the climate of Britain are responsible for considerable differences of climate within North England. The alignment of the major physical features athwart the track of the prevailing winds combines with strong relief to emphasise contrasts between western and eastern sides of the isthmus, and between windward and leeward sides of individual ranges.

The most striking differences are in precipitation (Fig. 11). In the Lake District we find the wettest district in England, but round Tees-mouth and in places elsewhere on the east coast are found some of the lowest rainfall recordings in Britain. The mountain tops in the Scafell area are drenched by a rainfall which on the average exceeds 150 inches per annum, but the Tees valley east of Darlington gets less than 25 inches. In the west only a small area at the head of the Solway has as little as 30 inches, whereas on the eastern, lee side of the main highland backbone most of the lowlands up to a height of 400 or 500 feet receive less than this amount. The uplands of mid-Northumberland even at altitudes of 800 feet or more get only 40 inches, an amount that is attained only by the highest summits of the North York Moors, where the high ground is encircled by the 30-inch isohyet. On the windward side of the Lake District, even the coast has 40 inches south of Whitehaven, though the more sheltered lowlands farther north, as well as the vale of Eden, are appreciably drier. Over a large tract of the summits of the Lake District fells precipitation is more than 80 or 100 inches, and even at Keswick is 55 inches; the vale of Eden, in contrast, is a pronounced rainshadow, Penrith and Appleby receiving about 35 inches and Temple Sowerby barely 30 inches. Along the crest of the Pennine escarpment, the amount increases again rapidly to 70 inches or more, and from there diminishes steadily eastwards in Teesdale to 30 inches at Barnard Castle, and only 22 inches near Redcar on the coast. Farther north, where cuesta features are well developed, the progressive decrease east of the main watershed is interrupted. Thus

[1] Acknowledgment is made to Professor Gordon Manley not only for his published work on the climate of North England, upon which this section draws heavily, but also for his kindness in reading an early draft and in making helpful suggestions that have been incorporated.

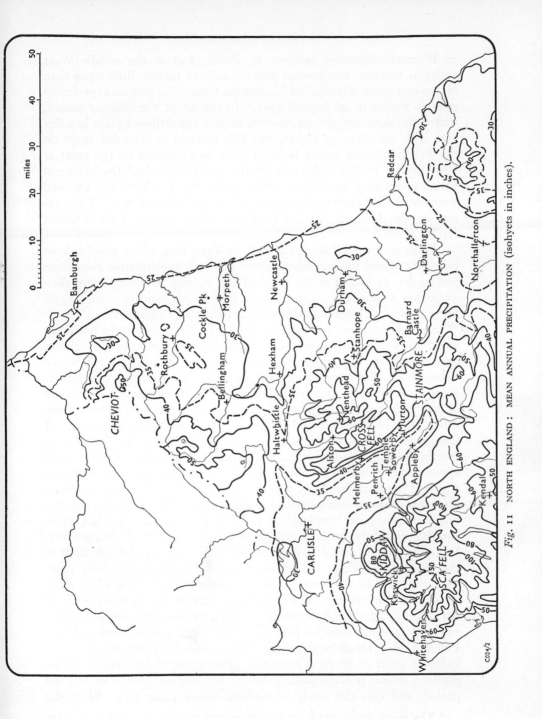

Fig. II NORTH ENGLAND : MEAN ANNUAL PRECIPITATION (isohyets in inches).

in Weardale Stanhope receives 35 inches, but in the middle Wear valley at Durham the amount falls to only 27 inches, little more than on the east coast, whereas the Magnesian Limestone plateau experiences over 30 inches in its western part. In the lee of the Cheviot massif, where the summits receive over 50 inches, the Milfield plain is a dry area with less than 30 inches, but this amount is exceeded again on the Fell Sandstone moors before falling to 25 inches on the coast at Bamburgh. In the dales east of the main watershed the sheltered valley floors may have from 10 to 15 inches less than the exposed watersheds, but even so the upper dales are distinctly wet. They are not as wet, however, as the lowlying valleys of the Lake District farther west.

From west to east along the Solway-Tyne line, where relief is least pronounced and the watershed below 500 feet, precipitation rises from just under 30 inches at the head of the Solway to rather more than 35 inches in the Tyne gap west of Haltwhistle, and decreases again to 30 inches at Haydon Bridge and 25 inches at Tynemouth.

Summer temperatures increase slightly southwards, but the northerly situation of the province makes for relatively cool summers throughout, and the mean temperature for the warmest month is everywhere below 60°F. But whereas winters give a general impression of mildness along the west coast they are cold and raw in the east, and snow occurs at low altitudes more frequently in northeast England than in any other part of England and Wales. Along the southwest coast of Cumberland the January mean is above 41°F, but in the lowlands of Northumberland and Durham it exceeds 39°F at only a few favoured spots very close to the sea coast. A large part of the province, and even much of the settled country within it, lies considerably above sea level, and this reduces temperatures appreciably. In the heart of the northern Pennines, Nenthead at 1,500 feet above sea level has mean January and July temperatures of only 33°F and 54°F respectively. Professor Manley has drawn attention to the very rapid diminution in the effective length of the growing season,[1] from considerably more than 200 days in the lowlands below 700 feet (beginning of April to second week in November) to 165 days at Moor House in Teesdale at 1,840 feet (5 May to 28 September), and only 128 days on the Pennine summits as represented by Dun Fell (2,780 feet) a little south of Cross Fell (23 May to 28 September). This altitudinal rate of change is twice as great as in New England. Reduction in the length of the growing season is accompanied also by less intense growth during the period, and oats can rarely be ripened above 1,200 feet. Since the

---

[1] The period during which the daily mean temperature rises above 42°F. The dates given are the mean dates of first and last days with this critical temperature.

duration of cloud and the frequency and amount of precipitation all increase rapidly with altitude also, there are sharp gradations of vegetation and rapid variation in potential land use.

The juxtaposition of the lowlying vale of Eden and the high Pennine plateau along the great Pennine escarpment is responsible for one of the most strongly developed local winds in Britain, the notorious ' helm ' wind. When a cold and cloudy northeasterly air stream moves across the Pennine plateau a dense mass of cloud gathers and rests on the western summits like a helmet ; associated with it, the northeaster descends the escarpment with unusual vigour and blows very strongly at the foot, although a short distance farther west conditions become much quieter. The helm wind may develop at any time of year, but is most liable to occur in late winter or spring. It may be experienced anywhere along the length of the escarpment and on any single occasion may extend for several miles in breadth, but it is most frequent between Melmerby and Murton, where many shelter-belts of trees have been planted along the scarp foot to give some protection against its icy blasts.

In enclosed lowlands such as the vale of Eden, Glendale, and the middle Wear valley, acute temperature-inversions frequently develop and substantially increase the risk of damaging frost. Where the floors or haughlands of incised valleys are fairly wide, remarkably low minimum temperatures may be recorded, as at the Durham county agricultural station at Houghall in the Wear valley near Durham city, where −6°F has more than once been noted. The hollows in the often-irregular drift cover of the lowlands are also frequently local frost-pockets, while high in the Pennines in the frosty valley near Nenthead a temperature of −9°F was recorded in January 1881, and frost has been experienced even in August. The lowest August temperature yet known in Britain, 27°F, was recorded here in 1885.

The coastal areas do not compare unfavourably with most of the country in amount of sunshine, but over most of North England, and especially in the dales, cloudy conditions are very prevalent. The poet Swinburne aptly wrote of the ' cloud-clogged sunshine ' of his native north country. Rain may be expected in the dales on more than seventeen days in August and on more than fourteen days in both July and September. The summers are relatively cool, moist, and cloudy, and quite apart from disabilities imposed upon cultivation of corn, the winning of hay, which is the main crop over most of the area, is a difficult and protracted operation. The traditional practice after mowing is to rake the hay into small heaps (kyles) for preparation into larger ones (pikes) for leading in when dried. The whole process often drags on far into September in the upper dales. At best the harvest is late, for grass growth is late in commencing. Late snowstorms after Easter frequently cause serious losses of sheep at lambing time. Even in the coastal lowlands on the east side spring is tardy, owing to the strong influence of the North Sea at this time of year, and even in May or June raw, cloudy weather and sea-frets are common along the coast.

The relatively high frequency of winds between northeast and east during spring, which is a well-known feature of our British climate, has noteworthy effects throughout the isthmian area of North England. The characteristic 'helm' wind of the fellside villages above Edenside has already been mentioned and tends to be most frequent in spring ; but the effects of the cold, dry, descending air west of the Pennines extend more widely. Grass makes but little growth, and the Lake District and Solway shores suffer much more frequently from a combination of cold, clear nights and spring drought than might at first be thought. In a countryside so largely dependent upon the grass crop a dry May, such as may happen from time to time, can be a serious matter. East of the Pennines, on the other hand, the frequency of northeasterly winds, accompanied by a good deal of low cloud, keeps afternoon temperatures low, and it is understandable that the mean temperature for May does not begin to exceed 50°F until we are south of the Tees or west of Stainmore and the Tyne gap. In a cold April or May, moreover, the rate of fall of temperature with height tends to be more pronounced than otherwise, and it is quite probable that there are years when at the heads of the Pennine dales no growth whatever begins until June. The vicissitudes of spring weather are especially serious here.

The general breeziness of the climate of North England confers the benefit of a general absence of fog. Away from the industrial areas of the northeast, lowland fog sufficient to impede traffic is rare. Even sheltered industrial and mining areas, where the otherwise slight valley mists are all too often reinforced by smoke so as to create poor visibility, do not suffer such dense fogs as are prevalent round Manchester, Glasgow, or London. If lowland fog is uncommon, low cloud often shrouds the hills in mist, however, and the traveller may cross Hartside Height many times without enjoying the wonderful prospect to the west which this road can offer to the fortunate motorist.

In the inland valleys thunder is heard on only about ten days in the year, far less often than in the English Midlands. Even so, occasionalc atastrophic floods have been known when, as in 1930, peculiarly intense storms develop locally in the Pennines. Long-continued orographic rains are more often responsible for bringing the rivers to spate, and even in the east this may happen at any time of year, as in August 1956. The worst floods known were those of

November 1771, which destroyed almost every bridge in the northeast including the old Tyne bridge at Newcastle. It seems that a deep snow-cover on the uplands was suddenly melted by extremely heavy and persistent rain.

The occasional heavy orographic precipitation on an east wind means that extremely heavy snowfalls are perhaps more liable to occur on the northeastern slopes of the Pennines than anywhere else in Britain. By far the heaviest widespread snowfall yet recorded was that of February 1941, when snow fell continuously for over fifty hours and attained a measured depth of 42 inches even on low ground at Durham.

Snow scarcely lies at all on the west coast, however, and on the Northumberland coast may be expected to cover the ground only on 7 or 8 days in the year. Inland, the duration of snow-cover increases to 10 days at Carlisle, and from 10 to 15 days in much of the Tyne valley. At Durham city it is already 17 days, and with increasing altitude the liability to snow increases rapidly as compared with the diminution of temperature, so that in the dales at 800 feet a snow-cover may be expected for an aggregate of from 30 to 35 days. At Alston, 1,000 feet above sea level, the period averages about 40 days; at Nenthead, 500 feet higher, it is 55 days; and around the highest habitations in upper Teesdale, above 1,800 feet, it is as much as 80 days. Cross Fell summit is covered with snow on about 120 days in the year; scattered drifts, however, last longer. During the winter of 1950–1 the summit was white on 191 days, and in that year snowdrifts lingered on Helvellyn until mid-July. Such persistence, however, is very rare. What is more important is that the highest fells of the Lake District, northern Pennines, and the Cheviot are all liable to be covered by snow in the aggregate for about four months of the year. Although a warm rain at any time will wash it all away, later in the season snow-cover quite frequently lasts through March and in some years through April into May. At high altitudes, moreover, snowfalls are often heavy and drifting severe, and snowploughs are regularly needed to clear roads in the dales. The main roads over Carter Bar, Hartside, and Stainmore are blocked by snow on one or more occasions every winter.

Soils

Under the prevailing cloudy, moist conditions, over much of North England the soils are strongly leached and bereft of mineral salts, and since they are derived for the most part from materials that are non-calcareous they generally tend to be acid. Moreover, there is frequently a prominent development of 'gley' characteristics. Waterlogging in the subsoil, and the occurrence above of a zone in which there is seasonal alternation of oxidising and reducing conditions, give the rusty streaking and mottling of a ' gley ' horizon.

On the extensive tracts of rain-drenched and only gently sloping upland, waterlogging is often so severe that widespread sheets of peat have formed. Much of the thick peat that occurs, however, is rather to be regarded as a residue from a past climate. The peat cover is often heavily eroded and shows manifest signs of wasting. Peaty soils are very extensive over the moorlands, and occur frequently in small basin-like hollows of the hummocky, drift surface in the lowlands. The ' mosses ' or ' flows ' around Solway head, Prestwick ' carrs ' in south Northumberland, and Bradbury, and Morden ' carrs ' in south Durham, are larger lowland tracts of black peaty soils, but the peat is ' mild ' compared with the acid moorland peats.

Parent materials that yield a large amount of detritus in weathering, and do not disintegrate to permit good subsoil drainage, are general. Not only is the prevalent drift mainly of this character, so also are the widespread grit and shale outcrops of the areas that are free from a covering of drift. The porphyritic slopes of the Cheviot and the outcrops of limestone that occur in the Carboniferous succession are exceptional. In the northern Pennines, and farther north in Northumberland these limestone beds are only thin and their outcrops are narrow, but the more massive limestones of the west give more extensive outcrops round the margins of the Lake District. These formations are well drained, and their thin soils are rich in alkalis. Although they are susceptible to physiological drought, their dry, stony loams are much more fertile than the prevailing acid soils of the uplands, which require drainage and heavy liming for their improvement and maintenance.

In the farmlands of the north country the physical characteristics of the soil, upon which its use for agriculture so largely depends, vary greatly with rapid variations in the depth of the drift, in its derivation and associated texture, and in the related conditions of subsoil drainage. The drift that is mapped uniformly by the Geological Survey as boulder-clay is really of very varied texture, and, quite apart from the more extensive spreads of sand and gravel, its surface is greatly diversified further by irregular patches of fluvio-glacial deposits. These in turn comprise a varied assortment of materials that display widely different degrees of coarseness and of removal of finer silty matter by washing. There can be few farms in the north of England on which soil conditions can be regarded as really homogeneous. In their broader distribution soils are especially variable in the vale of Eden and in the coastal plain of north Northumberland. So complex

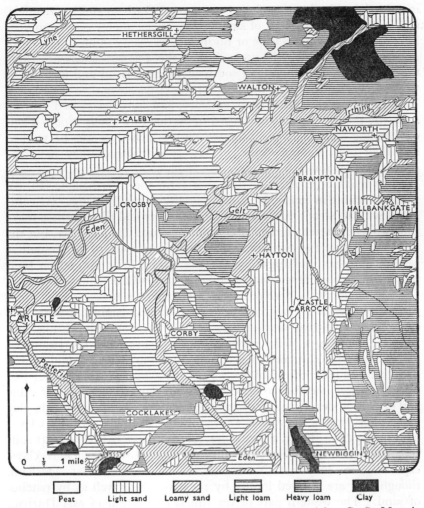

Fig. 12 SOIL-TEXTURE MAP OF THE AREA EAST OF CARLISLE (after G. S. Memoir, Sheet 18, Plate ix).

are the geographical distributions of those soil characteristics which matter most to the farmer that it is not surprising, but no less regrettable, that such little progress has been made towards provision of detailed soil-maps. For an area of 125 square miles in the district east of Carlisle a valuable soil-texture map is available, thanks to the praiseworthy enterprise of the surveyors who revised the Geological Survey 1 inch to 1 mile map (Sheet 18). Figure 12 is based upon this.

The fluvio-glacial sands extensively represented in this area at the mouth of the Tyne gap, and again in central Durham and in Glendale, and in widespread patches of smaller extent elsewhere, vary from very light sands that contain little or no humus to loamy sands. The latter are also typical of the drift derived from the Triassic sandstones along the west coast of Cumberland south of St Bees Head and in parts of the Eden lowlands, as well as of the terrace strips along the river valleys. These soils are all light, friable, and dry, and were designated ' turnip soils ' by the reporters to the Board of Agriculture about 1800. Their outstanding advantages are the ease with which they can be worked and their good natural drainage. In special degree they have the property of ' arability '.

The tracts of young alluvium that form the river-haughs (Pl. 8), though variable in constitution, are also often gravelly loams. As compared with adjacent areas, their relative fertility and their flatness make the haughs important agricultural tracts, especially in the dales, but the high water-table and liability to flooding cause them to be avoided as settlement sites. Buildings keep to the firmer, drier ground on their margins, as is well illustrated in Glendale around the Milfield plain.

The boulder-clay derived from Carboniferous rocks or even from Triassic shales and clays, and more locally the laminated lacustrine clays, yield soils that may usually be described as heavy loams, but they are sometimes sticky clays. The soils overlying the laminated clays differ from the boulder-clay soils in being stoneless, and on the warp lands round the head of the Solway the marine silts have developed deep, stoneless, medium to heavy soils with clay subsoils. Their value and utilisation depend upon drainage conditions. Heavy, reddish, clay loams are typical of the vale of Tees and there is an old saying : ' Cleveland in the clay. Bring in two soles, Carry one away.' The drift soils that cover much of the coalfields are also heavy, tenacious clays, especially in southeast Northumberland and northeast Durham, though they are relieved locally by rock islands as well as by patches of sand. The western part of the limestone plateau of east Durham is covered by only thin, dry, and stony loams, but coastwards the spread of drift becomes more continuous and the soils heavier. Cold, stiff, stony soils are also typical of much of the drift areas in the dales.

Vegetation

When man first appeared upon the scene the lowlands of northern England must everywhere have been clothed with broad-leaved deciduous forest, in which there were variations of richness and density according to altitude and exposure as well as soil and drainage. The prevailing heavy soils were probably densely covered with damp oakwood, with alder and willow swamps where the water-table was especially high, as on the haughs and other stretches of lowlying alluvium. Drier terrains, such as the sheets of fluvio-glacial sand and gravel, the valley terraces, and the limestone outcrops, probably carried a more open type of oak-birch or ash woodland. Along the upper limit of the woodland was a fringing zone where pine and birch were more typical than oak—remnants of the earlier pinewoods that oak and other deciduous trees had replaced. Today the removal of this tree-cover is almost complete except for hedgerow trees and scattered, small woods, which most frequently remain on steep valley-sides (Pls. 3, 5, 13, 16), notably in the post-glacial valleys where these are cut deeply into drift and rock. In the vegetation pattern the gills and denes often appear as birch or ash streaks.

Above the limit of farmland, which usually lies between 700 and 1,000 feet, are open moorlands (Fig. 13), but it is certain that woodland once covered most of this upland area. Not only do scattered trees, and even fragments of woodland, extend much higher, there are also abundant evidences of tree remains, especially birch and pine, preserved in peat up to altitudes of 2,000 feet. In sheltered sites they have been found even higher, though on the exposed western flank of the Lake District hills it has been suggested by Professor W. H. Pearsall that the tree-line may never have risen above about 800 feet.

The warm, dry (boreal) conditions that formed one phase in the progressive amelioration of the climate after the retreat of the ice lasted until about 7000 B.C., and allowed colonisation of northern England by woodland, at first birch and pine, followed by oak and other deciduous trees. About 5500 B.C., however, the climate appears to have become much wetter. During this ensuing Atlantic phase, oak forest reached its maximum development in Britain, but in the uplands of the north extensive tracts became so waterlogged that peat accumulated on a large scale. Spreading over the smooth upland surfaces as blanket bog, it encroached down the hillsides at the expense of the earlier woodland. Although the growth of basin peats and channel peats, which occupy areas of anomalous, indeterminate drainage, mainly glacial channels at a variety of levels, may have been continuous down to the present time, that of the hill-top peats slowed down or stopped altogether during the relatively dry and warm sub-boreal phase. Peat formation is no longer active on the drier eastern moorlands, and in the North York Moors, where the annual precipitation is less than 40 inches, all the existing peat is a relic from the past. Much of the shallower peat surfaces of North England, however, where the peat is less than 3 feet deep, are probably of fairly recent origin, and may be ascribed to the wetter sub-Atlantic phase since about 700 B.C., when

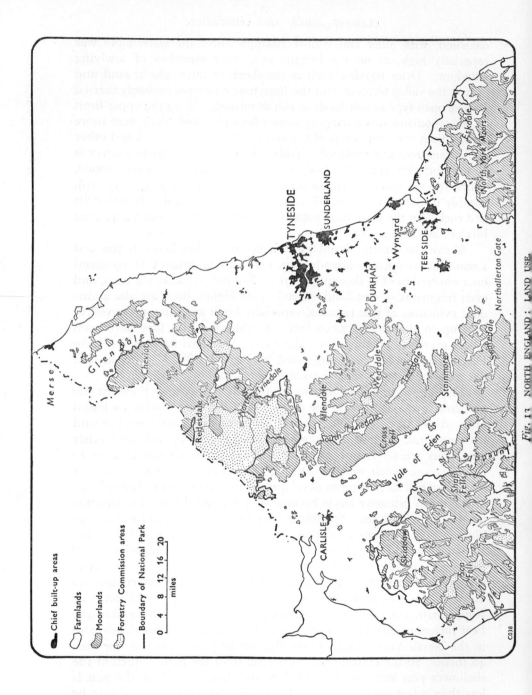

 labels (as shown on map):

Merse

Glendale
Cheviot
TYNESIDE
SUNDERLAND
North Tynedale
Redesdale
Allendale
DURHAM
Wynyard
TEESSIDE
South Tynedale
Weardale
Teesdale
Cross Fell
Stainmore
Swaledale
Vale of Eden
Cronkley
Northallerton Gate
CARLISLE
Skiddaw
Shap Fell
Sca Fell
North York Moors
Eskdale

Legend:

Chief built-up areas
Farmlands
Moorlands
Forestry Commission areas
Boundary of National Park

0 4 8 12 16 20
miles

C038

Fig. 13 NORTH ENGLAND : LAND USE

peat formation was renewed after the check or retardation it had suffered during the previous sub-boreal phase. But much of the deep peat is almost certainly much older, the product of a past climate. These deep hill-peats may be as much as 15 or 20 feet thick, but their upper surface is almost always eroded. It is characteristically ' hagged ', that is dissected by deep drainage channels cut down to drift or rock so that the peat remains only in blocks, which are being eroded by undercutting of their matted vegetation and dried by the drainage of their marginal channels. Once the mat of roots and foliage is broken, removal of peat by erosion is rapid along the channel sides.

Extension of moorland, with recession of the tree-line, has not been by any means a purely natural process that can be related simply to changes in climate. Since the Atlantic climatic phase, during which Neolithic man appeared in North England, human activity has contributed materially, and indeed principally, to modify the vegetation cover. Long before the direct attack from below began to make substantial encroachments upon the woodlands as land was cleared for agriculture, the vegetation along the zone of tension between the two major types of vegetation—woodland below and moorland above—was being profoundly altered by the presence of man, especially through the grazing activity of his animals. But even within the modern cultivated zone much of the land was deforested by pastoral and other human activity long before its reclamation for agriculture. There can be little doubt that the existing upland grasslands and much of the more truly moorland vegetation have succeeded woodland, and that the rest of the highland vegetation is derived ultimately from blanket bog.

Variations in the wild vegetation that has succeeded the woodland beyond the zone of cultivation depend partly upon soil and drainage conditions, and to a less extent directly upon climate, differences in which are chiefly an expression of altitude. The peat-clad tracts of upland surface, with acid conditions, are for the most part heather (*calluna*) and bilberry (*vaccinium*) moors. Heather and bilberry are closely associated elements of the moorland vegetation, but the latter extends higher, and above about 2,000 feet *vaccinium* moor tends to replace *calluna* moor, while below this altitude the dominance of heather has been accentuated by burning. Although heather is typical of really acid soil conditions it is intolerant of extreme conditions of saturation. For it to flourish there needs to be drying during part of the year, so that heather is characteristic of dried ' mor ' peats and of gley soils. Where the peat-layer is deep and natural drainage practically non-existent are found waterlogged areas from which heather is absent ; such tracts are no better than sedge moors, characterised by the sedge plants, especially so-called cotton-grass (*eriophorum*). Such water-logging, as compared with the ' mor ' peats or gley soils of which heather is more typical, occurs in the western moorlands, with their heavier precipitation, on steeper slopes than farther east. With lower precipitation, a more gentle slope is needed to produce the same degree of waterlogging.

At its worst the bog is dominated by *sphagnum* moss, a blanket of moss through which shoots of other bog plants protrude. But although *sphagnum* and other bog plants are well-represented species in the moorland vegetation, tracts of *sphagnum* moss, such as are much in evidence in the Pennines farther south, are not extensive in North England. It is evident from the structure of the underlying deep peat, however, that it has been derived chiefly from sphagnum. Everything points to the succession of the present vegetation from the blanket bog of an earlier climate. Sedge moor, and even some heather and bilberry moor overlying deep but hagged peat, represent degeneration of blanket bog. Indeed there are localities in the Stainmore area where burning or grazing is known to have brought about this succession within the last half-century. Undoubtedly, drainage operations have greatly extended the tracts of dried ' mor ' peat.

Heather moorland is very typical of the Fell Sandstone hills between Glendale and the Northumberland coast, and of the grit moorlands that extend southwest across mid-Northumberland, including Rothbury Forest. It covers extensive areas of the northern Pennines at intermediate altitudes, including especially the grit moorlands that fall away towards the Durham coalfield ; and it is equally typical of the drift-free summit plateau of the North York Moors. Large areas of the upper surface of the northern Pennines rise above 2,000 feet along the main watershed and the prongs radiating from it, and here *vaccinium* replaces *calluna*, but boggy conditions are widespread and sedge moor is extensively present over large areas of the summit-plateau. The highest parts of the Pennines, including Cross Fell itself, as well as the mountain tops in the Lake District, show interesting associations of Alpine heath, including Alpine plants which may be survivors of the Pleistocene vegetation that existed on nunataks amid the sea of ice. The associations so far considered are all typical of peaty, acid conditions. Locally, however, there are permanently wet tracts enriched by mineral salts, where water carrying these salts leached from the higher ground runs down slopes or issues in springs. *Molinia* grass is especially typical of these ' flushes '.

Grasses, chiefly *molinia* and *nardus*, may become important and even dominant constituents of the moorland vegetation, and large areas are now grass moor. *Nardus*, or mat-grass, is especially characteristic of highly leached, acid soils, but also of fairly well-drained conditions such as exist on relatively steep slopes or on only thin, dry peat. 'White grass', another name by which *nardus* is commonly known, relates to its bleached appearance during much of the year. *Molinia*, which is known as purple moor-grass or flying bent, is more typical of wet patches, and is indeed a feature of the retrogression of mosses, where tussocky clumps have replaced the blanket cover. Though found on deep peat, it is also typical, as has been noted, of surfaces saturated with running water, the 'flushes'. *Molinia* pastures, with much rush (*juncus*) are common on relatively lowlying areas that have cold, wet soils, such as are so widespread on the drift-covered uplands that extend towards the Border north of the Tyne valley and farther west. Some of this *molinia*-rush country is the product of neglect of formerly farmed fields, which have become sub-marginal land. With undergrazing and failure to maintain drains, *molinia* and rushes have spread. On the other hand, drying and heavy grazing lead to the replacement of *molinia* by *nardus*. On limestone surfaces and on the steep porphyritic slopes of the Cheviot, where conditions are not acid, sheep's fescue is found in association with *nardus*, giving much richer grazing. In the areas where limestones are present as members of the Yoredale facies, they are often noticeable in the relief as benches on the valley-sides ; but they are even more conspicuous in the colouring of the landscape at certain seasons by their verdance. They stand out as bright green strips of fresh grass, known as ' gairs ', in contrast with the dull and sombre shades that prevail. Instead of tussocky clumps of *nardus* and *molinia*, a turf composed of relatively short, sweet grasses, such as sheep's fescue and meadow grass, makes these outcrops altogether richer, and much less seasonal, pasture.

Above the low tree-line, the Lake District mountains are predominantly grassy, apart from interruptions of the plant cover by crag and scree. Much of the surface is so steep that peat, although it is present locally in basin-like hollows among the crags, is not developed over extensive moorland surfaces as in the Pennines. The Lake District fells are thus usually grasslands, *agrostis* and *festuca* on drier tracts, *nardus* and *juncus* on damper, drift-covered slopes. Heather moors are found chiefly on parts of the Skiddaw slate country in the north and on the Bannisdale flags and grits in the south.

It would be a mistake, however, to express the distribution of different types of moorland simply in terms of physical correlations. The present vegetation can be understood only as the product of a succession of changes since the retreat of the ice, and if the changes were at first entirely natural, they have later been a combination of natural and man-induced modifications of the earlier plant-cover. The present-day vegetation of the moorlands, hardly less than that of the farmlands themselves, is held in delicate balance which depends upon the manner and intensity of its human use and treatment. That this is manifestly so is frequently shown by the sharp, sudden changes in plant associations that exist along arbitrary lines of man's making, notably the striking differences that may often be seen on opposite sides of a boundary wall.

Grassland in particular is not a natural formation, but a product of grazing. This is the main and often the only factor that maintains the dominance of grasses over the extensive areas which they cover beyond the present limit of enclosed farmland. Great expanses of grass moorland cover the Border hills, and elsewhere an irregular fringe of grass moor commonly interposes on the dale slopes between the moorland edge and the other moorland associations of the higher areas. If grazing is at all relaxed the grasslands below about 1,200 feet are invaded by bracken, and in modern times this has taken place on an extensive scale (Pls. 2, 15). It has greatly modified the colour pattern of the Lake District landscape since the time of Wordsworth. The replacement of cattle by sheep has removed the most effective check, that of heavy trampling, and the alternative of systematic periodic rolling is too costly now. Sir George Stapledon has drawn attention to the great areas of bracken-covered country on the Border hills as evidence of eminently improvable land.

Bracken, however, does not extend above about 1,200 feet, and undergrazing at higher altitudes leads rather to invasion by heather. That heather moor is so prominent a feature of the moorland landscapes in North England reflects the use of large areas of moorland for grouse-shooting (Pl. 7). Young heather is the essential food of grouse, and grouse moor is managed with the object of stimulating its growth. This is done by periodic burning at intervals of from seven to fifteen years, which assists heather as compared with less woody plants and as compared with *vaccinium* because the latter does not seed so heavily. If, however, heather moor is subjected to too-frequent burning or is overgrazed by sheep, it passes into *nardus* moorland. Much moorland is of course put to the twin uses of sheep-grazing and grouse-rearing; its relative value for these purposes can quickly be modified through control of the vegetation as between grass and heather.

The grasslands themselves vary a great deal locally in constitution according to the grazing pressure to which they are subject, though they show marked tolerance of a variety of soil conditions. When heavily grazed, *molinia* gives place to *nardus*. *Nardetum* is in fact an index association of moorland that is heavily stocked, or even over-stocked, with sheep. It may be mentioned, however, that in recent decades the rough grazings have not been so heavily stocked with sheep, for wethers are no longer kept to graze the moors in winter, and their winter carry is reduced to the flocks of breeding ewes.

In early times the upper edges of the woodlands among the open stands of birch and pine, and the adjacent moors, were the haunts of red deer. In the Middle Ages large areas of North England were claimed and reserved as deer forest for the king and the Border lords such as the Bishop of Durham, whose deer forest covered an extensive area in Weardale. The later extension of sheep grazing not only pushed back the tree-line; above it sedge moor was converted into grass moor, and the deer retreated into ever more restricted fastnesses as the sheep increased in number and spread. In the Lake District both upper Ennerdale and Wasdale were deer forest as late as the seventeenth century, but the single herd of red deer that range in the Helvellyn area are the only survivors, the last truly wild deer in North England. Sheep are the grazing animals of the moorland today. Hill-sheep farming was important early as a specialised activity in the areas operated by or for the Cistercian monastic houses; but the emphasis of the pastoral life elsewhere was upon cattle. Summer grazing of the moorlands by cattle was the basis of widespread transhumance until comparatively modern times. It is of interest to note, moreover, that in the wilderness of the Border fells herds of wild cattle roamed late. A surviving herd of wild white cattle is preserved in Chillingham Park, Northumberland (near Wooler), though it was almost exterminated by the severe winter of 1946–7.

The different uses made of the moorlands at different times and in different areas—deer hunting, cattle grazing, sheep grazing, and grouse shooting—different combinations of some of these, and especially different intensities of grazing, have all played a significant part in producing the complex and essentially unstable pattern of the moorland vegetation. Apart from the effects of his grazing animals upon the moorland, man has further contributed to the differences by his deliberate treatment of the vegetation to modify its constitution. Periodic burning and paring, and measures taken in attempts to improve drainage, have undoubtedly transformed extensive tracts. No wonder that all transitions between grass heath and true moorland communities are found.

The interplay of such a diversity of physical and biotic factors, both past and present, means not only that the moorland vegetation is mixed so that it consists of various blends of the constituent species, but that it is also essentially a complicated mosaic of patches of the different types of moorland vegetation we have described above. The map on the scale of 1 inch to 10 miles, published in 1946, is very much

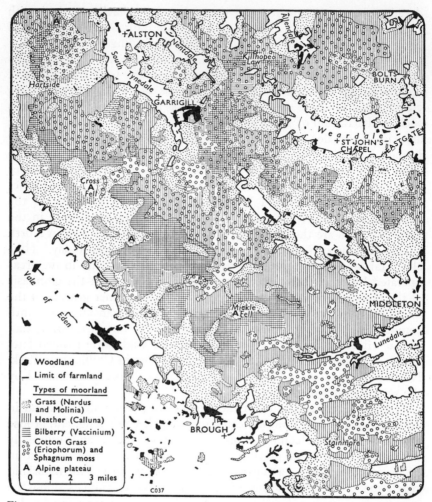

Fig. 14 VEGETATION OF THE NORTHERN PENNINES ABOUT 1900 (adapted from F. J. Lewis).

generalised, and the moorland tracts have in reality nothing like the simplicity of vegetation pattern and homogeneity over extensive areas that it might suggest. Figure 14 shows a more detailed representation of the vegetation of part of the northern Pennines as mapped by Dr F. J. Lewis half a century ago; but even this is considerably generalised, and locally there have been significant changes since.

The mining activities carried on with varying degrees of intensity over a long period in various parts of North England have been responsible for some direct clearance of woodland. For smelting the

66

silver-lead ores worked in the Middle Ages in the northern Pennines charcoal was used, and an important right granted by the Crown to the medieval miners of Alston Moor was that to cut timber. The sixteenth- and seventeenth-century mining activity in the Lake District resulted in considerable destruction of the local forests, as did the working of the iron ores of Furness over a longer period. In 1700 we find that three of four forges then operating in Furness were transferred to Scotland because of depletion of the local timber supplies. In other ways, too, the operations of the palmy days of mining activity, especially the smelting and large-scale mine-drainage undertakings and waterpower projects, have played their part in modifying the character of the moorlands, the first by spreading poisonous lead fumes, the others by altering run-off conditions over considerable areas.

There were scattered bloomeries in several districts of North England, but charcoal smelting of iron ore never developed so intensively here as in some other parts of the country, and some of the most voracious consumers of timber—domestic heating and certain types of industrial operation—early found a satisfactory alternative available locally in the form of coal. The needs of primitive coal-working itself for timber props were not comparable with those of more modern mining, pursued for long distances underground. Indirectly, however, the growth of the coal trade, by creating a need for collier vessels to ship the coal, so stimulated shipbuilding that great inroads were made into the woodlands which until the sixteenth century had clothed the sides of the Derwent valley southwest of Tyneside.

These factors, although they might be of local importance, had nothing like the general effect of agricultural colonisation in reducing woodland. While pasture encroached upon the forests from the moorlands above, farmland ate into the woodland along the valleys and up the valley sides. The deforestation was virtually completed by the eighteenth century, a considerable time before the farmland had been extended to its present limits, and the later accessions to the cultivated area were wrung entirely from the moorlands. These extensions were made during the century preceding 1850, the period that also saw the beginnings of afforestation.

From that time there has been much planting, though not with trees that were typical of the former woodlands. The planting by private landowners that was extensively carried out during the nineteenth century was especially characteristic of the farming zone, where the plantations often served also as useful shelter-belts. Conifer plantations with rectilineal outlines are a conspicuous element of the landscape (Pls. 5, 8), especially in the upper zone of farmland, where they fleck the grass-green countryside with sombre patches of darker shade.

67

Some of the nineteenth-century plantations, however, were established on very marginal land, as for example those of the Beaumont estate at the head of Allendale and others made elsewhere in the Pennine dales by the London Lead Company. Above Allenheads plantations ascend alongside the road to a height of 1,750 feet, and in a side-valley of upper South Tynedale east of Garrigill the uppermost trees of the large Ashgill plantation extend up to 2,000 feet. These are probably the highest woodlands in England.

More recently afforestation on a much larger scale has been undertaken by some of the municipal water-supply authorities in their water catchment areas surrounding highland reservoirs, as notably in the Thirlmere valley, and especially by the Forestry Commission (Fig. 13). On the outer fringes of the Lake District the Forestry Commission undertook extensive planting in the inter-war years, but on a far larger scale the Border fells are now being reclothed with forest. Since 1920 a total area of over 170,000 acres (about 280 sq. miles) has been appropriated on the Border, most of it on the English side. Kielder, the largest of these State Forests, occupies a remarkably extensive and compact area at the head of North Tynedale above Falstone (Fig. 59). Planting began here in 1926, and the programme of establishing 45,000 acres, mainly with Sitka and Norway spruce, is nearly fulfilled. The forest ranges from 500 feet in the valley-floor to 1,250 feet for regular planting and 1,500 feet for experimental planting. By 1975 it is expected that the output will reach nearly $1\frac{1}{4}$ million cubic feet per annum (40,000 tons), and thinnings are now producing pit-props for the coal-field. A planned new forestry village of 250 houses is being built on the dale floor (Pl. 4) near the pseudo-medieval castle which the Percies erected as a shooting lodge in 1775. Smaller, but considerable, forests have been established in the neighbouring dales of the Rede and the Kershope Burn, while farther south are other new forest blocks in the desolate wastes north of Hadrian's Wall. The gritstone hills of mid-Northumberland near Rothbury and farther southwest at Harwood, and the flanks of the northern Pennines in Hexhamshire at Slaley and near the margin of the Durham coalfield in Weardale and Derwentdale carry other Forestry Commission plantations.

To preserve the fell scenery of the heart of the Lake District, although this is a man-induced landscape with a mantle of vegetation that is far from natural in any true sense, the Forestry Commission gave an undertaking to the Council for the Preservation of Rural England in 1936 not to acquire land for afforestation within a prescribed area of roughly 300 square miles (Fig. 66). This agreement has more recently been modified to allow some temporary softwood planting in this area to replace tracts which were under timber trees in

1936. The decision to maintain the characteristic scenery of the reserved area and in particular not to transform its hardwood vegetation has been reaffirmed. Just outside the reserved area the Forestry Commission has undertaken extensive planting of conifers to the east of Skiddaw at Greystoke, but especially on the western side of the Lake District hills at Thornthwaite, Ennerdale, and in the Forest Park of Hardknott astride the Duddon-Esk watershed. In the last-named area forestry policy has been integrated with preservation of scenery in a tract of country to which public access is assured by its designation as a national park.

There is still a heavily wooded district in the south of the Lake District round Windermere (Pl. 14), and this is of long standing. Charcoal burning was for long an important feature of its economy, and when the smelting industry of Furness underwent changes that reduced the market for charcoal, the woodland economy was re-oriented to find outlets for its products in the manufacture of gun-powder and especially of cotton bobbins. For these purposes the woods were generally maintained as some form of coppice, and even today they are noteworthy for the abundance of small timber (hazel and birch) as well as for the considerable variety of species.

The Census of Woodlands of 1947–9, which recorded 180,000 acres of woodland in the four northern counties, shows that the proportion of the total area that is wooded conforms to the national average, but a considerably higher proportion, altogether one third, is State Forest, concentrated in large blocks. About two-thirds of the woodland area recorded by the Census, which ignored plots of less than 5 acres, was classed as high forest. Of this about 40,000 acres were broad-leaved stands, and 84,000 acres conifers. Coppice is an inconsiderable element in the woodland cover of the northern counties, except in Westmorland, and most of the woodland area not classed as high forest by the Census was felled, the remainder being either scrub or devastated.

Before proceeding to a consideration of the people whose successive appraisals of the environment in terms of developing capacities and changing needs have developed the country from its primeval state into the present humanised landscape, one may venture to summarise the salient contributions to the distinctiveness of the environment of North England, considered both as a regional entity and as a complex association of varied sites and surface facets.

A surface that is in general conspicuously smooth, its outlines bearing witness to extensive bevellings in pre-glacial times in relation to successive base-levels and to the further rounding and infilling actions of the ice-sheets themselves, soils that have been derived largely from the extensive coating of ground-moraine left behind by the ice, and a climatic range of limited latitudinal extent, all make for a measure of homogeneity in the aspect of North England and in the significance of the country as a setting for the people by whom it has been colonised and developed.

Within this broadly homogeneous natural frame, however, considerable variety of rock formations, earth sculpture, soil conditions, and climate is responsible for a wealth of scenic contrasts and of human opportunities that the standard maps available would hardly lead one to suspect. Under the uninformative term, ' Lower Carboniferous ', or the misleading one, ' Carboniferous Limestone ', a uniform colouring on small-scale geological maps fails to do justice to the rapid local changes of rock-type that arise from the rhythmic Yoredale sequence of North England. The Geological Survey drift maps tell little of the variations in the constitution of the drift that are so important for farming, and no soil map exists to portray the complexity of the actual distribution of soil types. The special significance of small changes in altitude and orientation gives an effective range of climate out of proportion to a range of relief contained within a mere 3,000 feet, yet precipitation is the only element of this climatic variety that is familiar from maps. The Land Utilisation Survey makes no attempt to distinguish the fine detail of the vegetation mosaic in the extensive areas that lie above the limit of farmland, and even the 1 inch to 10 miles Vegetation map generalises the moorland vegetation for large tracts in terms of the most prevalent constituents.

In a countryside of coastal lowlands, cuesta ridges, and rolling plateau surfaces, the assemblage of landforms inherited from the Ice Age, and the vigorous post-glacial dissection by a drainage system related to a new coastline and corresponding very imperfectly to the detailed lineaments of the pre-glacial surface, are especially responsible for local scenic variety ; but it is man, reacting to the different opportunities of the varied environment of slope, soil, and climate, who has been responsible for the patchwork mantle of vegetation that now clothes the surface. Wild and untamed though much of this may appear to be, it expresses a fine adjustment between man and nature. The fells and moorlands, as well as the farmlands, bear witness to the duty exacted of the land by its people, and the changing scene they present is the product of successive calls and pressures exercised upon them by man.

Special and striking individuality has been imparted to certain districts by the winning of their mineral wealth, but outside the still restricted industrial and urban areas a farming economy holds sway.

Appreciation of the deep roots of the occupation of the land by a farming community, and of the fundamental stability of its geographical pattern, must not lead us to overlook the delicate balance presented in detail by the pattern of land-use and the geographical margins that apply at any particular time.

CHAPTER 5

THE EARLY OCCUPATION—PREHISTORIC AND ROMAN

THE colonisation and development of any territory are the result of appraisals by human societies, and express their particular outlook, ideas, and technical equipment. It is important, therefore, to examine the various constituent peoples who have contributed to the society concerned. Yet even in this very process the situation and physical character of the area in relation to the sources of the colonists have played an important part, favouring the entry of certain elements, excluding or filtering others.

Immigrants from the mainland of Europe have reached Britain by two distinct ways of approach—along an outer, western, or Atlantic front, and along an inner, eastern, or North Sea front. By the former, entry was made along the west and southwest coasts of Britain, the newcomers approaching either from the south from the coasts of western Europe and the Mediterranean Sea or from the north from the Scandinavian fiords. On the other hand, the east and southeast coasts of Britain have been approached directly from the mainland of Europe across the shallow continental seas. In relation to these respective ways of immigration and cultural penetration the western and eastern sides of North England, separated as they are by a broad backbone of highland, have played diametrically opposite rôles. By their orientation and framing physique the two faces of North England have been as singularly isolated from the currents that have entered from opposite sides of the isthmus as they have been accessible and open to penetration from the seas they front.

The eastern approach did not become important until the second millennium B.C., a fact which is perhaps connected with the process of evolution of the coasts of the North Sea and English Channel. Thus in Neolithic times the external human relations of Britain seem to have been mainly along the Atlantic side. In relation to this early occupation of Britain, before the Bronze Age, by people of Mediterranean stock who have contributed strongly to the racial composition in certain districts, and who have left widespread evidences of their culture in the form of their great stone monuments or megaliths and the long barrows in which they buried their dead collectively, the eastern side of North England was very much a negative region. It was a remote, isolated corner, far from the main centres of population such as Salisbury Plain, and not in easy connection with them by belts of continuously open and attractive country.

A few scattered Neolithic remains show that some infiltration took place by land routes that were probably offshoots from the northward spread of these people along the ridgeways of the English lowland. From these ridgeways there was certainly some intrusion on to the intermediate slopes of the highlands of central Britain. Such terrains

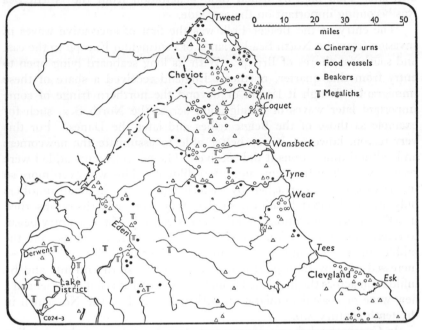

Fig. 15   NORTH ENGLAND : SOME PREHISTORIC DISTRIBUTIONS.

were the most attractive for the early immigrants, who avoided alike the heavily forested lowlands and floors of the dales and also the high, exposed, and ill-drained moorlands. Everywhere Neolithic settlement came late, and no long barrows have been found in North England. Megaliths, however, which are almost absent from Northumberland and Durham, are more numerous in Cumberland (Fig. 15). Stone circles are most thickly distributed in south Cumberland, along the coastal belt south of St Bees Head (Pl. 36), where their presence points to colonisation by a seafaring people. Others are found up the Derwent valley as far as Keswick and in the Eden valley, where they include Long Meg, but all are confined to the lowlands below 500 feet, in what must have been forested country. The distribution of polished stone axes corresponds very

73

closely with that of the megaliths. These axes are usually regarded as contemporaneous with dolmens, but since the latter are not found in the northwest, the axes here must be assigned to a later date. R. G. Collingwood believed that both the megaliths and the axes are the relics of a single people and of a period after 1800 B.C. Indeed, it seems likely that the first significant influx of settlers spreading inland from the primary area of Neolithic settlement on the west coast was only after 1700 B.C., by which time penetration from the North Sea was becoming important on the east side.

The entry of the Beaker Folk was the first of successive waves of invasion from the North Sea lowlands of continental Europe to the east and southeast shores of Britain. With its long seaboard lying open to entry from this quarter, northeast England received a share of these immigrants, though it lay on or beyond the northern fringe of some important later waves of immigration across the North Sea, such for example as those of the Belgic tribes and later the Danes. For this very reason, however, it was better able to assimilate the newcomers and cultural innovations it did receive. The new elements added were relatively small, infrequent, and often diluted. This was even more so in the west country, reached by eastern immigrants in small numbers only and in limited localities, so that they were effectively absorbed into the earlier population. While the eastern side of the country began to receive along its sea front periodic accessions of immigrants from the middle of the second millennium B.C., the population of the west increased only by multiplication of its earlier western entrants and by infiltration across the highlands from the east, until at last it experienced a new wave of coastal immigration with the arrival of the Norsemen in the tenth century A.D.

In Cumberland the evidence points to a Neolithic people extending their areas of settlement as they grew in number, and coming into slight contact with trickles of new cultures from the east. Some new characteristics were acquired in this way, but there was probably no great cultural change. As R. G. Collingwood has emphasised, there is no evidence of change such as cannot be explained simply as the product of peaceful development within the area itself and of gradual infiltration of new ideas from the more highly civilised outer world.

The relatively small number of finds of bronze implements in the east of Cumberland do not tally in distribution with those of Beaker burials, which are clearly related to ingress by the Tyne Corridor (Fig. 15). This would suggest that the Beaker Folk from the east did not introduce bronze, but that it came much later, probably after 1000 B.C., by way of the trade connections of the old-established Neolithic communities along the coast of south Cumberland and Furness. We may envisage in the west a people with lingering strong Neolithic traditions and few features of the latest type of Bronze culture, increasing in numbers and gradually spreading over the uplands. The indices of the later phases, notably the cinerary urns, show how the occupation had extended, especially on the fringing uplands that surround the Lake District (Fig. 15). This society had not adopted iron, and was virtually unaffected by Iron Age culture, before the coming of the Romans. As in Scotland, the Bronze Age lasted on into Roman times ; even then the extent of change was slight and locally restricted.

New cultures were late in reaching this remote area, and all dates of culture periods B.C. must be scaled down. The conventional divisions of the Bronze and Iron Ages into more or less definite periods and type phases are quite inappropriate anywhere in North England. Rather should we envisage a gradual infiltration of some elements that elsewhere belong to such periods, but which were here absorbed into a culture that was little affected by them and that changed only very gradually over a long period.

Throughout North England a high degree of cultural continuity has been characteristic, with gradual blending of the old and new. Such a blending followed the early Bronze Age immigration along the east coast. After the entry of the Beaker Folk about 1700 B.C., a long period of internal peace and stability seems to have followed, during which the newcomers intermingled with the earlier inhabitants. Illustrative of this are the food vessels that became the distinctive type of pottery. In design and ornament they owed much to the native tradition and are generally regarded as a local development from the cord-ornamented Neolithic ware. Adoption of the custom of burial after cremation, which gave the cinerary urns typical of the later Bronze Age burials, is not likely to have taken place before 1000 B.C.

Later still, intermittent invasions of continental people brought both the Celtic language and the use of iron to Britain. From these newcomers were descended the Brigantes, whom the Romans found on the eastern side of the country south of the Tyne, a warrior-aristocracy of Celts in possession of an early Iron Age culture. The primary settlements of later Celtic-speaking peoples, who reached Britain after 450 B.C. with an Iron Age culture of la Tène type, are not found north of Scarborough, and any who entered North England must have done so by infiltration from districts farther south. Before the Roman advance into North England under Agricola in A.D. 69, the Brigantes had concentrated their power upon their great fortress at Stanwick south of the Tees. At this time, north of the Tyne the Votadini occupied both sides of what is now the Border country in Northumberland and south Scotland. They had numerous hill-forts, the greatest

75

of which was at Traprain Law near the Forth. Remains of such forts and settlements are especially numerous in the Tweed basin and on the Northumbrian side of the Border hills, where about four hundred have been recognised. The technique of fort building, with the other archaeological evidence, points to the spread of refugee members of the Celtic aristocracy from districts farther south about the time of the Roman conquest. These were probably the first users of iron to establish themselves north of the Tyne, and the country must have been mainly inhabited by a substratum of population with old-fashioned ways and equipment.

Numerous earthworks, ' camps ', and stone remains are the most conspicuous and widespread evidences of the pre-Roman settlement, as well as of the British occupation that was contemporaneous with the Roman phase as Britons were pushed north in front of the advancing legions. While it is still impossible to assign all these remains to definite periods, their general distribution shows clearly the areas of concentration of early settlement. Further progressive stages in a process of colonisation can be envisaged, at least in broad outline, from study of the distributions of index finds of successive phases, such as beakers, food vessels, and cinerary urns, which have been analysed by Raistrick, Elgee, and Collingwood.

In these distributions (Fig. 15) the unattractive peat-clad moorlands of the highland summits appear as empty areas, as they do in the modern settlement distribution. It is the presence of extensive empty lowland areas and the concentration of most of the prehistoric settlement in an intermediate zone that mark the essential differences between the prehistoric distribution of settlement and that of today.

The warm, dry, sub-boreal climate that prevailed during the early part of the Bronze Age, although it failed to effect regeneration of the forest, which had receded during the preceding moist Atlantic climate, must have favoured the advance of grass-heath rather than moor. On the open grasslands between the peaty summits and the forested lowlands prehistoric man would find the most attractive conditions. Such an area is indicated by a pronounced concentration of prehistoric remains in an aureole round the Cheviot, above the valleys of the Breamish and Till, and in upper Coquetdale [1] (Fig. 16). These prehistoric settlements were situated below the 800-foot contour line, and were densest near that of 400 feet. The rigorous climate and acid, peaty soils of the granite outcrop repelled settlement from the higher ground, while the heavily forested, swampy floor of Glendale was equally unattractive. Between these negative regions, on the well-drained slopes with light soils derived from porphyritic material

[1] See *County History of Northumberland*, vol. xiv (1935).

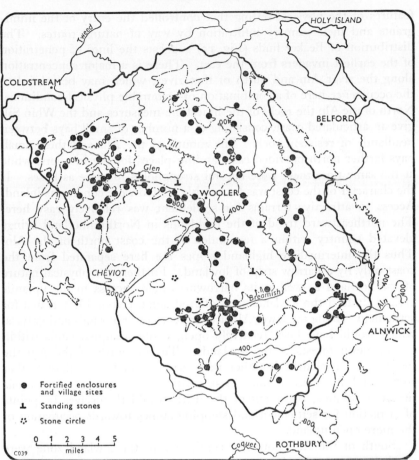

Fig. 16 PREHISTORIC SITES IN GLENDALE (adapted from the *County History of Northumberland*, Vol. XIV).

or glacial sands, prehistoric colonists found a zone that was easy to occupy. It provided extensive and good pasture lands for their live-stock, easily worked and moderately fertile soils for cultivation, and numerous defensive sites for their settlements. In this zone, which mostly lies above the limit of modern settlement and enclosure, there is scarcely a valley spur without its ' camp '. The prehistoric economy seems to have been predominantly pastoral, and must have differed considerably from that of southern England, for air photography has not here revealed widespread field-systems.

The specially dense concentration in this northern area may be more fully appreciated by reference to the ways of ingress of immigrants from across the North Sea, and by consideration of those features of the physical setting that controlled the entry of the immigrants and their primary infiltration by way of natural routes. The distribution of Beaker finds (Fig. 15) suggests the lines of penetration of the earliest invaders from the east. There is a major concentration along the river Aln and north of that river, which may be related to the occurrence here of a combination of favourable physical conditions. North of the Aln the rocks of the limestone measures and the Whin Sill give an articulated coast, consisting of a number of small bays between headlands of resistant rock. The mouth of the Aln and these small bays farther north provided easy landing-places for the invaders, while at the same time there were natural strongholds to serve as bases. If the character of the coast was favourable, so too were conditions inland. Access to attractive terrains for settlement was relatively easy here. The northeastward trend of the highlands in Northumberland brings elevated country within a few miles of the coast north of the Aln. Thus the intermediate highland slopes are here separated from the coast only by a narrow strip of lowland. Further, the physical nature of this lowland as well as its narrowness made access to the uplands easier ; indeed the lowland itself offered some favourable terrains for settlement. Along the lower Aln are stretches of light sands and gravels, which would have been relatively open, easily occupied lands within the primeval forests of the lowlands. To the north of the Aln the mantle of glacial drift is rather more sandy and lighter than farther south, and it is also a much less continuous covering. Numerous limestone islands, rising out of the drift, would themselves be points of attraction for settlement and stepping-stones towards occupation of the more open uplands.

South of the Aln, however, conditions in the lowland zone were much less favourable for penetration and settlement. Good landing-places are less common on this coast, and even more important is the fact that behind the coast lies a wide stretch of heavy boulder-clay lowland. In its natural state ill-drained and covered with heavy forest and swamp, this lowland widens southwards and near the coast is rarely interrupted by rock outcrops. The estuaries of the Coquet and Wansbeck, and the sand and gravel terraces along their banks, afforded lines of penetration and patches of easily occupied land, but the main concentration of Beaker finds south of the Aln lies significantly along the Tyne valley. Well-drained sites for settlements occur along the lower Tyne, where the valley has steep sides cut in the Coal Measures sandstones, while extensive sand and gravel terraces along the valley floor to the west favoured settlement and penetration up North Tynedale, and also through the Tyne Corridor into the vale of Eden, where eight or nine Beaker burials have been found. It is noteworthy that these all lie in the east or northeast of Cumberland and Westmorland, away from the chief concentration of megaliths, with which they are clearly not related.

South of the Tyne, as far as Hartlepool, the Magnesian Limestone plateau meets the sea in cliffs. The inhospitable coast is without natural harbours except where the Wear estuary breaches the limestone. Beaker finds on the limestone plateau south of the Wear, and on the glacial sands of the middle Wear valley, point to entry by the Wear, but there is no evidence of penetration up the valley much beyond Durham. The extensive heaths of the northern Pennines were apparently too distant from the coast and too isolated by forest to be reached by the early settlers.

The cliff coast of Durham is succeeded southwards by a very different, but in its natural state no more favourable, stretch—the flat, marsh-fringed estuary of the Tees, with shifting channels and sandbanks. Behind lies flat, heavy, clay country which must have carried very dense forest in early times. At Saltburn the land again rises in cliffs, as the rocky coast of the Jurassic highland begins. But here the coast, although generally inhospitable and difficult to approach, offers a few small harbours as landing-places, backed by small and disconnected patches of more fertile ground, hemmed in by the moorland plateau. In these areas, too, the Beaker Folk established themselves.

The distribution of Beakers thus indicates that the main region of entry of the newcomers was in north Northumberland, where they spread from the coast across the narrow lowland of the Cheviot gate to the heaths of the highland slopes. Other colonies were established at favourable points along the coast farther south, and immigrants made their way inland by way of the valleys, notably along the Tyne. The areas of occupation, however, remained very restricted.

The food-vessels of later date show a wider distribution, a natural result of the growth of population and the progressive colonisation of favourable terrains from the initial nuclei. During this period effective occupation of the regions that were accessible and naturally attractive was carried out. But the northern Pennines still remained an empty area, presumably because of the difficulty of reaching its favourable terrains. The distribution of cinerary urns of the late Bronze Age, when cremation had been adopted, reveals a further stage in the process of expansion, and is not likely to be earlier than 1000 B.C. In many cases it reflects a spread outwards, beyond the optimum areas of earlier occupation, into less favourable country. This may have been due to the pressure of the natural increase of population or of an influx of new invaders, driving some of the earlier inhabitants to occupy regions that had hitherto been avoided. Thus Elgee has

79

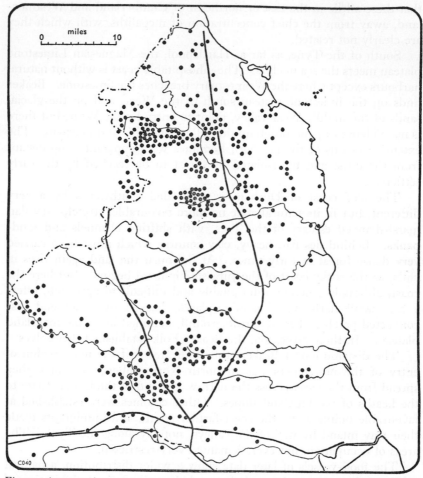

Fig. 17 ' BRITISH ' SETTLEMENTS IN NORTHUMBERLAND (after A. H. A. Hogg). The lines of Roman roads are also shown.

argued that the urn people of northeast Yorkshire were pushed by newcomers on to the inhospitable high moorlands.

A noteworthy feature of the late Bronze Age extension of the occupied area is that then for the first time the archaeological distributions show the major settlement areas on the Cheviot slopes and in the Tyne valley interconnected across the moorlands between the North Tyne and the Coquet. The Wear and Cleveland areas, however, appear to have remained separate, isolated groups. It is to be emphasised that the late Bronze Age extension of settlement from the areas of major concentration on the intermediate slopes of the highlands was a spread upwards, towards the moorlands, rather than downwards into the lowlands and valleys. There the forest remained uncleared. At the same time the spread on to the moorlands seems to have been only local and nowhere extensive.

Large numbers of what are loosely called ' British ' settlements, consisting of circles of stone-built huts that represent villages or, more often, family farms, generally enclosed within a ring fence, are found on the uplands (Fig. 17). They are certainly not all pre-Roman. They belong to a period which began before the entry of the Romans, but they were extended during and after the Roman occupation. That some of the remoter among them are found in country beyond the areas where they are accompanied by Bronze Age remains may be attributed to the presence after A.D. 550 of Anglian settlers. It is reasonable to believe that these newcomers pushed the Britons up into the hill country, where they may have continued to live without much change in their habits right into the Middle Ages. Elgee has suggested that in this way Britons found refuge in the secluded dales of the North York Moors.

As Figure 17 shows, the greatest density of such remains is in the Cheviot hill country, but it may be that many lower-lying sites have been destroyed. The frequent occurrence of ' chesters ' as a place-name may point to the former sites of some of these, for this name is more often associated with such British sites than with actual Roman sites. Numerous as the extant remains are, little archaeological work has been carried out upon them since Collingwood excavated and described those on Crosby Ravensworth fells, near the Roman road. Here eight British settlements occur within a radius of one and a half miles of Crosby Ravensworth. At least six of them are collections of round huts, amidst groups of fields bounded by stone walls. Two are definite villages (Ewe Close and Burwens), the others probably family farms. Significantly they usually have groups of round barrows near by.

Wherever it can be proved that such a hut settlement was occupied in Roman times the proof comes only from a few potsherds ; otherwise the settlement might be altogether pre-Roman. It is evident that the people went on living in the same sort of settlements and practised the same way of life. The mainstay of their economy was cattle keeping, with which was combined a little hoe cultivation. The ring forts, some of them with multiple ramparts, show extensive systems of enclosures that were probably cattle paddocks. To most of the tribes living within the large blocks of territory that lay between the lines of the Roman roads both north and south of Hadrian's Wall (Fig. 18), the Roman period probably meant little more than the imposition of restraints upon lawlessness and some extension of the use of iron.

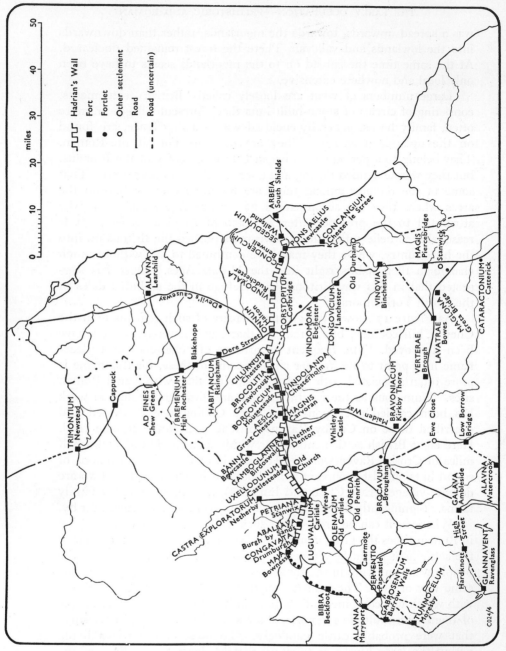

Fig. 18 THE ROMAN FRONTIER ZONE IN NORTH ENGLAND.

Over much of North England, as in Scotland, the Bronze Age lasted till Roman times, and the old ways of life persisted without much change until the coming of the Angles in the east, and in the remoter dales of the west until the settlement of the Norsemen. Similarly the characteristics of population distribution that have been described above were not appreciably modified until the Anglian colonisation. The three centuries of Roman rule were little more than an episode. In the Roman organisation of Britain, North England was a frontier district outside the area of civil occupation with its towns and villas. True, there were along the Wall considerable civilian settlements, if not towns, at Corstopitum (near Corbridge) and Luguvallium (Carlisle) ; and at Old Durham there was the most northerly villa estate known in the Roman world. But these were isolated features.

The surviving remains of the fortifications built by Hadrian between A.D. 122 and 126 from the Tyne estuary to that of the Solway (Fig. 18) are perhaps the most impressive monuments to their military genius that the Romans have left in Britain (Pl. 17). The Wall, however, was only part of a frontier system which is to be understood as a succession of schemes that were modified as policy changed with changing circumstances. Even while the Wall was under construction the conception of it was modified. Its duplication by the *vallum*, enclosing a narrow, heavily garrisoned zone along the Wall itself, and the strengthening of the Wall with additional forts as well as reconstruction of the turf portions of the west in stone, all point to its being called upon to play a rôle for which its original design and construction proved inadequate.

Between the extension of the military conquest of Britain into the north by Agricola after A.D. 69, and the demarcation of the linear frontier half a century later by Hadrian, the Roman occupation was based upon trunk roads, driven through northern England into Scotland from the legionary headquarters at York and Chester. Most important was the road from York that traversed the eastern foothills of the Pennines, its crossings of the east-flowing rivers marked by forts at Piercebridge, Binchester, Lanchester, Ebchester, and Corstopitum. From the Tyne valley here it struck with remarkable directness north-northwest through the Border hills to the Tweed basin at Trimontium (Newstead), crossing the Tweed-Tyne watershed below the Cheviot, but at a height of more than 1,600 feet, by Ad Fines. From Catterick a road branched northwest towards the Solway across Stainmore into the Eden valley, where at Brougham it joined another from Chester over Shap. Farther north the roads on the east and west sides of the main highland backbone were connected through the Tyne gap by the Stanegate. Important offsets from the main roads north, which ran some distance inland, kept them in contact with the sea at the mouths of the Tyne and Tweed, as well as the Cumberland coast. Other crossbraces completed an open network which divided the tribal territory into districts for military supervision by troops stationed at the forts established at road junctions and at stages along them.

Hadrian's Wall itself appears to have been designed to demarcate and seal the frontier, rendering it impenetrable to raiding and infiltration. It stretched right across the isthmus for 73 miles from tidewater on the Tyne to the Solway at Bowness beyond the lowest ford, with seventeen forts ranged at intervals along it and mile-castles and turrets punctuating the intervening stretches. Beyond the western end of the Wall, flank defences were extended along the Solway shore nearly as far as modern Whitehaven. They consisted of three more forts, like those on the Wall, with mile fortlets and signal towers between. Barely twenty years after the building of Hadrian's Wall the frontier was pushed north to the Forth-Clyde line, where the shorter Antonine Wall was built in A.D. 142. The mile-castles along Hadrian's Wall were thrown open, and between the two walls additional small patrol posts were established on the old roads, and new roads were built forward in the west. After temporary loss of control of the northern frontier at the end of the second century, Severus re-established the frontier and rebuilt Hadrian's Wall. But his policy continued the frontier strategy of defence in depth, combining the wall with powerfully garrisoned outposts that were pushed forward well beyond it. In the later phases of the occupation, however, the line of the wall was no longer a major frontier, and became obsolete as responsibility for defence was thrown more and more upon the local militia, and the real danger shifted from the northern land frontier to the eastern seaboard. An early fort at the Tees crossing was strengthened in this later phase to stem possible inland penetration from the Tees estuary.

Although North England lay at the ' vanishing point of Romanisation ' and the Roman period had generally little effect upon the tribes that occupied this distant country, the Roman roads persisted long after the withdrawal of the legions and were much used as lines of penetration by both raiding bands and settlers (see below, p. 88). Indeed, considerable sections of their lines are incorporated in the modern road system. The trunk road (A6) that branches northwest from the Great North Road at Scotch Corner and crosses Stainmore to descend into the Eden valley by Brough, Appleby, and Penrith to Carlisle for most of its course follows the Roman road. At Carlisle it is joined by a road from west Cumberland (A595), which likewise follows a Roman road in a straight stretch from Papcastle. Hadrian's Wall runs north of the Tyne valley, the settlements of which are linked by a later valley road. But this is doubled by the more northerly road between Heddon-on-the-Wall and Greenhead (B6318), following the course of the Roman road immediately behind the Wall. So slow and difficult were cross communications between the east and west sides of the country at the time of the 1745 rebellion that the Roman road was reconstructed soon afterwards as a strategic measure. Still known as the Military Road, it is a valuable fast through route that by-passes the Tyne valley settlements.

Elsewhere correspondence between modern and Roman road arteries is not close. The lines of Roman strategic roads, such as High Street, Maiden Way, and Devil's Causeway (Fig. 18), pursuing switch-back courses along the watersheds, stride wholly aloof from the present-day settlement pattern and have no part to play in modern communications. Naturally the forts along these stretches, such as Hardknott, are deserted sites. So are many of the lowland forts, although modern settlements near by give them the names by which they are commonly known. Corbridge, for example, lies a mile to the east of the important Roman civil settlement, Corstopitum. The modern village of Piercebridge (Fig. 19), displaying in its plan the outlines of the Roman fort on the site of which it has grown, is very exceptional.

The two great Border cities, Newcastle and Carlisle, both have origins that date back to Roman times, though continuity of occupation at either is at least doubtful. Near its eastern end the Wall was reached by an offshoot from Dere Street. Between the Wall and the bridge by which this road crossed the Tyne, precisely at the spot where successive low-level bridges have crossed the river to reach Newcastle, Pons Aelius was established and became a great base of supplies brought in by sea to serve the army of occupation. Luguvallium (Carlisle) grew as a civilian settlement south of the Eden, opposite Petriana (Stanwix), a fort on the Wall.

If the Roman occupation had generally little effect upon the mode of life and distribution of the British population of North England, locally, as for example along the line of the Wall, a greater degree of Romanisation and some concentration of British population are

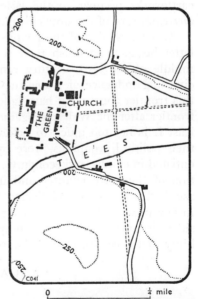

Fig. 19 PIERCEBRIDGE (CO. DURHAM). A later 'green' village occupying the site of a Roman fort where the road crossed the Tees above Darlington.

85

7

likely to have been achieved, at least for a time. It was the deliberate policy of the Romans that their garrisons should as far as possible be supported by the surrounding country, and the presence of the garrison troops must have encouraged farming and handicrafts, as well as the support of other camp-followers, in and near the fortified zone along the Wall. Not only for the construction and maintenance of the Wall, but even in manning the posts between the forts, reliance was probably placed to a considerable extent upon recruitment of the British population, and a considerable concentration of peasant militia must have been settled in the territory along the Wall.

Outside the forts, and at road junctions elsewhere in the Brigantian territory, there grew up fairly considerable settlements, *vici*, with concentrations of shops and taverns. Some of them, for example at Borcovicium, cover larger areas than the nearby forts. The occurrence of a concentration of fort sites of unusual rectilinear outline in the country that lies north of the Wall to the east of North Tynedale has called forth the interesting speculation that in this area the Romans may have carried out an exchange of population with the inhabitants of their Rhætian frontier. Brooch evidence [1] suggests that the settlers who were taken thither from Britain about the middle of the second century came from the Votadini country north of the Wall, while the rectilinear earthworks peculiar to the latter area show resemblances with the *viereckshangen* of the upper Rhine basin.

Our knowledge of the people who confronted the Angles when the latter began to establish their settlements along the east coast in the middle of the sixth century remains very vague and general. The civilising influence of Rome, never more than locally considerable in this frontier zone, must have faded since the final abandonment of the frontier after the Wall had again been overrun by Picts in 383, but at least it is not too much to believe that the Britons, quite apart from their political groupings, were by no means a single people undifferentiated in culture and economy. What differences in the later occupation of the north country and in its humanised landscape are to be ascribed to such old-established distinctions it is of course impossible in our present state of knowledge to pronounce, but that such a consideration may enter into a completely valid interpretation is a possibility that is certainly not to be excluded.

[1] A. H. A. Hogg, *op. cit.*

CHAPTER 6

THE AGRICULTURAL COLONISATION

THE settlement of North England by the Angles, as distinct from spasmodic incursions by their raiding bands, began late. Documentary evidence suggests that they did not gain an effective foothold in Northumberland until the capture of the British coastal fortress of Dinguardi (Bamburgh) in A.D. 547. This fortress became the base of the Anglian power and capital of the kingdom of Bernicia. At first it was only a foothold held with difficulty, but after the British had been decisively defeated in 603 the Anglian colonisation was free to proceed in security from this nuclear area.

The late beginnings of Anglian settlement are confirmed by archaeological and place-name evidence. Since the records suggest that effective Anglian settlement did not long precede the Christian mission of Aidan in 635, it is not surprising that very few pagan burials have been located in North England. Though it must be realised that pagan burials continued even after the introduction of Christianity, they have provided invaluable archaeological evidence of early Anglian occupation in certain localities of Britain. Another type of evidence is provided by place-names. It is generally agreed that place-names ending in -ing (where the terminal is derived from inga) and in -ingham indicate early settlements of what may be termed the entrance phase. There is, however, only one certain -ing name in the four northern counties (Birling, at the mouth of the river Coquet) and another near the southern border of our province at Gilling in the North Riding, with Cleatlam in south Durham as a dubious additional example ; in contrast there are nearly a score of names ending in -ingham. The -ingham names are old, and in the opinion of Ekwall probably as old as the -ing names. Their distribution, considered along with that of the few isolated pagan burial places and -ing names, is interesting and perhaps very significant (Fig. 20). Most of these evidences of early Anglian settlement occur as a group in north Northumberland ; a smaller number is found along the valley of the Tyne and that of the North Tyne, and the others are scattered in the areas farther south or west.

It would seem, therefore, that the early penetration of the Angles was influenced by very much the same physical controls that affected the ingress of the Beaker Folk. Like their predecessors, the first Anglian immigrants, coming maybe from earlier colonies round the

87

Humber, were attracted to settle in north Northumberland by the
favourable conditions for landing and establishing initial settlements.
Farther south, the Tyne valley offered them the best facilities for penetration, but elsewhere both coast and hinterland were unattractive.
This is borne out by Symeon of Durham's description of the land
between the Tyne and Tees in the sixth century as ' a deserted waste
. . . and thus nothing but a hiding place for wild and woodland beasts.' [1]

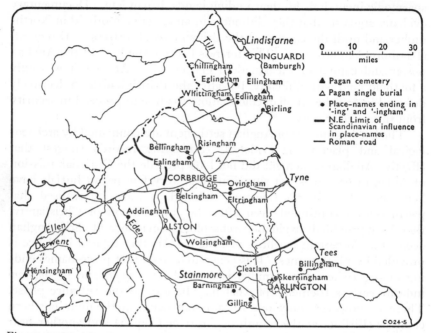

Fig. 20   NORTH ENGLAND : SOME FEATURES OF THE ANGLIAN AND NORSE COLONISATION.

A factor which facilitated the ingress of the Angles, however, but which
had not been operative in earlier immigration, was the existence of the
highways left by the Romans.   Many of the above-mentioned indications of Anglian settlement are at sites easily reached from Roman
roads ; and if they are not actually on the lines of the roads themselves
this is easily accounted for by the agricultural preoccupation of the
settlers and greater safety off the highways.   The more southerly
evidences of Anglian settlement are more readily explained in terms
of penetration from the south by land highways than by direct ingress
from the coast.

Only in the initial stages of the entry and occupation, however, did
the Anglian settlement show a close parallel with earlier immigrations

[1] *Life of St Oswald*, in *Opera*, i, 339, Surtees Soc. Pub. **51** (1868).

from the east. Once established in their new home, the immigrants began to clear and colonise the forested lowlands, extending their settlements at the expense of the forest, and establishing from them daughter townships in new clearings. Thus started the process which during the following centuries slowly transformed the lowlands and valleys, steadily extending farming and settlement in the former forest wilderness, and inscribing the lineaments of the landscape of today. This age-long process, begun by the Angles, was carried through by their descendants, the product of their mixing with the native population ; place-name and historical evidence alike support the view that the newcomers mixed with, rather than replaced, the British inhabitants.

Although Northumbrian political control had been rapidly and firmly established over the west during the course of the seventh century, and Anglian settlers spread into Cumberland and Westmorland through the Tyne Corridor and over Stainmore, the proportion of fairly early Anglian place-names in the west is small. Only two of them are in Cumberland—Addingham and Hensingham—and there is none in Westmorland. Even later -ham and -ington names are not common, and, except along the coastal strip, in a district east of Carlisle opposite the mouth of the Tyne gap, and in parts of the vale of Eden, it would appear that the essentially British character of the population was not much altered until the coming of the Norsemen.

On the other side of the highlands, in northeast England, the Anglian influx marks the last wave of immigration from across the North Sea that was of more than local importance in the peopling of the region. Other elements in the stock and culture of the people who carried out the colonisation during the Middle Ages and delineated in its main features the existing pattern of agricultural settlement were of importance only south of the Tees. Thus the later Danish settlement and influence were limited to the southeast, in south Durham and the North Riding. From the end of the eighth century the coast of northeast England suffered the ravages of raiding freebooters, but except in its southernmost districts it lay beyond the northern limit of Danish settlement. Certainly Halfdan penetrated north of the Tyne with his army in 875, but he left Bernicia under Anglian control. Although the area south of the Tyne became part of the Danelaw, Danish settlement, if we are to judge from place-name evidence, did not extend beyond the southern districts of Durham.

It is unfortunately impossible to distinguish as a rule between place-names indicative of Danish settlement and those resulting from settlement by other Scandinavian-speaking people. From about A.D. 900 Scandinavian immigration took place on a large scale in northwest England from landings on the west coast. These settlers were

Norse rather than Danish, and came by the western or Atlantic approach to make settlements on the coasts of Ireland and the west coasts of Great Britain in the ninth century. Their immigration into Cumberland and Westmorland, chiefly in the tenth century, was probably secondary, derived from earlier colonies on the coasts of Ireland, the Isle of Man, and the islands and west coast of Scotland. It has been pointed out, and it is surely significant, that their Norse speech was modified, so that instead of forming place-names in the normal Scandinavian (and Anglian) way, they inverted the order of compounds, as in Irish. Kirkoswald, Kirkandrews, and Aspatria may be compared, for instance, with Downpatrick. There is further evidence of their adoption of loan-words, among which an example of special interest to the geographer is -*erg*, equivalent to the Irish -*airigh* and having the same connotation as *shieling*. It is often represented in Cumberland as the terminal -*er*, as in Birker, Salter, Winder, and Cleator.

The Norse settlement in northwest England was very extensive, and it has given the region and its people a strongly Scandinavian character. It overlay some earlier Anglian settlement, but it was chiefly a British substratum on which it was superimposed. British place-name elements are especially common in northeast Cumberland on the rising ground towards the Border fells, on the northern edge of the Lake District highlands below Skiddaw, and on the western fringing uplands between the Ellen and the Derwent. In the heart of the Lake District, on the contrary, earlier place-names are little represented, and the Scandinavian immigrants here were probably pioneer farmers in an empty wilderness.

Earlier Anglian settlement had extended into the northwest by the Tyne Corridor and Stainmore, but the pressure of the tenth-century colonisation appears to have pushed back some of the earlier occupants, for there is mention of this ebb in historical records and even some place-name evidence of the penetration of colonists of Scandinavian speech into Northumberland by its western ' gate ', the Tyne gap. It is interesting to note the strongly Scandinavian character of the upper dale of the South Tyne, round Alston, which became and historically has always remained part of Cumberland, whereas the rest of the North Sea drainage area became parts of eastern counties. Much more important, however, than the Scandinavian spread by the Tyne Corridor into Northumberland was that from the upper end of the vale of Eden over Stainmore into Teesdale and north Yorkshire. The frequent occurrence of the -*thwaite* [1] element in the names of settlements in these southern districts suggests, moreover, that this colonisation was late,[2] and the historical records point to its basis. After the

---

[1] thwaite = piece of cleared land (Old Norse *þveit*, ' clearing, paddock ').
[2] H. Lindkvist, *op. cit.*

abortive rebellion in the north against the Normans in 1069, William the Conqueror set about the 'harrying of the north'. There followed the systematic and thorough devastation of the countryside, which suffered further ravages at the hands of the Scots under Malcolm. Domesday Book testifies to the depopulation of Teesdale and the lower vale of Tees, though the country farther north seems to have escaped. The re-settlement of the devastated districts was carried out in the succeeding centuries by Norse-speaking colonists from the vale of Eden, moving across Stainmore into the empty territory. But we have no warrant for assuming, as appears often to have been done tacitly, that these people were true Norse settlers. Their speech was Norse, but it seems more than probable that they were the product of intermingling in northwest England of British and Norse elements, with possibly even some Anglian admixture. We have suggested that the Scandinavian settlement of the northwest was itself secondary, derived rather from earlier colonies than direct from Scandinavia. The original settlers of Cumberland were possibly themselves not pure Norsemen, and certainly by the time of the colonisation of the depopulated districts across the Pennines the dilution of the Norse strain by intermixture of the immigrants with the earlier inhabitants of northwest England must have been far advanced.

Except in the region south of the Tees, where it has left a strong mark upon both the place-names and the dialect, Scandinavian influence is strikingly absent from northeast England (Fig. 20). Streams are 'burns', not 'becks'. There are no 'becks' in Northumberland, Wansbeck (earlier Wanespike) being misleading in this respect. The 'beck' names that now appear on maps of County Durham are all later than 1500; earlier, all the small streams were called 'burns'. The suffixes -by, -thorp, and -thwaite in names of settlements are not found in Northumberland and are rare in Durham, except in the south. Follingsby, Byker, and Walker, all on Tyneside, are possibly evidence of an isolated estuarine group of colonies established directly from across the North Sea. Lucker, in north Northumberland, is another isolated Scandinavian place-name that may have such an origin, but the other sporadic traces of Scandinavian influence that have been noted by Mawer in the place-names point by their distribution rather to infiltration from the west and south.

The speech of the Scandinavian settlers had many words in common with that of the no less Teutonic Angles (e.g. 'dale'), and others were very similar in form and meaning, so that of many place-names it cannot with certainty be determined whether they are the product of Anglian or Scandinavian settlement. Nevertheless it is broadly true to say that whereas place-names of distinctively Old English origin are uncommon in the west, those of Old Norse origin are almost unknown in the east, except in the southern districts.

The people of North England before the modern industrial period were essentially derived from the fusion of these Anglian and Norse immigrants with the earlier British inhabitants. The relative importance of the strains varied locally. On *a priori* grounds it is safe to assume that the British element was generally stronger in the west and in the highlands, and the place-names tend to support this assumption, except that the Lake District seems to have been little occupied at all until the Norse farmers established themselves there.

Nowhere, however, was the British element in the amalgam as important as in Wales or as the Anglian element in the English lowland. The Celtic language did not survive, though many Celtic customs did, and the Celtic influences are very apparent in the Christian decorated art that blossomed in the seventh and eighth centuries. Characteristically we find a high degree of continuity of much of the pre-Anglian cultural tradition, and only partial replacement. Less survived than in Wales, but less was superseded than in most of England. From the blending of Anglian or Norse with British elements, in varying proportions but, except locally, without either being really dominant, there arose in North England a new and distinctive society, a hybrid developed in the province, adapted to the distinctive milieu, and reacting in its own distinctive manner to new, intrusive features. The distinctiveness of this society in its relations with the country is apparent from study of the earliest fairly comprehensive documentary evidence concerning the manner of the agricultural occupation of North England, which dates from the twelfth century.

The four northern counties lay outside the scope of the Domesday inquest, and even the lands of the North Riding were recorded in that document chiefly as waste, following the recent devastations. An invaluable source of information on the bishopric of Durham about a century later, however, is provided by the Boldon Book. This document is a rental survey of the episcopal possessions, made for Bishop Hugh Pudsey in 1183, the units of the survey being the vills held by the bishop. It shows that at the end of the twelfth century there were three well-defined types of vills in the bishopric. By far the most numerous class were the pastoral vills, distinguished by the payment of ' cornage '. Cornage (from Latin *cornu*, a horn) was a due paid for the right to pasture cattle, and was the typical form of due rendered by communities that were primarily pastoral. It was not rendered by the vills of the Darlington Ward in the south of the county, these vills in the vale of Tees being the sole representatives in the bishopric of primarily corn-growing communities. Finally, in the west of the bishopric, there were a few forest vills, distinguished by 'drengage', service in the forest or in connection with the bishop's hunting expeditions. Although there is not available the direct evidence of a document such as Boldon Book, it is safe to assume that pastoral and, to a less extent, forest vills also prevailed throughout Northumberland, Cumberland, and Westmorland. Here, too, there is evidence of the widespread importance of cornage.

Although the basis for distinguishing these different types of vill is legalistic, the different services that were rendered reflect important differences in the economy. Except in the vale of Tees the true agricultural vill, which was characteristic of the English lowland farther south, was not found in North England, where the economy was much more pastoral in emphasis. The agrarian and social structure was correspondingly different from that which prevailed in the Midlands and South. To appreciate the nature and process of the medieval settlement of North England it is necessary further to examine these distinctive features, for in them we may see reflected the combined and inter-related influences of a distinctive physical milieu and a distinctive society.

In the first place, it must be emphasised that over most of North England the system of cultivation practised was more closely related to the Scottish *runrig* than to the open-field system of the English lowland. Jacobean surveys of townships in south Durham, as well as an Act of 1671 for the enclosure of the three open-fields of Bishop Auckland, show clearly that the latter system was not completely unrepresented, and investigation of the papers of the Percy family suggests that it may have been present farther north than has hitherto been suspected. The true three-field system, however, can never have had more than a very limited extension in North England, and was mainly confined to the southeastern parts, adjacent to the Northallerton gate connection with the English lowland. The vale of Tees represented, as it were, an annexe to the country of the three-field economy. It is probably highly significant that the only agricultural vills recorded in the Boldon Book were situated in this area where there is later evidence that the three-field system prevailed. Elsewhere, however, early cultivation based on co-aration was of the runrig type. As such, it was characterised by a fundamental distinction between the infield and the outfield, and by the annual re-distribution of strips among the cultivators. The infield, which received all the manure available, was cultivated continuously until soil-exhaustion necessitated fallowing. The outfield was land temporarily reclaimed from the waste, ploughed and sown for one year, and then left for a long period to recover. An Enclosure Act of 1840 clearly specifies the 'ingrounds' and 'out-

93

grounds' at Gunnerton in North Tynedale, and another, of 1814, distinguishes at Gateshead between the 'townfields' and 'other commonable lands and grounds'.

To recognise in the prevalence of this system of land use an adaptation to physical conditions of relief, soil, and climate is not in any way to disregard the fact that it reflects the strength of the British element in the society and the persistence of British custom. Indeed, these two aspects of interpretation seem to be essentially complementary; the physical conditions would tend to preserve the pastoral runrig system practised by the British. Where physical conditions were favourable to the development of more continuous and intensive cultivation, the three-field system of agriculture became established, but this was in only a small area of North England, mainly in its southeastern portion.

To the prevalent system of working the land may also be attributed the ease and therefore the early date at which enclosure of the old township lands was accomplished, and with it the establishment of many features of the landscape, such as field boundaries and roads, that still persist. The contrast in size between the settlement units that were associated with the runrig and the open-field systems of agricultural economy has been emphasised by H. L. Gray. With the scattered cultivation of the runrig system went small hamlets, as compared with the sizeable villages of the townships where the three-field economy was practised. The correlation is borne out in North England, where the general prevalence of small hamlets and the paucity of large village clusters characterise the texture of its old-established pattern of rural settlement, as they do in Scotland.

When the ecclesiastical parish organisation developed, the population of the northern bishoprics was so sparse and so scattered in small groups that the ecclesiastical parishes were made to include several of the townships that have in modern times become the civil parishes of our local government structure. The northern townships were grouped also for other purposes. A pastoral emphasis in a society is one that retards the growth of a completely feudal concept of property, and it is not surprising therefore to find that medieval feudalism did not here crystallise in the vill-manor. Professor J. A. Jolliffe has pointed out that the manorial system, with organic union of vill and demesne, did not obtain in Northumberland. Instead there was a more personal relationship between the peasant communities and their lords, a relationship more similar in nature to the allegiance of a tribe to its leader. The northern baron in the Middle Ages was primarily the military leader and protector of his dependants rather than their landlord. Lordship was exercised over large and unbroken estates, each containing several vill communities, and many of these groupings survived into the later Middle Ages as ' shires '.[1] This shire grouping of vills applied also for purposes of grazing organisation. Intercommoning by all the vills of the shire on the shiremoor was a usual practice. Such a shiremoor, pastured in common by the surrounding townships, has for example given its name to Shiremoor, a modern colliery settlement in the southeast corner of Northumberland, which has grown thereon.

To appreciate the basis of this practice it must be remembered that the amount of land under permanent occupation and utilisation was only a small part of the total area, set amidst the waste that was used for grazing. In the hilly country of North England there were large continuous tracts of moorland available for grazing in summer, but of little use in winter. These extensive seasonal pastures were in some cases situated at a considerable distance from the permanent settlements of the townships that used them. Hence arose the widespread practice of seasonal movement of men as well as of livestock. In late spring the animals were moved to the hill pastures, and during the summer the herdsmen occupied rude cabins and shelters, which were also dairies. They were usually called ' shiels ' or ' shielings ', but in the Cumbrian dialect both the old Norse name ' sæter ' and the Gaelic ' erg ' (*airigh*) were common terms for them.

It is not difficult to appreciate how the fertilisation of the land in the immediate vicinity of the shielings by animal droppings when the livestock were assembled there, would encourage reclamation of patches of land from the surrounding moor for cultivation and winter pasture and so, as population increased, would allow the originally temporary shelter to be converted into or replaced by permanent settlement. This process must have begun early, and it certainly continued late ; its importance in the colonisation of North England, especially in the upland country, is attested by the profusion of place-name elements such as *shields*, *bottle*, *-er*, *-sett* or *-side* in the names of present-day hamlets and farms. Such significant elements, like the *hafod* names in Wales, are represented in a very large proportion of settlement names in the highland country.

Colonisation, however, was not confined to the process whereby herdsmen's seasonal shelters became permanent settlements. As population grew, and increased the pressure on the older farmlands, new townships, planted outside the old townships, usually with the lord's permission, sprang up *ab initio* as permanent settlements. In

---

[1] Unlike the greater part of England, where parishes were grouped into Hundreds, the northern counties were divided into Wards, districts to which defensive duties were assigned (Fig. 21).

some cases place-names point to such an origin as offshoots from earlier settlements, as in Newton, Murton, and Newbiggin.

The natural and spontaneous process of multiplication of townships, with steady encroachment upon the wildernesss, was to some extent held up after the Conquest by the reservation of great tracts of land that were called 'forests'. The term refers not to the vegetation cover, but to the nature of the jurisdiction—land outside (*foris*) the common

Fig. 21   NORTH ENGLAND : ANCIENT 'FORESTS' AND TERRITORIAL DIVISIONS (counties, wards and liberties).

law, subject to special law. It must not be interpreted in its modern restricted and changed meaning as necessarily implying thickly wooded country. South of Carlisle, stretching right to Penrith and occupying an area of more than 150 square miles, was the royal forest of Inglewood (Fig. 21), but in North England much of the forest was alienated to the barons to whom the king entrusted the defence of the frontier and the maintenance of law and order in the Border country. The great feudal lords, including the Bishop of Durham, had extensive hunting domains. The forest of Cheviot (Chevy Chase) is perhaps best known, but great stretches of country farther south were occupied by other 'forests' (Fig. 21). The largest forest areas were naturally in the highlands, but considerable areas of more lowlying country, with much greater agricultural potentialities, were also reserved, as in Inglewood. The large modern civil parish of Denwick, lying in two portions north and south of Alnwick, more or less corresponds with what was still in the sixteenth century the deer-park of the Percies, of which Hulne Park and North Demesne are surviving remnants. Acklington Park similarly represents the deer park of the lords of Warkworth. Other fragments of the ancient ' forests ' survived the Middle Ages and persisted into modern times as reserved deer-parks. Such for example was the bishop's deer-park in Weardale, which Leland described about 1540 as ' rudely enclosed with stone of a twelve or fourteen miles in compass '. The hamlets of Westgate and Eastgate mark its limits along the floor of the dale. Such prolonged reservations were exceptional, however, and even these were not entirely without farm-steads. In describing Stanhope Park in Weardale Leland says, ' There be some little ferme holdes in this park ', and it was reported during the sixteenth century that deer were becoming scarce owing to the advance of cultivation and the encroachment of the dalesmen. Little ' forest' was left as such in Northumberland in the time of Leland, but in the Lake District the upper parts of both Ennerdale and Wasdale were still deer forests in the late seventeenth century.

Disforestation and gradual settlement in the one-time ' forests ' were an important aspect of colonisation during the thirteenth and fourteenth centuries. Comparison of the vills recorded in Boldon Book (1183) with those recorded in the Halmote Rolls of the fourteenth century shows clearly the progress of colonisation in the western part of the bishopric of Durham. Many new vills, of which there was no mention in Boldon Book, make their appearance in the Halmote Rolls and in Hatfield's Survey, and doubtless bear witness to the birth of new settlements. Thus, in the Halmote Rolls we find a group of eleven vills in northwest Durham where Boldon Book records the single vill of Lanchester. Several of them have names that end in -ley. These vills were characterised by the rendering of services in connection with the great chase held regularly by the bishop in Weardale. Moreover, under Stanhope in Weardale, there is specific mention of free tenants and their scattered holdings in the ' forest '.

The fact is that when it was to their advantage or convenience the lords did not hesitate to permit, and even to encourage, the establishment of new settlements in their ' forests '. In the royal forest of Inglewood revenues were increased during the fourteenth century by assarting large stretches and granting them to lessees for cultivation and pasturing. Mining settlement in the ' forests ' of the north Pennine dales was especially fostered rather than restricted, for mining activity provided a profitable source of revenue for king and bishop. The mining of silver-lead, which gave the chief stimulus to the colonisation of these dales, was responsible, for example, for the creation of the parish of Alston and the erection of its church in the twelfth century. The exploitation of the metalliferous ores brought rude settlements to high elevations in the upper parts of the dales, and pastoral farming was associated with the mining colonisation. This combination, as well as the scattered, shifting nature of the mineral workings, kept the settlement pattern predominantly dispersed. The miners' shielings were either scattered or in small hamlet-groups in the upper dales.

In North England, as elsewhere, monastic houses played an important part in stimulating and directing the development of farming and settlement in the Middle Ages. The three Cistercian houses that had been established by the end of the twelfth century in North England at Calder, Newminster, and Holme Cultram (Fig. 21), together with that at Furness, were active throughout the Middle Ages in developing sheep farming. The monks of Newminster used the pastures of the Cheviot, and from 1181 to 1536 held the lordship of Kidland there, with a right of way from Newminster. Furness Abbey acquired grazing interests in the heart of the Lake District, in upper Eskdale in 1242, and even across the central watershed in Borrowdale (1209), where the hardy local sheep, possibly of Norse ancestry, were reared for wool on their outlying sheep-runs or 'herdwicks', and where the monks had their 'grange'. The passes over Esk Hause that are now so frequented by holiday walkers in summer follow the tracks developed by the monks. Other religious houses also, endowed with extensive possessions by the king and local lords, played their part in the promotion of economic development by establishing new farms, as well as by maintaining flocks of sheep for the sale of wool. The Augustinian Priory of Guisborough, for example, held Castle Eden in Durham among its great possessions, and there William de Turp gave pasture for one thousand sheep throughout the year and for one thousand lambs till Michaelmas.

Stimulated in various ways, farming and settlement were thus making a progressive encroachment upon the woodlands and moors of the north country during the Middle Ages. In the process, the pattern of settlement was not only extended and increasingly filled in but also became more and more dispersed. Fundamentally, the clustered type of rural settlement is associated with an economy based upon communal arable farming. Such groups are a far less prominent feature of the settlement pattern in North England than in the English lowland. The practice of co-aration never applied to such a large proportion of the total area, and it also began to be superseded at an earlier date. In the absence of such dependence upon arable land for grazing livestock and of all the obligatory constraints that accompanied it, the way was open for early enclosure. The annual re-allotment of the cultivators' holdings in the open field contributed to the same end, by providing simple and repeated opportunities for new arrangements to be made. By the fourteenth century the degree of nucleation of settlement had probably already passed its peak, as more and more secondary settlements between earlier clusters were being established, and the farmland was being progressively extended by piecemeal encroachment upon woodland and moorland. Certainly the proportion of the rural population that lived in clustered settlements was much greater then than it is now. Almost all the village groups that exist today were already established, and there were many village sites occupied then which have subsequently been deserted. It is doubtful whether the distinction between clustered settlement and marginal and intercalated dispersed settlement was ever very clear-cut ; it has certainly been blurred by later developments. It can confidently be claimed that the rural settlement-groups as they exist today in the lowland areas that lie on each side of the highland backbone are, with few exceptions, relics of the early phase of co-aration (Fig. 24). These elements of the rural settlement pattern were established by the fourteenth century, by which time a stage of maturity in the process of agricultural colonisation had been attained. Late thirteenth- and early fourteenth-century records suggest that the rural population in many districts was comparable in numbers with that of today, and almost all the present village and hamlet groups had by then become crystallised.

Valuable, if incomplete, documentary evidence exists concerning the numbers and distribution of population in Northumberland at the end of the thirteenth century. A Lay Subsidy Roll of 1296, which enumerates the taxable population of those wards of Northumberland that were under the direct control of the king's sheriff, has been analysed by F. Bradshaw. Unfortunately the outlying parts of the County Palatine north of the Tyne, as well as the liberties of Hexhamshire [North] Tynedale and Redesdale,[1] do not come within the scope of this document, and it is doubtful whether the Roll represents anything like a complete census of householders even in the wards with which it deals. The statistics that can be gleaned from it do not appear to justify the pseudo-accuracy of cartographic representation, but certain generalisations may safely be made.

The vills, although they varied considerably in size, were generally

[1] Until they were abolished in the sixteenth century, all these liberties lay outside the control of the royal sheriffs of Northumberland and were governed by the officials of their various lords—Norham and Bedlington shires by the sheriffs of the Bishop of Durham, Hexhamshire by the bailiffs of the Archbishop of York. The earls of Angus and the royal house of Scotland were for long lords of Redesdale and Tynedale, but later these dales were controlled by keepers (*custodes*) appointed by the king of England or by his local representatives, the Wardens of the Marches.

small, the average number of householders enumerated being about ten. The highest proportion of larger vills, with as many as thirty or forty householders in a few places, was in the coastal belt north of the river Wansbeck. Interspersed among these larger vills here were many very small ones, and small vills were general in the western and southern districts of the county. Indeed, many were so small as to seem to be mere family-hamlets. The first direct numerical evidence that we can find thus corroborates the picture of settlement distribution as a sprinkling of small hamlets with but few larger village clusters.

The distribution of population outside the coalfield areas would seem to have been much as it is today. Most of the names of existing groups are recorded in the Roll. The numbers enumerated point to a generally close correspondence with the more striking variations in the density of rural population at the present day, and also suggest that the agricultural population of the rural northern and middle parts of the county was not very different in number from that of today. Apart from Newcastle, the coalfield area in the southeast of the country was a relatively poor and sparsely peopled tract, not nearly as rich and populous as some other districts.

For the bishopric of Durham, the fourteenth-century records in the Halmote Rolls and Hatfield's Survey are also obviously incomplete in their enumeration of the settlements of the county, but nevertheless provide much valuable evidence concerning their distribution. The principal concentrations were in the vale of Tees and in mid-Durham, along the Wear valley and the scarp-edge of the Magnesian Limestone plateau. Here the townships were numerous and close-set, but on the plateau farther east they were fewer and more widely spaced. In the hilly districts of the western part of the coalfield there were large empty tracts on the watersheds, but the valleys were settled and encroachment from them upwards on to the waste had progressed considerably since the time of Boldon Book. It may be gathered from the records that settlements in these districts consisted, as in Northumberland, of small and scattered hamlets. The units of Hatfield's Survey did not here correspond with single groups of settlement, as farther east, but were composite, containing several constituent units of settlement.

Since such evidence as is available suggests strongly that the rural population of many districts, particularly in the lowlands of North England, was comparable with that of today, it is appropriate to consider at this point the nature of the sites occupied by the medieval agricultural settlements.

In the dales, and in the broken upland country of the western part of the coalfield in Durham, there were few villages. Such as there were kept closely to the valley lines, where they were usually sited on the sand

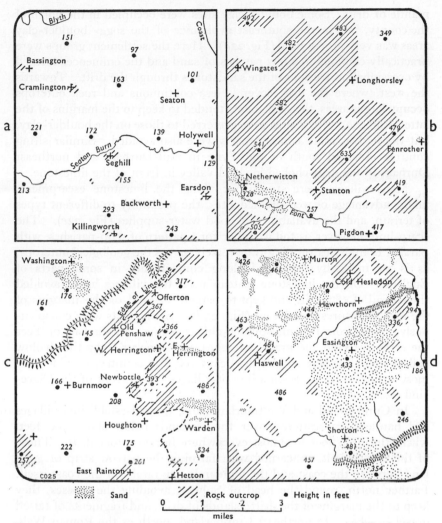

Fig. 22   NORTHEAST ENGLAND : VILLAGE SITES IN SAMPLE AREAS.   (*a*) The boulder-
clay plain of southeast Northumberland.   (*b*) The uplands of mid-Northumberland.
(*c*) The Wear vale and the Magnesian Limestone escarpment in Durham.   (*d*) The
east Durham plateau.

and gravel terraces.   The villages and hamlets in the drift-covered
coastal lowland of Northumberland were rarely sited on the prevalent
expanses of boulder-clay.   The terraces along the rivers, and other
scattered patches of sand and gravel interspersed among the clay country,
offered more favoured sites alike in respect of drainage, water supply,
and ease of cultivation.   Many of the settlements were concentrated on
such terrains and on the rock islands that rise here and there out of the

mantle of drift. Some boulder-clay sites were occupied in the north of the county, but in the southeast avoidance of the soggy boulder-clay areas was very pronounced (Fig. 22a). Here the settlement groups were practically confined to a few patches of sand and the eminences formed by occasional protrusions of the sandstones through the drift. Towards the west, where the drift cover is less continuous and rock outcrops occupy larger areas, the settlements tended to keep to the margins of the latter (Fig. 22b). Rock sites were preferred to those on the boulder-clay, but the higher, more exposed parts were also avoided. Similar siting controls obtained south of the Tyne in mid-Durham and northeast Durham in the drift-choked lowland valley in front of the limestone.

Many villages were strung out along the limestone escarpment, taking advantage of well-drained sites, the proximity to different types of terrain, and the availability of good water-supplies (Fig. 22c). The scarp-line, however, is too irregular for a pattern of strip-parishes, with parallel boundaries running transversely across the geological outcrops, as is so markedly developed along contact-lines in some parts of England. On the limestone plateau itself the villages again avoided the spread of clay drift and kept to patches of sand or the margins of the rock exposures in the west (Fig. 22d). Settlements were conspicuously absent from the inhospitable cliff coastline. In the vale of Tees the extensive sand and gravel stretches, which occur along the shallow valleys and elsewhere amidst the heavy red-clay country, provided the most attractive sites. Such a line of villages lies in front of the Cleveland escarpment.

In Cumberland and Westmorland, too, the old-established villages and hamlets are scattered over the lowlands below about 700 feet, where the rock floor is almost everywhere buried under drift. Those of the coastal belt, concerned with farming the narrow strip of good land between the coast and the highlands, are rarely on the coast itself. Farther north, round the head of Solway, avoiding the mosses, they keep to the margins of the drift, islands of drift, and fragments of raised gravel beaches. In northeast Cumberland, north of the Roman Wall, there is very little grouped settlement at all, but farther south, in the vale of Eden, a remarkable line of scarp-foot clusters runs from near Brampton to Brough beneath the Pennines. Elsewhere the villages lie in grooves of the drumlin-streaked landscape, more often on the banks of small tributary streams than on the main rivers, which are usually deeply entrenched. The marginal hamlets often lie at the mouths of the small dales of the Lake District highlands, with a few outlying clusters in the great U-shaped valleys that penetrate into the heart of the highlands. Here they occupy favourable valley-side and lake-side sites such are as provided by alluvial fans.

These features of the rural settlement pattern were well established by the fourteenth century. The areas that then remained empty were negative areas agriculturally, and extension beyond the frontier of settlement that had been reached by this time was for long held up by the reduction in population brought about by the ravages of the Black Death and the slow recovery during the ensuing period.

If the sites of the vast majority of rural settlement clusters and some at least of the dispersed steadings can be traced back to the Middle Ages, not so the buildings. The medieval dwellings of the peasantry were rude and insubstantial, and they have not survived. Among buildings, only churches and castles, solidly built of stone, persist from the earlier medieval period. But from the fourteenth century to the sixteenth a considerable number of buildings sprang up in the north country which, with modifications, have survived, either occupied or in ruins, to the present day, as significant and distinctive features of the Border landscape, reminders of its most troubled period of history.

The fourteenth century ushered in a long period of disturbed political conditions in the Border counties, which continued even after the Union of the Crowns. Over a wide belt along the Border the insecurity of life and property arrested agricultural development and further extension of settlement. Repeatedly devastated, the Border counties remained miserable and backward until the re-establishment of peace and security allowed economic revival during the last two centuries. Nowhere was the change in the later Middle Ages so pronounced as in Glendale, which in the thirteenth century had been one of the most prosperous and thickly settled districts. In the sixteenth century, on the contrary, a report on the Scottish marches refers to the periodic evacuation of the area lying west of the river Till. ' So soon as there is an appearance or suspicion of war the most part of the inhabitants do withdraw themselves with their goods to other fortresses for their defence and leave the said border by west of the river of Till almost desolate and waste ; and if war continuing long these tenants provided them of other farms. And so there is a season after the end of every such war before the frontier and border can be again peopled and replenished." [1]

Such havoc was wrought by the endless incursions and forays of the lawless Border dalesmen, no less than by the organised invasions of Scottish armies, that special measures for the defence of life and property were absolutely necessary. Whereas the erection of fortifications by vassals was in general regarded with jealousy and suspicion by

---

[1] Bowes and Ellerker, *View of the castles, barmekyns, and fortresses of the frontier of the East and Middle Marches* [Northumberland] (1541), quoted by C. J. Bates, *op. cit.*

the royal power as its authority extended, the practice was encouraged on the Border as a help towards solution of the problem of defence. Licences to crenellate were liberally granted, especially after the devastation wrought by the Scottish army before the battle of Neville's Cross in 1346. Thus fortifications of various kinds, ranging from

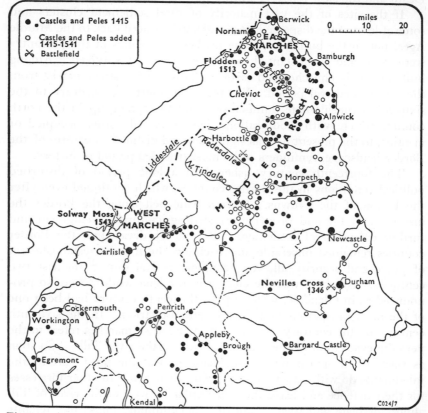

Fig. 23 THE ENGLISH MARCHES TOWARDS SCOTLAND IN THE FIFTEENTH AND SIXTEENTH CENTURIES.

baronial strongholds to turreted and strongly built farmsteads, sprang up till the countryside literally bristled with such towers.

A list of the fortified buildings in Northumberland in 1415 is extant ('List of castles and fortalices, 1415'). Their distribution (Fig. 23) shows a concentration in an arcuate zone extending across the county from the district between the coast and the river Till in the north to the Tyne valley in the south. From the middle of this belt a salient extended northwest towards Harbottle, the centre for the organisation of the defences of the Middle Marches. Throughout this broad zone fortified buildings were a very prominent feature of the settlement pattern. Many more were added during the fifteenth century, so that scarcely a village or hamlet was without such a strong point. In his translation of Camden's *Britannia* Holland wrote in 1610, ' There is not a man amongst them of the better sort that hath not his little tower or pele.' Such towers were typically rectangular, with very thick walls, and were crenellated. The living-quarters were above the byres and store-rooms that occupied the ground floor. Outside the immediate protection of such fortified buildings the other settlements of the Middle Ages were makeshift structures, mere huts or shiels. But of necessity the peles were much more substantial and enduring than the ordinary medieval dwellings. Built of stone, which was everywhere plentiful, their grim, solid structures have often survived, either wholly or in part, to the present day. In more or less modified form some are still occupied as farmhouses (Pl. 18). Many of the sixteenth-century priests lived in peles, and the rectories at Elsdon and Rothbury, as well as the vicarages at Alnham, Embleton, and Shilbottle are surviving examples. Some churches, too, were provided with strong towers, and the town-fields of some villages were surrounded by earthen dykes, the only openings (' barras gates ') being strongly trenched ; without doubt these dykes were manned by the villagers when need arose. Such earthworks are traceable at Dalston, Salkeld, and elsewhere. It is tempting to relate the characteristic lay-out of the numerous ' green ' villages of the northern counties to these needs of defence. Juxtaposed buildings surround an open green (Pls. 21, 22), making an enclosure with strictly limited ways of access. But the origins of the green villages are still obscure, and the type may well be associated first and foremost with the agrarian structure and may pre-date the period of Border turmoil. At least it may be observed that it was a lay-out admirably adapted to give some protection, and provide a stockade into which livestock could be driven, at time of raids and invasions.

On the outer side of the heavily fortified zone was a no-man's land, crossed for centuries by almost ceaseless tides of raid and counter-raid. Physically this tract is the highland Border country that is largely waste even today, but penetrated by narrow tongues of lowland and cultivation in Liddisdale, North Tynedale, and Redesdale, as well as by the deep, confined glens of the Cheviot. Until quite modern times the lack of security made settled life and the development of the limited agricultural resources of this country wellnigh impossible. Yet the position and character of the country, while denying the practice of a lawful livelihood, offered great opportunities for harbouring and maintaining outlaws and robbers. For long these dales were inhabited by wild tribesmen, whose chief occupations were fighting and livestock-stealing. Clan organisation persisted long, and there were bitter clan feuds. There were branches or 'graynes' of every surname, each family was under the leadership of its chief or headsman, and gavelkind was still practised as late as the seventeenth century. The tribesmen lived scattered in family groups in the fastnesses of the small 'hopes' or side-valleys, whence they raided indiscriminately on both sides of the Border, and whither they retreated across the treacherous bogs by difficult and tortuous paths that defied pursuit. In summer they grazed their cattle on the peaty moors, occupying scattered shielings from April till September. Their thieving was also characteristically a seasonal activity, carried out chiefly between Michaelmas and Martinmas when 'the fells are good and the cattle strong to drive'. In October 1593, for example, a thousand horsemen of the Elliott and Armstrong following raided Tynedale and drove away more than one thousand head of cattle, more than one thousand sheep and goats, and twenty-four horses. It would seem that the Border freebooters or 'moss-troopers' were numerous, more so than the farming resources of the Border dales would themselves warrant. Sir Robert Bowes, reporting in 1541, estimated that these dales could provide about six hundred men 'on horseback and on foot', and he refers to the over-population 'whereby the young and active people, for lack of living be constrained to steal or spoil continually, either in England or Scotland, for maintaining of their lives'.

The southeastern plain of Northumberland, the country south of the Tyne, and, in the west, the secluded valleys of the Lake District, were less affected by the disturbances that raged in the country nearer the Border. But even here recovery of the position in agricultural development and colonisation that had been reached before the scourges of plague was slow. Perhaps the chief field of further colonisation during the fifteenth and early sixteenth centuries was in the north Pennine dales. These dales were at least relatively immune from Border raiding, and ore mining made considerable, if not continuous, advances. Pastoral colonisation of the upper dales proceeded with mining settlement, and the developments appear to have been accompanied by considerable periodic immigration into the dales. There is evidence of more than one influx of German miners, as well as of mining families from mineralised areas in the Pennine dales farther south.

It has been emphasised that the mature stage of colonisation of North England, with the grouped settlements of agricultural communities in occupation of the good farming land, had been reached in the Middle Ages. Since then its pattern has been obscured in modern times by the superimposition of another pattern that belongs to the

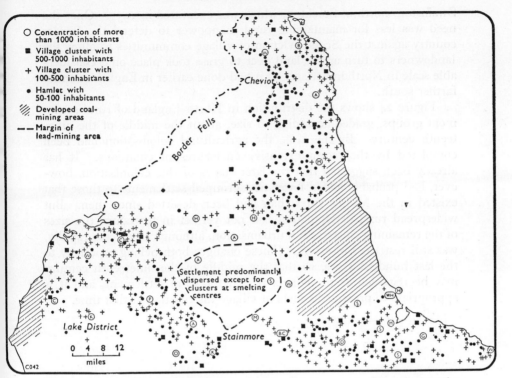

Legend:
- O Concentration of more than 1000 inhabitants
- ■ Village cluster with 500-1000 inhabitants
- + Village cluster with 100-500 inhabitants
- ● Hamlet with 50-100 inhabitants
- ▨ Developed coal-mining areas
- — — Margin of lead-mining area

?Cheviot

Border Fells

(Settlement predominantly dispersed except for clusters at smelting centres)

Lake District

0 4 8 12
miles

Stainmore

C042

Fig. 24 NORTH ENGLAND: RURAL SETTLEMENT CLUSTERS ABOUT 1850. Among the grouped settlements in the lowlands and in the fringing zone between these old-established areas and the moorland edge, recently pushed back by enclosures of commons, were many scattered farmsteads. The latter predominated in the dales, including the lead-mining dales. In the coal-mining areas urbanisation was rapidly transforming the older pattern.

industrial colonisation. Moreover, its outlines and clarity have been blurred by extensions of the frontier into marginal land and by scattering from the old nuclei. While new farmsteads have thus appeared beyond and between the old-established clusters, the number of the latter has almost certainly been reduced. New villages since the medieval period are outnumbered by lost villages. There is little evidence of lost villages in Cumberland and Westmorland, but that they are numerous in Northumberland is suggested by the *County History* and borne out by the direct evidence of the returns of a commission set up under statutes of 1581 to inquire what tenancies and houses had been ruined or decayed since 1535. In the Border counties two thousand houses are recorded as having decayed in this half-century, and villages with substantial decays are listed. Most of them are in Northumberland, but there are some, too, in Durham, including a well-known example at Archdeacon Newton, near Darlington, and

Swainston, north of Stockton, which was excavated in 1957. Once the need was less for maintaining rural manpower to defend the Border country against the Scots, eviction of village communities to allow the landowners to turn arable land over to grass took place on a considerable scale in Northumberland, as it had done earlier in English counties farther south.

Figure 24 shows the distribution in North England of rural settlement groups, graded according to size, about the middle of the nineteenth century. By this time the agricultural colonisation had been completed by the recent extensive enclosures of commons. It has already been suggested that the later stages of this colonisation, however, had probably added fewer new grouped settlements to those that existed in the Middle Ages than had been deserted since then. But widespread rural depopulation had not yet set in to reduce the sizes of the remaining clusters, and urbanisation, although advancing rapidly, was still restricted in extent. These changes both belong especially to the last hundred years, so that the middle of the nineteenth century may be regarded as the climax period for rural settlement, and it is appropriate to present the facts of village distribution at that time.

CHAPTER 7

THE ORIGINS AND EARLY GROWTH OF TOWNS

AT least until the latter part of the sixteenth century North England remained almost purely agricultural. The germs of industrial development were present in the form of coal mining and ore mining, but the urban communities that had come into existence were essentially administrative centres and garrison towns, ports for farming hinterlands, or simply local market-centres. Such commercial activity as existed was still based very largely upon the products and needs of farming.

It is important not to misconceive the early phases of urban development. Present-day connotations must not be read into the medieval usage of terms relating to urban status and character. It is neither safe to assume that places called ' boroughs ' before the Norman Conquest were towns, nor that communities in possession of medieval borough charters were therefore necessarily in any real sense urban in character. Carl Stephenson's warning against regarding borough and town as synonymous must be applied to the pre-Norman usage of the term ' borough ' and must also be extended to the later period. Neither before nor after the Conquest may a ' borough ' be assumed to discharge urban functions and to possess the other characteristics of townhood.

As in other parts of the country, there were in North England a number of places known before the Conquest as *burhs* and *caesters*, but the only significance of these names *per se* is that they indicate enclosure by a defensive earthwork or wall. On the other hand, many ' boroughs ' in the later sense of the word, signifying communities that enjoyed certain special franchises and privileges, did not become truly urban and develop into fully-fledged towns. Under the system of feudal tenures introduced by the Normans, the lords could proclaim a borough within their own jurisdiction wherever they chose. Many boroughs that were thus proclaimed never became urban, for the simple reason that they were not well enough situated to develop in competition with others that enjoyed greater advantages of geographical position. Incorporation and burgess privileges were almost invariably associated with urban life in the Middle Ages when we do find it developed, so that it is true to say that the towns were almost all boroughs. Many of them had developed, moreover, from *burhs*. This association of the terms may explain, but certainly does not justify, their loose use as equivalents.

Thus, although a *burh* must not be assumed to be a town, it is not difficult to appreciate that the *burhs* had definite advantages for becoming focusing points of trade as a widening and more highly organised economic life emerged. The revival of trade appears to have been a slow and gradual process that took a leap forward after the Norman Conquest, so that its fruits in urban growth acquired such a new prominence that Carl Stephenson was led to suggest the sudden appearance of the medieval town in Norman England as an entirely new feature, unaccountable in terms of any pre-existing institution. This thesis has been strongly challenged by other scholars, such as Sir Frank Stenton, who prefer to regard the development of the eleventh and twelfth centuries as the quickened growth of shoots the roots of which reach into the obscure soil of the Dark Ages. The Anglian *burhs* served as the centres for the organisation and administration of the surrounding districts. As economic life developed, therefore, it was natural that it, too, should focus upon the *burh*, a point of relative security at which to establish a market.

In North England, however, such continuity from Anglian *burh* to medieval town is clearly discernible only at Darlington. The ravages of the Danish marauders obliterated any urban character that the fairly important *burh* of South Shields may have begun to assume ; and, although others escaped extinction, most of the Anglian *burhs* in North England had certainly passed their zenith as military and administrative centres before the economic development of the region was sufficiently advanced to give them an independent existence as trading centres. Such was the case with Bamburgh, which had been by far the most important centre of the Anglian power. From the commencement of the Anglian penetration this stronghold, on a headland of the Whin Sill on the coast of north Northumberland, was the centre of Anglian organisation. Here Ida planted his *burh* on the site of an earlier British camp. From being at first the coastal base that ensured a foothold for the invaders and a centre of diffusion of early colonisation, Bamburgh, by virtue of its strategic position in the gateway between north and south, was able to grow in importance as the Anglian power was extended into a kingdom stretching from Forth to Tees. When, however, this kingdom broke up during the ninth and tenth centuries, the importance of Bamburgh likewise declined. In 1018 the Northumbrian frontier receded to the Tweed, and thenceforth Bamburgh lay in an exposed frontier situation. The political conditions under which it had risen to importance as an administrative centre had passed, and after the Norman Conquest the organisation of the defence and administration of northeast England was based upon centres farther south. When a Norman castle was established at Bamburgh (Pl. 19) it was an outpost, part of the frontier fortifications; and although Bamburgh was still styled a borough in 1296, it was by then merely a fort with a small agricultural settlement attached. As a focusing point for local trade it had been outstripped by the new feudal stronghold of Alnwick, which enjoyed greater natural nodality, as well as greater strategic importance in the frontier defences.

Corbridge was another royal seat and important centre of Anglian administration. One of the earliest Anglian settlement sites known in the north of England, it was established near the principal Roman civilian settlement along the Wall, where the road from the south crossed the river Tyne to reach the Wall (see p. 85). Long afterwards it carried the advantage of this momentum, but although it was still called a borough in 1296 this was mainly a tribute to its earlier status, and it is doubtful whether any settlement that could really be called urban had ever existed. Certainly it was by this time overshadowed by nearby Hexham.

The achievement of urban character in the Middle Ages by places that enjoyed an early administrative importance in the Anglian period depended upon the possession of geographical advantages adequate to maintain their regional importance in competition with younger foundations of the feudal era, as well as upon mere survival of the political hazards of the time. Darlington alone had such an adequate natural endowment. Like Corbridge it was the site of one of the earliest Anglian settlements and a fortified Anglian *burh*, and it was already definitely a district centre with dependent vills when in 1003 it became part of the patrimony of St Cuthbert. Its importance was derived from its central situation in the vale of Tees, near a crossing of the river. At some early date it possessed a market, and the nascent town grew after the Conquest as the market centre of a rich agricultural district. In the bishopric it was by the end of the twelfth century second in importance only to Durham, and it maintained this status throughout the Middle Ages. Leland described it about 1540 as ' the best market-town in the bishoprick, saving Duresme '.

The other medieval towns of North England cannot be linked with pre-Conquest centres. Their foundations were of later date, though this does not necessarily mean that their sites were previously unoccupied. The eleventh century marked the coming of a new order, and although the medieval trading communities are quite commonly found to have grown round military strongholds, their nuclei were the new Norman castles rather than the older Anglian *burhs*. Before the eleventh century there are some obscure references to a settlement called Monkchester on the north side of the Tyne near the Roman fort of Pons Aelius, but the existence of any urban settlement there certainly post-dates the new Norman castle. Nor can the urban character of Carlisle and Durham be established before the Conquest. In the Norman organisation, however, Newcastle and Durham super-seded Bamburgh in the northeast, and in the northwest Carlisle was supreme.

For some time after the assertion of Norman authority over the eastern side of North England, Cumberland remained outside the kingdom. As long as this was so the country west of the Pennines, and thereby the western entrance to the Tyne Corridor, remained unsecured and open to Scottish armies; and the situation of the 'New Castle' that had been established on the Tyne in 1080 could not have first-class strategic value, for it was liable to be outflanked. This castle was probably only a wooden stockade, designed to afford some protection to the bridge that had recently been built there across the Tyne. Its functions were local and restricted, and the real burden of the defence of the north was entrusted by the Conqueror to the prince-bishop at Durham, for whom the county palatine was created south of the Tyne.

Until the closing years of the tenth century the site of Durham had been covered with thick woodland. The meanders of the Wear are deeply entrenched here, and the smooth summit of a sandstone pro-montory rises precipitously one hundred feet above the river, which sweeps round it, leaving only a narrow isthmus in the north, less than two hundred yards across (Pls. 40, 46). This small, but well-defined site enjoyed wonderful natural defences, and here in A.D. 995 a suitable resting-place was at last found for the remains of St Cuthbert. The site, says Symeon of Durham, was ' a place strong by nature, but not easily rendered habitable, as it was overgrown by a thick forest'. Return-ing from his campaign in Scotland in 1070, William I recognised the natural strength of the site and its appropriateness for a fortress to serve as a bulwark against the Scots and to hold in awe the unruly inhabitants of the district. Under his authority the building of a castle was begun, and under one of his own men as bishop the organisation of the patrimony as a county palatine was undertaken.

During the twelfth century, however, Newcastle became of primary importance as a fortress. After Rufus's annexation of Cumberland in 1092 and his establishment of a fortress at Carlisle to guard the western entry into England and control the new province, the strategic import-ance of Newcastle's position was greatly enhanced. The western entry to the Tyne Corridor was in the hands of the English king, and Newcastle itself commanded the east-coast route where it crossed the Tyne, the only way by which large forces could penetrate from Scotland into Durham and Yorkshire. In the frontier defence system of William

Rufus and Henry I Newcastle on the east and Carlisle on the west were the key positions, but during the war of succession and the anarchy that followed the death of Henry I both fell into the hands of the Scottish king. In 1157, however, Henry II again asserted English authority over the Border counties, and to secure his control he replaced Rufus's castle in 1172 by the massive keep that still overlooks the Tyne bridge. That the importance of the site was first and foremost related to the bridge it guarded is reflected by the facts that the bridge gave its name, Pons Aelius, to the Roman fort, and that the site was insignificant during the period between the withdrawal of the Roman authority and the coming of the Normans, when it seems certain that no bridge existed. Between the lowlying clay land south of the Tyne estuary in northeast Durham and the extensive haughs of the drift-choked pre-glacial valley through which the diminutive Team meanders to the Tyne, the cuesta formed by resistant sandstones above the High Main coal-seam marks the natural line of approach to the river from the south (Figs. 8, 46, and Pl. 42). Here the Tyne valley becomes constricted between steeply rising ground on both sides, and here the river was bridged. The site of the Roman fort, like that of the later Norman castle, was strengthened by the natural flank protection afforded by the deep ravines or denes of the burns which dissect the highland mass of sandstone that rises high above the north bank of the river (Fig. 25 and pl. 43). These denes were once more numerous than appears today, for several of them have been filled in during the modern development of the city. Originally Castle Hill descended abruptly eastwards to the valley of the Lort burn, a tributary of which gave additional protection on its north side. Only to the west of the castle was there a fairly considerable stretch of more level ground immediately adjacent.

Towards the other end of Hadrian's Wall, just east of the point where it crosses the lower Eden to pass behind the river towards the south shore of the Solway Firth, Carlisle (Fig. 56) was in some respects, but not in all, the western counterpart of Newcastle. Its site, a sandstone bluff that rises from the alluvial flats of the wide, deep, and swift-flowing river Eden between the valleys of its left-bank tributaries the Petteril and Caldew, was easily defended, and Agricola had established a fort there. But when the Wall was built, this fort was replaced by Petriana (Stanwix) across the Eden to the north; and from the second to the fourth centuries Luguvallium was a civilian settlement in the shelter of the frontier fortifications. Highways from the west coast and down the vale of Eden here converged upon the line of the frontier, which passed from west to east across the isthmus through the Tyne Corridor.

After the withdrawal of the legions, Luguvallium (corrupted to

113

Lugubalia, and Luel, whence the modern Ca(e)r-lisle) remained for some centuries the centre of territorial rule of the surrounding district, until the settlement was sacked by the Norsemen about 875. From this time it remained in ruins until after the Norman Conquest when, in 1092, Rufus restored the settlement and initiated the building of a castle. But it was his successor Henry I who carried through the establishment of Carlisle as the key fortress of the west. Visiting Carlisle in 1122, he recognised the strategic importance of the situation and the potentialities of the promontory site, and the work of building the great castle and the city walls was pressed on.

Under the protection of these fortresses, both religious houses and trading communities gathered at Durham, Newcastle, and Carlisle during the twelfth and thirteenth centuries. While the castle was being built at Carlisle and before the civil administration had been put into the hands of a vassal, the Austin Canons had arrived and had been endowed by the king and encouraged in the building of their great church behind the castle. Their prior was created the first bishop in 1133. At Durham the cathedral had been begun before 1100, and a convent of Benedictine monks had been founded. The bishop granted to the monks the vill of Elvet, to the east across the river, to be held as a borough, while the trading community that gathered on the Durham peninsula itself, in the first place to minister to the needs of the garrison and its retainers, remained under the bishop's direct control. Early in the twelfth century the defences were strengthened by a wall, and the first bridge (to the west) was built (Pls. 40, 46). The trade of Durham was growing steadily, and already the annual fair of St Cuthbert was being held. This early development received a check during the anarchy of the middle of the twelfth century, when the see was usurped and the growing town largely destroyed by fire. Fortunately there followed the reign of the greatest of the medieval prince-bishops, Hugh Pudsey (1153-94), under whose ambitious and strong direction the see became a miniature kingdom.

Pudsey rebuilt the borough of Elvet and restored it to the monks, but bound it closely to his own borough by means of a new bridge. He restored and extended the defences of Durham itself, and granted the burgesses a charter modelled upon that of Newcastle. Further, he created the new borough of St Giles outside the city, to the north. Even so, Durham had by this time fallen far behind Newcastle in regional importance—not only because of the latter's superior position for trade, but also because of political circumstances. Newcastle was a royal borough, and its burgesses enjoyed far greater freedom to develop their opportunities than those of Durham, who lived under the immediate surveillance of their lord. Furthermore, while the disturbances of the period 1137–54 spelt temporary ruin to Durham, Newcastle thrived during occupation by the Scots. Till then it had scarcely extended beyond the small area that had served the Roman fort. The first medieval walls enclosed a small site lying northwest of the castle, and Hadrian's Wall was probably still standing to serve after some repair as the northern wall of the original borough, while a new wall was built on the west side from what is now the head of Collingwood Street to Tuthill Stairs. To the southeast the castle precincts overlooked the steep descent to the Lort burn and the Tyne. Here houses of traders occupied the slopes above the wharves on the Lort burn (Pl. 43).

During the thirteenth century, however, the prospering town outgrew these narrow confines. The influx of religious bodies, on a scale unparalleled elsewhere in Britain outside London, and the growing importance of the fortress and its garrison in themselves gave rise to a considerable aggregation of dependent civilians. At the same time the commerce of the port was growing. The special privileges of the burgesses, already recognised by Henry I, were confirmed and extended in the municipal charters of Henry II and his successors, and laid the foundations for the great power exercised later. They marked the legal recognition of the growing trade of the port and the wealth and eminence of its merchants. The chief products, derived from the pastoral hinterland of Newcastle, were wool and hides ; less important, but already in existence, was the trade in coal. There is no specific reference to the export of coal until 1325, but the evidence justifies the assumption that the coal trade existed during the preceding century. In 1239 the burgesses obtained a licence from the king to dig for coal in the fields outside the town, and at the inquisition held in Newcastle in 1281 the figure of £100 at which the fee farm had stood since 1213 was doubled, and the increase was attributed to the prosperity that the new industry had since brought to the town. The population is estimated at about two thousand by the end of the thirteenth century, and Newcastle had considerably outgrown its original walls. Monastic settlements and burgesses' houses had spread to the west, giving rise to the new parishes and churches of St Andrew and St John, while another new extension sprang up on the east across the Lort burn. Here, at the lower end of Pilgrim Street, which followed the ridge between the Lort and Pandon denes towards the hospitals of Mary Magdalene and St James and the shrine at Jesmond, the parish of All Saints developed. Farther north on this ridge the Grey Friars were established in 1240.

To include these extensions and the monastic houses, new walls were planned and begun on the west side at the end of the thirteenth century (Fig. 25). The outbreak of the Scottish wars quickened the desire of the burgesses and religious bodies to carry out the task of surrounding the enlarged town with a new wall. In so doing the

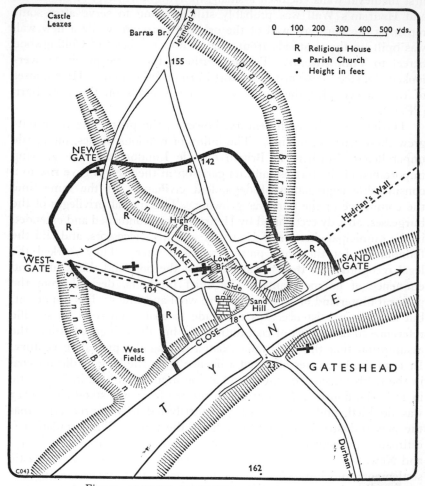

Fig. 25   MEDIEVAL NEWCASTLE : SITE AND LAY-OUT.

burgesses coveted the inclusion of the commercial facilities of the mouth of Pandon burn and the defensive knoll beyond it, and managed to obtain the king's sanction to purchase the vill of Pandon. The eastern wall of the city was extended to include it, with its convent of White Friars. When the walls were built, and for long afterwards, there remained extensive open spaces within their limits. The newly annexed Pandon, for instance, was connected with All Saints by rural lanes (Dog's Bank and Silver Street) and a foot-bridge across Pandon burn made of logs or ' stocks ' (Stockbridge).

The strongly walled city continued to grow in prosperity during

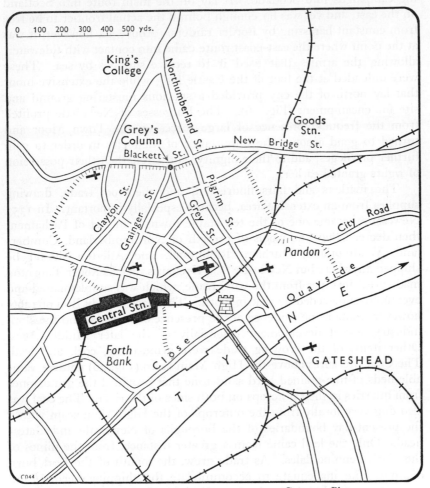

Fig. 26   MODERN NEWCASTLE : CITY CENTRE.   Compare Plates 41-4.

the fourteenth and fifteenth centuries, a period when urban develop-ment in the Border counties was generally inhibited because of the repeated invasions of Scottish armies and raiders and the ravages of the plague. Although Newcastle did not escape these recurrent visita-tions, it grew in spite of them. From the Scottish wars, which proved disastrous to other towns, it reaped positive benefits as a great military base. The strength of its city walls, a measure of its early advance and prosperity, together with a rare combination of advantages both of situation and of site, pointed to Newcastle as the unchallenged centre for the organisation of defence against a major invasion and for launching campaigns into Scotland. It lay on the main route into Scotland on the east, and yet was far enough behind the actual frontier to be free from constant harassing by Border raiders. Above all, however, it was at the point where the east-coast route came into contact with tidewater, allowing the armies that used it to receive supplies by sea. These were unloaded at the foot of the Castle Hill, while the extensive moor that lay north of the city provided a spacious mustering ground and site for encampment (Fig. 46). The burgesses of Newcastle profited from the frequent presence of large forces on the Town Moor and turned to good account the importance of their city in order to gain further privileges, add to their dignity, and strengthen their possession of rights granted earlier.

The markets and fairs flourished, and the wool trade, drawing supplies from an extensive area, became especially important. In 1353 Newcastle became one of the ten staple towns ; an Act of Parliament then decreed that ' no wools of growth of Northumberland, Cumberland, Westmorland, Durham, Richmond, and Allerton should be shipped anywhere but Newcastle '. Merchants such as Roger Thornton made great fortunes from the wool trade, which was supplemented and eventually superseded by that in cloth. The Lay Subsidy Roll of 1296, however, contains no evidence of the presence of weavers, and the cloth industry was a development essentially of the later Middle Ages. Other items of the growing trade were grindstones, coal, and lead. The Coal Measures above the High Main seam (Fig. 46) contain valuable beds of fine-grained hard sandstone that provided the grindstones from quarries in their outcrops on both sides of the river. The coal was also dug very locally from the outcrops of the High Main seam within the present-day boundaries of the boroughs of Newcastle and Gateshead. Only the lead came from a greater distance, from the mines of the north Pennine dales. As trade grew, the mouth of the Lort burn became quite inadequate to accommodate the shipping needed, and commerce moved to the bank of the Tyne itself. Merchants' mansions, the Exchange, Guildhall, and other buildings gathered there, and the quayside was gradually extended east of the Lort burn to meet the need for increased wharfage. The market had been shifted from its original site hard by the castle and port, and spread north along the main thoroughfare of the town that led from its earliest nucleus towards the ' new ' gate of the extended north wall.

There are a few clues to numerical assessment of the growth of population that accompanied the medieval development of Newcastle.

An estimate of 2,000 inhabitants for the end of the thirteenth century has already been cited. The poll-tax returns of 1377 recorded 2,647 persons over the age of fourteen, which suggests a total population of the order of 4,000 at a period when the immediate effects of the Black Death must still have been felt. By 1539 the population had increased to about 10,000. The muster roll of that year enumerated 1,907 able-bodied men, perhaps about one-fifth of the total population. With this increase in population, the area within the city walls was gradually being filled in with buildings, but the religious bodies continued to maintain considerable open tracts. Meantime the town was made more compact by the construction of cross-lines of communication, such as bridges over the Lort burn, the approaches to which became lined with houses. Thus streets such as High Bridge, Low Bridge, Butcher Bank, High and Low Friar streets were formed. Similarly the lanes connecting All Saints and Pandon came to be lined with dwellings, and by the end of the fifteenth century small extensions had made their appearance outside the gates. The largest of these was Sandgate in the southeast, since it was not only the best protected of the extra-mural suburbs but also the most conveniently situated for housing the increasing number of persons engaged in manning the port. The dissolution of the monasteries did not mean such an economic and social upheaval at Newcastle as might perhaps be assumed, for many of the religious bodies by that time had dwindled greatly in numbers. However, on the eve of a period of great commercial expansion associated with the coal trade, it made centrally placed sites available for development.

That no other settlement was able to rise on the banks of the Tyne and attain urban status during the Middle Ages must be attributed to the power of Newcastle rather than to lack of natural bases for such development. From the first the waterway of the Tyne and trade upon it were regarded by the burgesses of Newcastle as their special prerogative, and the monopoly was maintained successfully, if not entirely without challenge. The banks of the river just within the bar at its mouth enjoyed a certain advantage over Newcastle, in that ships trading there might avoid navigating the river up to Newcastle. But attempts during the Middle Ages to exploit this advantage met with the determined resistance of Newcastle and were all in turn stifled. On the south bank Newcastle's authority was never seriously challenged, but at North Shields the priors of Tynemouth more than once established an incipient trading community. Towards the end of the thirteenth century, and again in the fifteenth century, we find the burgesses of Newcastle successfully appealing to the king against infringement by the prior of their exclusive rights of market and port.

Although the bishop of Durham held the south bank of the Tyne, the power of Newcastle caused him to look elsewhere for ports to serve his palatinate, and such importance and status as were enjoyed by Gateshead sprang from his concern to maintain his territorial claim to the south bank and the southern half of Tyne bridge against encroachment by Newcastle, rather than to any serious attempt to challenge Newcastle's trade monopoly. The small cluster of dwellings that gathered at the southern end of the Tyne bridge was never a possible rival. Gateshead from the first was only the poor neighbour of Newcastle. Its charter reflects its small importance, being little more than a grant of protection from the oppressions of the bishop's foresters and of privileges in the forest. There is no mention of a market or of trading rights, and the market probably did not appear until the fourteenth century.

The bishop's ports were at Wearmouth and Hartlepool. Between the Tyne and Tees estuaries the exposed cliff coast provided only two natural sites for port development—the estuary of the Wear and the shelter of the Hartlepool peninsula. Farther south, the Tees estuary, a wide tract of sand and mud threaded by the tortuous, shifting, and shallow channels of the river and fringed by salt-marshes, offered little attraction for shipping. Until about 1200 Wearmouth was the only port of the bishopric and with this initial advantage expanded its trade, especially in the salt and fish that were essential to the medieval economy. It had served in a small way as a port during the seventh and eighth centuries, when Benedict Biscop's monastery occupied the north bank of the river mouth and used the favourable shipping facilities of the opposite shore. But it suffered the fate of other places on the coast exposed to Danish raids, and remained in eclipse until revived by the bishop of Durham. Its medieval trade, however, never reached large proportions. Once the bishop acquired Hartlepool in 1200 its relative importance was reduced. It appears to have suffered especially severely from the Black Death, and Leland had no more to say about it than that it was situated twelve miles from Durham.

Hartlepool (Fig. 50) was also the site of a seventh-century monastery that was later destroyed by the Danes. Soon after the Conquest, before it had become part of the palatinate, its trade was developed by the Brus family, and before the king handed its overlordship to the bishop he granted Brus a market and gave the burgesses a charter. During the thirteenth century the haven was improved and the town was walled across the peninsula. As there was no port on the Tees itself, Hartlepool served the productive agricultural district of the lower basin of the Tees. It was frequently mentioned during the fourteenth century and supplied five ships for the siege of Calais, and during the Scottish wars it was often used to transport provisions to the various garrisons occupied by the English in Scotland.

Berwick and Whitby lie beyond the limits of our province, and the stretches of coast intervening between these ports and the Tyne and Tees respectively were little used for trade. The rocky, exposed coast of the North Riding offered neither shelter nor a productive hinterland, and although the Northumberland coast had a number of small harbours in the shelter of headlands, the trade of that county was largely concentrated upon Newcastle. A few of the coastal vills farther north developed fishing communities and a small local trade, e.g. Newbiggin, Warkworth at the mouth of the Coquet, and Alnmouth, which became fairly prosperous in the fifteenth century as the port of Alnwick.

On the west coast there was little trade. Unlike Newcastle, Carlisle was not a port, for the Eden was not navigable. Skinburness on the Solway, the port of the monks of Holme Cultram abbey, was used to bring supplies by sea for the Carlisle garrison, but the Cumberland coast was of little commercial importance throughout the Middle Ages. Workington was only a small fishing port, and the other ports are much later creations, engendered by the needs of the coal trade.

Moreover, in spite of its early market-rights, Carlisle was slow to develop the functions of the centre of a rich agricultural lowland. To the south a large sector of its natural market hinterland was for a time reserved as a royal forest (Inglewood), from which normal agricultural development was precluded, though by the fourteenth century there is evidence of extensive assarting. Medieval Carlisle was first and foremost a great fortress. Throughout the Middle Ages and into the modern period, Carlisle held its key position commanding the constricted lowland entry into England from the northwest, between the head of the Solway estuary and the hill country. Exposed to constant danger of attack by organised forces from Scotland, the city remained confined within the relative security of its medieval walls. Indeed, for some time after the Stuart rebellions, in which Carlisle played a prominent part, the drawbridge was raised and sentinels were posted at night. The 1745 rebellion, however, marked the close of the long period of insecurity and warfare on the Scottish border, and with it the end of Carlisle's importance as a fortress. The Norman castle, now used as a depot for the 34th or Border regiment, remains to remind us of this long phase of the city's history.

Within the medieval walls, which confined the built-up area until the eighteenth century, the main features of the layout of old Carlisle were derived from the relative positions of the castle, cathedral, market-place, and the three city gates (Pl. 45). The roads approaching the town converged upon the three gates, situated to the south, northeast, and northwest of the town. The road from the vale of Eden and the south entered by Botchergate or English gate. The roads from Scotland and other districts north of the Eden entered by Rickergate or Scotch gate, leading from the Eden bridge. Those from the east, according to whether they approached on the south or north side of the Eden, also came in by one or other of these gates. From the west and southwest, roads converged upon the Caldew bridge to enter the city by Caldewgate in the northwest, behind the castle. With some slight modifications caused by the positions of the cathedral and castle, the street-plan showed a simple radial arrangement, three main arteries leading from the gates into the market-place in the centre of the city. These features of the layout of the old fortress town have been inherited by the core of the modern city, and the minor features of the plan have also been but little altered.

The other towns of North England grew from rural vills that were more favoured either by circumstance or position to become district centres and thereby assume urban features. It has already been pointed out how this was notably the case at Darlington, chief centre of the fertile vale of Tees. One cannot say at what stage in their development such communities emerged as towns. Non-agricultural activities gradually assumed importance, and with these functions came townhood. The date of incorporation is not decisive, for in some cases it marks the recognition of an already acquired urban status, in others an attempt to foster or implant the germs of urban development. The mere possession of the right to hold a market is by itself no indication of urban character, even where the right was practised and not allowed to lapse into desuetude, as sometimes happened. The privilege was enjoyed by places that were no more than mere villages, where the inhabitants remained predominantly engaged in agriculture, despite their markets. In some cases, moreover, early advances towards urban status were not maintained, and nascent towns stagnated or declined during the more difficult times of the later Middle Ages, when warfare and plague offered setbacks.

In the palatinate of Durham the bishop's boroughs of Stockton and Auckland both owed much to his patronage; at each the establishment of an episcopal residence brought an influx of retainers and gave an impetus to trade. Both received charters from the bishop and developed as small market centres, but neither approached Darlington in size or importance, and neither appears to have been prosperous or growing during the later Middle Ages. Stockton was not yet a port, and, although it lay in the midst of fertile farming country, its development as a district centre was restricted by the fact that it had only ferry connection with the country on the south side of the river. Auckland enjoyed early importance as one of the bishop's favourite residences, for it lay within easy access of both Durham city and his hunting domain in Weardale. Situated where the river Wear emerges from its dale into the more open lowlands of mid-Durham, and just above the point where the old Roman road from the south crossed the river, its market was well placed to develop trade. The erection of a

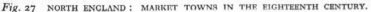

Fig. 27   NORTH ENGLAND : MARKET TOWNS IN THE EIGHTEENTH CENTURY.

stone bridge across the Wear about 1400 improved its connections with the surrounding district, but it was not of great importance when visited by Leland. The bishop of Durham also held Northallerton, south of the Tees in the lowland corridor that connects the main lowlands of England with their annexe in the northeast. It was Bishop Pudsey who provided it with some defences and who was responsible for stimulating its early growth as a market centre.

In the frontier region of the marcher counties of Northumberland and Cumberland the protection of a feudal stronghold was an indispensable factor in the origin of medieval towns. Along the main south–north highways on both sides of the country, market towns developed beneath the shelter of Norman strongholds (Fig. 23). Such were Morpeth and Alnwick on the main route into Scotland from

Newcastle through Northumberland. On the western side of the Pennines, after the reassertion of English control in 1157, earlier earthworks along the Roman military road down the Eden valley from Stainmore were transformed into strong castles that commanded the principal fords—at Brougham on the Eamont, at Appleby in a meander loop on the Eden, and at Brough below Stainmore.

But the feudal castles were crystallising points for urban development only when they could offer, in addition to the advantages of protection and patronage, those of natural nodality. In the central district of the vale of Eden it was the town of Penrith, alongside a late fourteenth-century castle commanding another crossing of the Eamont, that emerged as market centre, and not Brougham where an earlier castle had been established along the line of the old Roman road. In Tynedale urban functions and the rôle of district centre developed neither at the feudal stronghold of Prudhoe (Pl. 20) nor the old-established Anglian *burh* of Corbridge, but at Hexham, where the town grew under the patronage of the religious community established there by Wilfred in the seventh century. Already in Anglian times Hexham had assumed leadership in the ecclesiastical organisation and was for a time the seat of a bishopric. Later, although it lacked the protection of a feudal castle and seems never to have been incorporated as a borough, its advantages of nodal situation proved decisive. Situated on a well-defended site (a steeply rising gravel-terrace south of the enlarged Tyne, a little below the confluence of its two components), the abbey town became the undisputed centre of Tynedale.

On the Wansbeck an incipient borough at Mitford was superseded by Morpeth, which had a superior situation. Mitford, the seat of the Bertram family, was situated on a peninsula formed between the rivers Font and Wansbeck above their confluence, but it declined in importance after 1200 because of the rise of Morpeth, which was better placed on the direct north–south route. Morpeth Castle, occupying a defensive site on the south bank of the Wansbeck between the confluences of two small tributaries, commanded the crossing of the Wansbeck; the town grew up on the opposite bank. Like Morpeth, the borough of Alnwick was a trading community attached to a feudal castle (Pl. 25) at an important river-crossing on the direct north–south line of movement. But its position was much more important. The highland country that lies west of Morpeth strikes towards the coast farther north, and the Aln flows across the southern approach to the narrow belt of lowland between the hills and sea—the Cheviot gate. Its upper valley also connects the back-door approach to the direct coastal route by the sub-Cheviot groove behind the sandstone highlands. Thus the feudal castle that De Vesci had established came to have great strategic importance in the period of Border wars. Under the house of Percy, Alnwick was in the fourteenth and fifteenth centuries the great military stronghold of the actual frontier zone. In 1315 its garrison numbered more than two thousand men-at-arms, and it had many military retainers even in time of peace. A borough community had made its appearance beneath the castle soon after its foundation, and was nourished by the De Vescis who granted it charters and land. Although the surrounding district suffered grievously from its frontier position, and the town itself was more than once devastated, trade increased thanks to the nodality of the situation and the size of the local garrison. In the fifteenth century the burgesses were rich enough to defend themselves by building round the town a wall with four gates, strongly defended by towers, and they developed at Alnmouth a small port for their trade.

That no town such as Alnwick or Morpeth grew at the other important river-crossing of the east-coast route—Felton on the Coquet —is indicative of the rôle played by feudal castles in the urban origins in this region. Felton was not an important feudal seat in the early Middle Ages, although it later came to possess one of the numerous pele-towers that studded the frontier zone. On the other hand, Barnard Castle is a town that owes its foundation entirely to the enterprise of a Norman lord, whose name it perpetuates. At the beginning of the twelfth century Bernard Balliol, to whose father Rufus had granted the forest of Teesdale, chose for his castle a site on the Tees in Marwood. There is no earlier mention of the spot, and even the parish in which it lay took its name from the vill of Gainford. The new feudal seat, however, became the district centre of lower Teesdale, and under the protection of the castle a community of dependants and traders gathered. Besides those already mentioned, other Norman castles at Cockermouth (Pl. 26), Egremont, and Kendal were nuclei of towns, while Millom, like Penrith, grew up in the shelter of a later fourteenth-century castle. At Guisborough, as at Hexham, the trading settlement attached itself to a religious foundation—the twelfth-century Augustinian priory established in a lowland embayment of the Cleveland hills.

The advance in prosperity of all the towns of North England except Newcastle itself was severely checked during the Border wars, but they emerged from this period in a strengthened position as district centres to enjoy the peace-time benefits of this function. With the limited accessibility permitted by undeveloped means of transport and poor roads, provision of services, chiefly market facilities, had perforce to be local, and a small scale of urban mesh was necessitated. Between the major centres of town development, small though many of these remained, markets were also held at intermediate points. Figure 27 names the eighteenth-century market centres.

In varying degrees these places advanced towards townhood, but later several of them decayed as their markets became redundant, and they have failed to assume the modern functions of towns. This has also been the fate of Yarm, a port that flourished in the seventeenth century at the head of navigation on the Tees (Fig. 36). It lost its trade to Stockton, farther downstream, when the stone bridge was erected there in 1760.

The centres of the lead-mining dales, Alston, Allendale Town, Stanhope, and Middleton became thriving towns as mining in their dales prospered and population increased. Their markets lapsed after the mines declined, and the servicing of the reduced communities of the dales has become concentrated in urban centres outside. After flourishing in Elizabethan times as a mining centre, Keswick also declined ; but it has been revived by the tourist industry.

The new towns, Sunderland and Whitehaven (Pl. 27), created by development of the coal trade in the seventeenth century, have however become permanent additions to the ranks of towns. Inconsiderable at the beginning of the seventeenth century, and unmentioned by Camden, they grew rapidly as coal ports and industrial centres and became firmly established as service centres for the inhabitants of the surrounding districts. Finally, within the past century, urban functions have developed at some of the larger mining settlements that have come to be service centres in densely populated colliery districts, at some new ports created by the coal trade, and at a few resorts and residential settlements that have sprung up. These developments will be dealt with in later chapters.

CHAPTER 8

EARLY INDUSTRIAL SETTLEMENT

IT is still a matter of conjecture whether the silver-lead ores of the northern Pennines were worked by the Romans, and it may be mere coincidence that the Roman boundary corresponds so closely with the limit of the ore-bearing rocks (Fig. 52). It is quite certain, however, that silver-lead mining in the Alston Moor district (Fig. 61) was actively pursued during the Middle Ages. A document of 1130 refers to the Carlisle silver mines, and the source of supply was in all probability Alston Moor. It is probably significant that the foundation of the church at Alston and creation of the parish date from 1154. More specifically, in 1234 royal protection was granted to the miners of Alston Moor, and a century later a charter defined their liberties and immunities, which included the right to cut down trees. The miners lived then in ' shielings ', rude huts made of turf walls with roofs of turf or heather thatch. There is Pipe Roll evidence of the large rent paid for the mines, which would suggest the medieval prosperity of the industry.

In the fourteenth century the Alston Moor mines were leased to Germans from Cologne, who founded a colony of their countrymen there. Their links with Europe were through Newcastle, and at least from this time the Tyne was the outlet for the lead, and the earlier association with Carlisle was broken. At the head of navigation of the Tyne, Blaydon is a place-name which may well be derived from the German word for lead, as Blagill in the Alston Moor district certainly is. A fifteenth-century document refers to the royal grant of mines at Fletchers and Gerrards Gill (Garrigill) in the Tyne valley, and also at Blanchland, which points to extension of the activity into a district farther east. There is also some other evidence of developments in the late sixteenth and early seventeenth centuries in Allendale, and at Fallowfield in Tynedale ; in 1550 a royal grant was made to Bowes of all the lead mines in the forest of Teesdale. But the history of metalliferous mining is not one of steady, uninterrupted progress. With primitive techniques and very limited geological knowledge, mining was a transitory and shifting activity, and after the medieval phase there is little record of much activity in the northern Pennines until the late seventeenth century. A survey at the beginning of that century reported that the mines of Alston Moor were almost exhausted, but meantime mining was flourishing for a brief spell in the Lake District.

In the heart of the Lake District mining on any significant scale began later than in the Pennines, though lead-mining operations on Caldbeck Fells, north of Skiddaw, probably date back to medieval times, and the haematite ore of the limestone fringe of the west and south of the district was certainly worked by the monks of Holme Cultram, Calder, and Furness. There is a record of an iron-ore mine at Egremont being granted in 1179 to Holme Cultram abbey, and in the next century the account-books of Furness abbey clearly show the importance to the monks of their profits from ironworking.

Seeing a promising field for enterprise in the Keswick district, a group of Germans, equipped with a charter as the Company of the Mines Royal, started copper- and lead-mining operations on an ambitious scale in the latter half of the sixteenth century. During the Civil War, in 1648, their extensive works were destroyed, and the industry did not recover, but for eighty years previously Keswick had thriven greatly as the centre of the industry, with smelt-houses and smiths' shops. The river Greta was harnessed to work the bellows and stamps, and was also used for washing the ore. The chief mines (Fig. 28), including Goldscope (*Gottes gab*) and Brandelhow, were on the west side of Derwentwater and in the Newlands valley, but others lay to the north in the gills of Caldbeck Fell, and some additional supplies of ore were drawn from Coniston. As in the case of the Alston Moor mines, Newcastle was the port, whither ore was conveyed by pack-horse through the Tyne gap, although in 1569 Curwen erected a wharf at Workington with the intention of developing a west-coast outlet. There was some local smelting, six furnaces being active in 1567. Mining and smelting were both voracious of timber and made great depredations into the local woodlands. Charcoal burning was carried on as far afield as Windermere and Coniston. Also, in 1565 the iron bloomeries of Furness had been suppressed in order to stay the destruction of the woodlands, and not until the monopoly of the Company of the Mines Royal came to an end was iron smelting resumed, about 1650 at Coniston, and after 1700 at a number of other places, including Backbarrow. By 1752 local supplies of charcoal were becoming so difficult to obtain that the ironmasters shifted their smelting operations to Bonawe in Scotland.

It was the scale of the Elizabethan and Stuart industrial activity localised at Keswick that made this short-lived venture distinctive in the northwest as compared with what had preceded it. On a much larger scale there were contemporaneous industrial developments in northeast England that also dwarfed their precursors. For the first time industry may be said to have assumed a major rôle in regional differentiation, although its field was still restricted, and it dominated the scene only in a small area on Tyneside. Coal mining there has a continuous history right back to the thirteenth century, and numerous references throughout the later Middle Ages recall the working of coal in many other places in North England. But it is very doubtful whether before Elizabethan times coal mining, any more than ore mining, con-

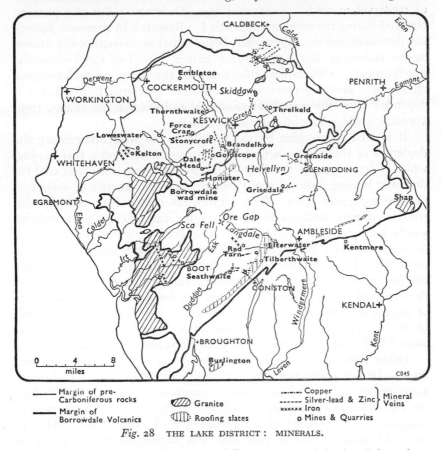

Margin of pre-Carboniferous rocks
Margin of Borrowdale Volcanics
Granite
Roofing slates

Copper
Silver-lead & Zinc } Mineral Veins
Iron
o Mines & Quarries

Fig. 28   THE LAKE DISTRICT : MINERALS.

tributed much to the geographical differentiation of the localities where it was carried on or employed any significant proportion of the population of the region. Shipments of coal from the Tyne rose to considerable amounts during the fourteenth century, but there was little further increase for a long time after that. They were no greater in 1513 than in 1377, and throughout the intervening period were probably never more than fifteen thousand tons per annum. Coal was very little used as a domestic fuel except in the immediate vicinity of its outcrops, and its other markets were practically confined to some use for lime burning and by smiths. Throughout the Middle Ages, in fact, coal

129

working was merely an adjunct to predominantly agricultural pursuits, except around Newcastle itself, which provided the sea-borne coal. So were the sporadic ironworking and ' bloomery ' smelting industries and the small saltpans scattered along the coast. Even at Newcastle it was the wool trade rather than the coal trade that made the fortunes of medieval merchants such as Roger Thornton. But the position changed during the reign of Elizabeth I. Research in economic history has demonstrated the importance, before what is conventionally known as the Industrial Revolution, of an earlier period of rapid industrial development. This earlier quickening of the tempo of technological change was nowhere more significant than in North England, for it depended upon the extended use of coal and marked the change from a wood-burning to a coal-burning economy.

It is well known that by the middle of the sixteenth century the depletion of the country's timber resources threatened a fuel famine, which at last overcame the deep-seated prejudice against use of coal for domestic heating, especially in London where the scarcity of wood fuel became especially acute. The seriousness of the fuel problem also stimulated new methods in industry, for example in glass making, which increased the use of coal. The growing demand for coal as domestic fuel and its extended industrial uses both affected Tyneside especially. Land transport of so bulky a commodity was impracticable except for very short distances, and the easily worked outcrop coal on the banks of the navigable Tyne (Fig. 29) provided the nearest source of supply to London by water. So great was the resulting growth of the Tyne coal trade that shipments increased fivefold during the second half of the sixteenth century, from 35,000 to 160,000 tons.

Other industries were directly stimulated by the expanding coal trade. In this connection the availability of cheap coal and of cheap water-transport were of paramount importance. It was not only that on Tyneside easily accessible coal and navigable water were present together ; the existence of a flourishing coal export trade added to these advantages. Small coal that was unsuitable for shipment to London was available for local industry at an almost nominal price, and bulky raw materials could be the more cheaply brought to the Tyne since they served as ballast for returning colliers. These were powerful attractions for such industries as the making of salt, glass, pottery, and copperas [1] (Fig. 30). First of these to become important was brine evaporation, an industry which in our British climate consumed great quantities of coal, although not necessarily coal of good quality. The large demand for ships and their accessories, which was

---

[1] Copperas (green vitriol or ferrous sulphate, used as a mordant) was made from iron pyrites (' brass ') found in coal seams.

created by the coal trade, provided yet another stimulus for local industry,[1] and shipbuilding expanded in step with coal shipments.

This intimate connection between the coal trade and industrial development explains the essential features of the early industrial settlement in northeast England, the effective beginnings of which date from

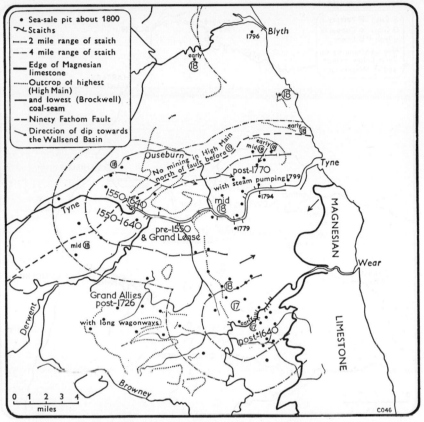

Fig. 29   EARLY MINING IN NORTHEAST ENGLAND.

the middle of the sixteenth century. Specialised and distinctively industrial settlements first appeared at that time. The workers were concentrated in groups to a degree previously quite unknown, for the industrial expansion involved a striking increase in the scale of organisation. The growing demand for coal required and called forth technical improvements to allow the pursuit of mining at greater depths, and market conditions were so advantageous that capital was sunk lavishly in applying the new inventions. With deeper mining came an increase

[1] Nef suggests that at the time of the Restoration (1660) the tonnage of colliers exceeded that of all other British merchantmen.

131

in the size of pits. Likewise in other industries the application of new methods connected with the use of coal meant an increase in the size of their units, both because of the capital expenditure required and the high degree of localisation involved. In yet another way, however, the coal trade helped to concentrate population on the Tyne. Besides the

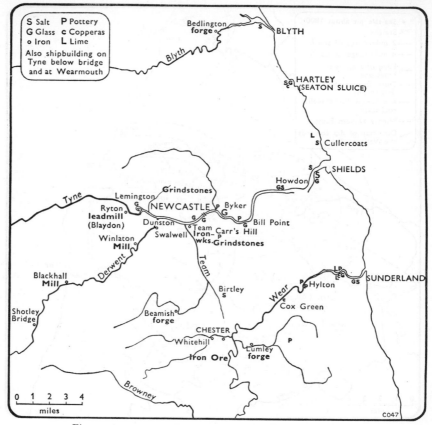

Fig. 30   EARLY INDUSTRIAL SITES IN NORTHEAST ENGLAND.

workers employed in the actual winning of the coal and its transport to the shipping points or staiths, there was a numerous body of lightermen or keelmen engaged in the transport of coal on the river (Pl. 32). The presence of the low Tyne bridge and the difficult state of the waterway made it impossible for sea-going vessels to negotiate the Tyne estuary and make their way right up to the staiths. All loading had therefore to be done by the keels, which plied to and fro between the staiths and the ships, so that a large proportion of the total employment in the coal trade was actually engaged on the river. The keelmen, employed by the Hostmen of Newcastle, the merchants who monopolised the coal trade, were a distinctive social group with their own dress and customs, and lived in colonies on the river banks. Chief of these was Sandgate, an eastern annexe to Newcastle just outside the city wall, but there were other smaller colonies, for example at Dunston and Swalwell. The keelmen seem to have been recruited from the Border dales, both on the English and Scottish sides, and an early seventeenth-century document put their numbers at more than 1,800. Not all of them brought their families to settle permanently on Tyneside. Winter was an off-season in the coal trade, and many of the men who came to Tyneside for the summer returned in winter to their families in the Border dales.

The appearance of clusters of industrial workers, however, affected only a very restricted area. Naturally, the keelmen's settlements clung to the river banks, and the mining groups did not extend much farther afield. The jealously organised power of Newcastle in the coal trade, together with less favourable conditions for shipment, prevented any comparable trade from the Wear or from the Northumberland coast before the middle of the seventeenth century. On the Tyne, it is true, the increase in production in Elizabethan times involved some extension of the mining area (Fig. 29). Previously practically all the sea-coal had come from the pits in the manors of Gateshead and Whickham, that is from the south side of the river between the mouth of the Derwent and the Tyne bridge. In addition to considerable intensification of activity there, new pits were opened farther west on the south side of the river above the Derwent confluence ; and at the beginning of the seventeenth century similar development took place on the north bank west of Newcastle at Newburn, Denton, Elswick, and Benwell. But the limits within which spread of mining was possible remained extremely narrow. Technical advances, especially in drainage and ventilation, were allowing mining to be carried to greater depths, but the deep coal of the buried coalfield east of the Tyne bridge still lay beyond the physical limit of production, and mining was confined to the outcrop field on upper Tyneside. Here the heavy cost of transporting coal to the staiths severely limited the area that could produce for shipment. The least extension away from the river added significantly to the cost, and a distance of more than about two miles was still considered prohibitive. Other industries, with their colonies of workers, depended, as we have seen, upon the facilities offered by waterside sites in contact with the coal trade. The salt industry, earliest to attain prominence, of course needed sea-water in addition, and consequently a location either on the coast or right at an estuary mouth (Fig. 30). Its chief centre was South Shields, though it also developed on the coast farther north at Cullercoats, Hartley, and Blyth, as well as at Wearmouth. Indeed, the requirements of these outlying centres of salt making gave

133

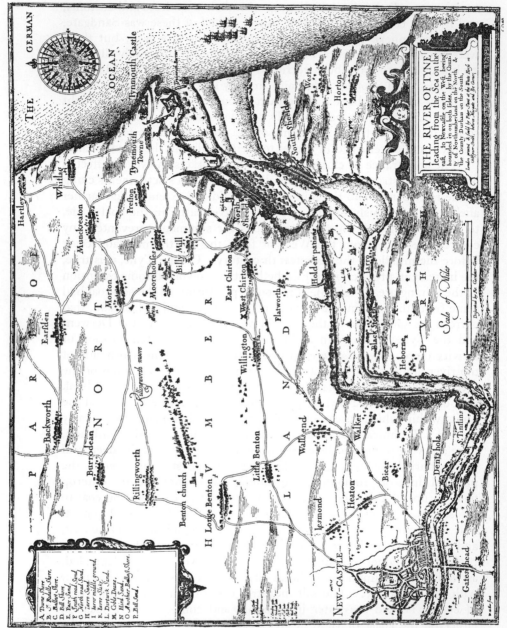

Fig. 31 W. HOLLAR'S MAP OF TYNESIDE, 1654. Note the unimproved nature of the estuary and compare with Figure 46.

THE RIVER OF TYNE leading from the Sea on the east, to Newcastle on the West, beeing bounded in on both sides, by the County of Northumberland on the North, & the County Durham on the South.

London printed & sould by Peter Stent at the White Horse in Guilspur-Street, betwixt Newgate and Pye Corner.

Sale of Miles

Designed by Wⁿ Gardner Gent.

THE GERMAN OCEAN

Tynemouth Castle

Hartley

Whitlay

Munckseaton

Easlden

Backworth

Burrodean

Killingworth

Rillingworth

Benton church

Morton

Preston

Tynemouth Towne

Moorehouses

Billy Mill

NORT HUMBERLA ND

West Chirton

East Chirton

Flatworth

Willington

Little Benton

Wall send

Lodge Benton

Jesmond

Heaton

Bicar

Walker

South Sheelds

North Sheeld

Holden pannes

Dent hola

Tintins

Heborne

Westa

Horton

DVRH

NEW-CASTLE

Gateshead

A. *Thune Shore.*
B. *J. Bradlu Shore.*
C. *Bullast Shore.*
D. *Bell Shore.*
E. *Pace Sand.*
F. *South mid Sand.*
G. *North mid Sand.*
H. *Barr Sand.*
I. *barr middle ground.*
K. *barr Slaty.*
L. *Dortwick Sand.*
M. *Coble Deane.*
N. *Herd Sand.*
O. *Another Ballast Shore.*
P. *Bell Sand.*

134

the first effective stimulus to coal mining outside the Tyne district, especially on the banks of the navigable section of the Wear that lies west of the Magnesian Limestone.

That the industrial communities were essentially riparian is illustrated by Hollar's map of the Tyne in 1654, which shows their linear layout along the river banks (Fig. 31). Except for Newcastle itself, they consisted at most of two rows of buildings lining the foreshore at intervals in front of the steeply sloping sides of the pre-glacial valley within which the Tyne flows.

During the course of the seventeenth century, growth of the coal trade and of other industries on the Tyne was not accompanied by a correspondingly important extension of the mining area. As production was intensified in the established mining districts, the mining settlements grew in size and some new ones appeared between the older sites; but upper Tyneside remained the great centre of mining throughout this century. Although the use of railroads, with large horse-drawn wagons, became general after 1640, cost of way-leaves held up extension of the range within which it was profitable to engage in mining. The outstanding new development was the rise of Sunderland as a coal port and industrial centre and the expansion of mining on the Wear in its hinterland. In 1600 the Newcastle Hostmen had been more strongly entrenched than ever as lords of the coal, thanks to the charter that legalised their pretensions to monopoly. So far as the Tyne was concerned their dominance was long maintained, but they were less able to deal summarily with competition from the Wear, and their policy of regulating the supply to keep prices high actually encouraged development on the Wear, where the restrictions could not be imposed. The coal trade and town of Sunderland, which had not been noticed by Camden, both grew rapidly. Its great opportunity to establish a firm footing in the London market came during the Civil War when supplies from Royalist Newcastle were interrupted. On the Wear, as on the Tyne, however, the coal was drawn from quite a small district, within a mile or two of the river between its bend at Chester and its entry into the gorge cut across the limestone plateau to the sea (Fig. 29).

Although the Wear district remained the chief addition to the mining area in the northeast during the century and a half following the death of Elizabeth I, some extension of the area that supplied the Tyne coal trade also became necessary as time went on. By the beginning of the eighteenth century the coal within reach of existing methods of mining had been worked out in many places on upper Tyneside, and the collieries were waterlogged. Foreseeing the impending exhaustion of the accessible coal in the existing mining area, certain coal-owners sought to strengthen their position by buying up leases for areas farther from the river in the western districts, where large reserves of coal lay well within the known range of exploitation (about 60 fathoms). This policy inspired the formation in 1726 of a powerful combination of coal-owning families known as the Grand Allies, who entered into an association to extend the mining field by securing large tracts of coal in northwest Durham (Fig. 29). Thus we find a colliery viewer stating in 1738 that there were pits eight miles from the river whereas twelve years earlier the farthest had been five miles from the river. Mines were developed in the Pontop-Tanfield district, and mining hamlets such as Dipton and Tantobie sprang up on the plateau between the Derwent and Team valleys, eight or nine miles from the Tyne. The joint resources and co-operative policy of the Grand Allies overcame the difficulties of establishing and working such long wagonway connections with the staiths.[1] In spite of these extensions, however, the developed coalfield remained small, and industrial activity, although it was expanding, also remained strictly confined to the riverside and the coast.

During the seventeenth century the salt industry was at its peak. Its chief centre was at the mouth of the Tyne, where just within the estuary mouth there were at one time 200 saltpans in operation at South Shields employing about 1,000 men. The industry declined later in the eighteenth century, but the communities which it had supported found alternative sources of employment through the expansion of other industries, such as glass, pottery, and shipbuilding and its ancillaries ; and these industries also added new settlements.

The largest concentration of industrial workers was near the Tyne bridge, the centre of the coal trade. The glass industry had first been established on the Tyne in 1619, on a ballast shore just below the mouth of the Ouseburn (St Lawrence) and about the same time at Howdon Pans farther east (Fig. 30). Towards the close of the century and early in the eighteenth century other glass houses were added in the Ouseburn district, and also on the south side of the river. Above the Ouseburn, shipyards, roperies, and the like lined the north bank of the Tyne as far as Sandgate, and during the eighteenth century several potteries were established near the river in Byker and Gateshead. Most of the works gathered east of the Tyne bridge, but there was some development on a smaller scale farther west near the mouths of the Skinner burn and the Team. On the Wear, too, the flourishing coal trade attracted industrial undertakings of similar type, while outlying industrial settlements came into being north of the Tyne at Seaton

---

[1] The Causey arch, built in 1727 to carry one of the wagonways across a deeply entrenched burn near Tanfield, survives as probably the oldest railway bridge in the world.

Sluice and Blyth. Seaton Sluice dates from the seventeenth century and owed much to the enterprise of the Delaval family. Their harbour works allowed the small salters' village to become a small port with a growing trade in coal and salt. Further improvements in the seventeen-sixties and the establishment of a bottle-glass factory and a copperas works added to the prosperity, in spite of decline in salt making. So, too, at Blyth, of which Leland makes no mention and which is not shown on Speed's map of 1616. The opening of the wagon-way (Fig. 35) from the Plessey pits to Blyth in 1709 revived the manufacture of salt and the coal trade, and by the end of the eighteenth century both shipbuilding and rope making were adding to the industrial employment.

All these industries, however, were more localised even than the coal mining. They were based upon the use of coal, the coal trade, and water transport. New industrial sites were occupied and new groups of workers' houses sprang up alongside, but their locations were still essentially of the same type—with few exceptions confined to the banks of navigable rivers or the coast within the outcrop coalfield.

The beginnings of coal mining on a considerable scale in west Cumberland, as on the Wear, date from the seventeenth century, although coal digging had been carried on much earlier, both for local domestic use and for saltpans. As W. H. Makey has emphasised, Dublin played a rôle in the Irish Sea coal-trade analogous to that of London in the larger North Sea trade, but it became important somewhat later. From less than 10,000 at the beginning of the seventeenth century, Dublin's population had grown to more than 50,000 in 1700, and by 1750 was approaching 150,000. Local timber resources were quite inadequate to meet the fuel requirements of such urban growth, and an important market for coal was created. It was Whitehaven and its immediate vicinity which, rather than any other part of the Cumberland coalfield and rather than any other coalfield round the Irish Sea, was able to profit from this situation in the century between 1640 and 1740.

Before 1640 coal was being worked and shipped to Ireland on a small scale from Workington and Parton, as well as from Whitehaven, where Christopher Lowther had begun to work coal about 1620 on his newly acquired estate. He converted the little creek at the northern end of the St Bees valley into a harbour by constructing a small pier to protect it from the southwest. On succeeding to his inheritance in 1642, Sir John Lowther undertook, on a much larger scale, the development of Whitehaven and its small hinterland in the southernmost part of the coalfield (Fig. 32). By the time of his death in 1706 the Lowther collieries were producing about 30,000 tons per annum, chiefly from

Howgill on the western flank of the St Bees valley. The workings were within two miles of the mouth of the valley, where the artificial harbour had been enlarged and the new town, laid out on a regular grid-plan, had grown into a community of more than 3,000 people. A fleet of 80 colliers plied to and fro, and most of the residents of Whitehaven were the families of seamen, though miners employed in the nearby pits were also numerous, and the copperas, salt, and lime works, which were also active, provided further employment.

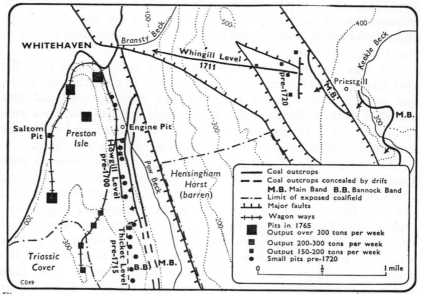

Fig. 32 WHITEHAVEN COLLIERY IN THE EIGHTEENTH CENTURY (after W. H. Makey).

Whitehaven was coming to monopolise the growing Irish coal trade. In the natural hinterlands of the ports farther north outcrops of good coal were for the most part concealed by drift, and the resources remained unrealised until well into the eighteenth century. But near Whitehaven, along the coastward side of the deep trench of the St Bees valley, the two best seams of the coalfield were exposed, and large tracts of coal, free from faults, lay above the limit of free drainage in the block of high ground to the west, known as Preston Isle. In comparison all other competitors for the Dublin coal trade suffered from one or other serious and, for the time being, decisive disability. The anthracitic coal of Pembrokeshire and the non-caking type of Ayrshire could not command adequate prices, the cost of hauling Lancashire coal to the coast was prohibitive, and drainage problems held up development of Flintshire coal near the Dee estuary.

The supremacy of Whitehaven in the Irish coal trade in the century before 1740 rested upon a remarkable combination of natural advantages, but it also depended upon the Lowther family, who supplied the capital and energy to exploit the favourable conditions. When, in course of time, the most accessible coal had been removed from the Howgill basin in Preston Isle, they had the resources and initiative to undertake expensive developments that expanded production to keep pace with the demand. The introduction of steam-pumping, from 1718, enabled much more vigorous pursuit of mining where previously only tracts that could be drained by adit levels were accessible. The Saltom pit was sunk on the coast to the Main Band at a depth of 80 fathoms, and undersea working of coal began here as early as 1731. Meantime, another tract east of Whitehaven, separated from the Howgill basin by an important fault, had been developed by means of the Whingill Level, and wagonways connected these pits with the north side of the harbour. By 1740 the Whitehaven pits were producing nearly 100,000 tons,[1] of which 80,000 tons were being shipped to Dublin. In comparison, the other Cumberland ports shipped only 4,400 tons, and the rest of the Irish Sea coal-trade amounted only to another 20,000 tons. The supremacy of Whitehaven in this trade was at its peak, and about the same time the port was enjoying a short period of prosperity as a colonial port, with the tobacco trade.

The Irish coal trade increased again fourfold during the next 50 years. In 1790 Cumberland still supplied two-thirds of the coal used in Ireland, but Whitehaven's share had dropped from more than three-quarters to less than one-third. Never again could it enjoy such a monopoly. The Howgill pits continued to be the most important in the coalfield and their production was increased, but attention was also being paid to virgin tracts farther north (Fig. 33). Earlier workings had been scattered and confined to the drift-free outcrops along the sides of the coastal gills. Most of the field lay untapped, its resources scarcely suspected. The Lowther family showed the way in this extension of mining, and were responsible for considerable undertakings before 1750 behind Workington at Clifton and Seaton, where the outcrop of the Main Band was discovered beneath a covering of drift. Other landowners, notably the Curwens and Senhouse, quickly followed, developing pits on their estates by installing costly steam-engines and providing wagonway connections with the coast at Harrington, Workington, and Maryport. Writing in 1774, Pennant records the birth of a new port and town at the mouth of the Ellen in the north of the coalfield: 'Maryport, another new creation, the property of Humphrey Senhouse, Esq., and so named by him in

---

[1] In comparison, however, the Tyne and Wear together were shipping considerably over one million tons at this time.

honour of his lady; the second house was built only in 1750. Now there are above one hundred, peopled by thirteen hundred souls, all collected by the opening of a coal trade on the estate. For the conveniency of shipping (there being more than seventy of different sizes from thirty to three hundred tons burthen, belonging to the harbour) are wooden piers with quays on the river Ellen, where ships lie and

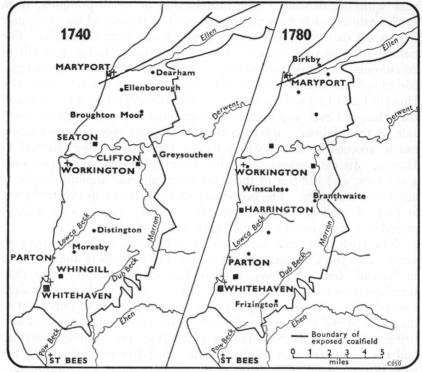

Fig. 33 WEST CUMBERLAND COLLIERIES IN 1740 AND 1780 (after W. H. Makey).

receive their lading.' [1] By the end of the eighteenth century these other ports together shipped more coal than Whitehaven, and their wooden shipbuilding and allied trades were flourishing.

Cumberland's annual output of coal at the end of the eighteenth century did not amount to more than half a million tons, however, as compared with as much as three million tons from Northumberland and Durham. In 1792 McNabb estimated that in the area tributary to the Tyne more than 38,000 persons were supported by the coal trade, and in the Wear district more than 26,000.[2] These figures included about 12,000 pitmen and an even greater number of seamen,

[1] Quoted by Isaac Fletcher, *op. cit.*
[2] Quoted by J. Bailey and G. Culley, in *A General View of the Agriculture of Northumberland*, 3rd edition (1805), p. 10.

together with numerous keelmen, trimmers, and ballast-heavers, coal factors and clerks, shipwrights, and workers in ancillary trades, and their dependants.

Towards the end of the eighteenth century the chief centre of coal-mining activity shifted definitely eastwards to lower Tyneside, the area of deeply buried coal east of the bridge (Figs. 29, 35). This area enjoyed obviously great advantages of position for easy shipment, but it had hitherto lain untouched because the coal was too deep (about 100 fathoms). With the application of the steam-engine to pumping, and improvement in its powers, it at last became possible to open mines in the High Main coal here, and the expected premium upon more distant tracts of coal anticipated by the Grand Allies was cancelled. In the older western districts there was stagnation or decline, so that we find Eden in his *State of the Poor* (1797) remarking upon the depressed state of the industry in Tanfield parish. But sinking was being vigorously pursued on lower Tyneside, and many of the new pits were within a mile of their staiths. The settlements that grew beside them were often practically on the river banks, and are among the nuclei of modern Wallsend, Hebburn, and Jarrow. These deep pits were larger units, employing on an average from 300 to 400 men at the opening of the nineteenth century, whereas few of those working in the western districts employed more than half this number.

The trough of the Wallsend basin was approached also from the north, where there were old workings along the High Main outcrop on Shiremoor. Extension southwestwards in the direction of the dip is commemorated in the name New York, one of the mining hamlets thus brought into being at the time of the American War of Independence. The tract of country north of the Tyne valley until this time had remained an extensive moor, but it was then enclosed and new roads were laid out.

The Tyne still accounted for about two-thirds of the coal trade, though the Wear coal trade also grew during the eighteenth century with the help of the steam-engine. The Wear trade remained focused upon the staiths on the reach of the river between Lambton Castle and Cox Green. Although the pits were smaller than those of lower Tyneside they were on the whole somewhat larger than those of the western districts.

The close association of industrial settlement with tidewater sites during the eighteenth century was relaxed a little in the case of the iron industry. The use of Coal Measures ore, sometimes actually worked with coal seams, and of waterpower to drive forge-hammers, were the bases of small-scale iron works at a few scattered points in the northeastern coalfield, notably within the mining area of northwest

Durham (Fig. 30). On rapidly flowing burns at Beamish and Lumley there were forges whose workers lived in the adjacent hamlets of Beamish and Breckon Hill; and the first blast-furnace to use coal in northeast England was established before 1750 at Whitehill on Chester

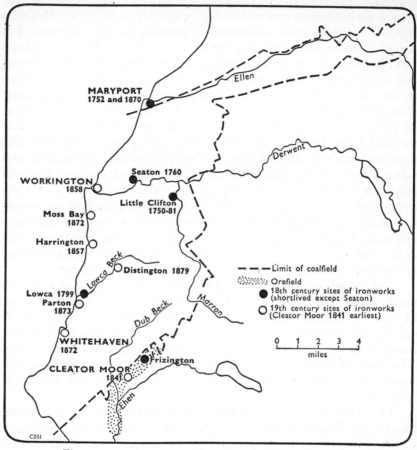

Fig. 34   WEST CUMBERLAND : SITES OF FORMER IRONWORKS.

burn, but it had been abandoned before the end of the century on account of the inadequacy of the water-supply upon which the blast depended. For this same reason, as well as because the local coal was very unsuitable for coking, attempts about this time to develop coke blast-furnaces in west Cumberland to smelt the haematite ore at various sites on the coalfield were also unsuccessful (Fig. 34). Except at Seaton, on the river Derwent behind Workington, they had all been abandoned by the end of the century. In each case foundries were attached to the furnaces.

The chief ironworking district in North England during the eighteenth century was the lower Derwent valley in northwest Durham, where Ambrose Crowley brought over German workmen to establish his works at Winlaton in 1690 in the busiest mining district of that time (Fig. 30). Soon afterwards the manufacture of the heavier articles, such as anchors and chains, was transferred to Swalwell, to which point the Derwent was navigable. Winlaton continued to make nails, files, and edge-tools ; there were forges and a slitting mill on the river near by (Winlaton Mill), and also higher upstream at Derwentcote and Blackhall Mill, where steel making by the cementation process was carried on. These sites lie near the modern centre of the steel industry at Consett. By eighteenth-century standards the Derwent colonies of ironworkers were large and attracted much attention. Arthur Young in 1770 described the works as ' supposed to be the greatest manufactory of its kind in Europe ', and in 1788 the striking change wrought here by the appearance of industry was described in the *Universal Magazine* [1] : ' Before Sir Ambrose settled his people the place [Winlaton] consisted of a few deserted cottages, but now contains about 1,500 inhabitants, chiefly smiths.'

Even in the iron industry, however, the market provided by shipping and other industries on the river and the use of imported raw materials attracted some of the main establishments to navigable water, especially those making the heavier articles. It has been noted that this was so at Swalwell, and another instance is provided by the Team Works of the Hawks family at Gateshead. This began in 1747 with a few forges working up old iron, brought by collier vessels as ballast, to supply the demand for anchors and chains created by the great increase in shipping. From small beginnings it grew steadily into an important concern by 1800.

Fostered by improved techniques, both of winning the ore and extracting its metal content, there was in the eighteenth century renewed activity in the old lead-mining industry of the Pennine dales. The London Lead Company, a group of Quakers who acquired the Ryton mill in 1704, quickly followed this by engaging in mining operations, first in South Tynedale and somewhat later in Derwentdale and on Alston Moor. They adopted the improved method of smelting in reverberatory or cupola furnaces, and built Acton and Jeffries mills in Derwentdale (Fig. 62). The old mill at Whitfield was supplemented by mills at Nenthead (1746) (Pl. 6) and Langley (1768), the latter built for Greenwich Hospital [2] to smelt their ore from Alston Moor.

[1] Quoted by Wm. Hutchinson, *History of Durham* (1787), vol. ii, p. 441.
[2] In 1737 the Commissioners had been granted the Derwentwater estates, confiscated by the Crown after the 1715 Rebellion.

In the closing years of the seventeenth century the Allendale mines had been acquired by the Blacketts, and although for a time the industry was not so prosperous in Allendale there was considerable revival later in the eighteenth century, when the Beaumont family (successors to the Blacketts) were also actively developing mines in Weardale, for which the new Rookhope mills became the chief smelting centre. They also operated the Allenheads mill to deal with ore from mines in the dale-heads round Killhope, but the largest of the Blackett-Beaumont mills was the Dukesfield mill, built before 1728, at Steel in Hexhamshire, on the route between the orefield and the Tyne estuary.

The workings, from numerous trials that shifted along the outcrops of the veins, continued to be carried on by farmer-miners. Grouped in ' partnerships ' or teams, they made ' bargains ' or contracts with the mining companies to work specified sections. They lived on their smallholdings in scattered cottages in the upper parts of the dales, where the veins were productive in the limestone beds. The smelt-mills, which, unlike the actual mining, were responsible for bigger clusters of settlement, were not restricted to the mining field of the upper dales, and, as noted above, some of the most important lay outside. Others were chiefly responsible for the appearance of new hamlets high up the dales, at Nenthead, Allenheads, and Rookhope.

There was no comparable revival of mining in the Lake District, but a number of scattered and diverse mining enterprises were pursued there with varying degrees of success during the seventeenth and eighteenth centuries. The Coniston copper mine was revived after the Restoration, and from 1690 to 1715 Dutchmen were responsible for re-opening and working the Goldscope mine and the Keswick smelting works. During the eighteenth century, lead mining was also pursued on the Caldbeck Fells, slate quarrying was particularly active at Honister and Coniston, whence slates were taken to Ulverston for shipment, and iron was worked in the volcanic rocks about Red Tarn and in the Ore Gap between Hanging Knotts and Bow Fell (Fig. 28). These iron workings respectively supplied charcoal furnaces situated at Langdale and in Langstrath. The ' wad ' or blacklead from the graphite mine near Seathwaite in Borrowdale, which attracted the notice of Camden, continued to be in demand for glazing crucibles and making dyes fast, as well as for polishing metals, and towards the end of the eighteenth century the mine was approaching the peak of its activity.

CHAPTER 9

THE NORTH COUNTRY ABOUT 1800

AT the opening of the nineteenth century coal-mining and coal-using industry were no new features on Tyneside and Wearside and in west Cumberland, but only small areas were affected by industrialisation. They were far less extensive than the industrial areas of today. Most of the present Northumberland and Durham coalfield was still rural, and if a larger proportion of the west Cumberland coalfield was already affected that was simply a reflection of the small extent of this coalfield and its virtual confinement to a littoral strip. Only where good household coal was easily mined within a few miles of tidewater did collieries, wagonways, and pitmen's cottages appreciably modify the prevailing rural character of the countryside (Fig. 35). Even there industrial settlements were small and scattered, except in the immediate vicinity of the coast and river banks, and outside these districts scattered outcrop workings of coal for local landsale scarcely affected the agricultural tone of the landscape and of the occupations of the people.

In west Cumberland, coal mining in the immediate vicinity of Whitehaven, Workington, and Maryport and shipments from these ports had created industrial towns [1] like those of the northeast coast, as well as some colliery hamlets near by. But the inland portion of the coalfield northeast towards Aspatria (Fig. 4) was still out of range, and like the eastern inland margin of the coalfield farther south was exploited only by small and scattered landsale workings.

Landsale workings such as were widespread over the outcrop sections of the main coalfields of the northeast and northwest coasts were hardly less typical of the string of small coalfields along the northern margin of the North Pennine massif in southwest Northumberland and east Cumberland (Fig. 63), and of Northumberland farther north, where coal seams occur in the lower Carboniferous rocks. These coals were being worked at a great number of localities on a small scale for domestic use and for burning limestone, which was quarried from the adjacent outcrops on many farms.

The area over which the landscape was in some measure transformed by industry and where the pattern of agricultural occupance was overlain at all heavily by industrial settlement was thus very restricted. By far the largest concentration of population was at the Tyne bridge (Pl. 44), where Newcastle and Gateshead together accommodated

[1] Whitehaven, with nearly 9,000 inhabitants, was the largest of these.

145

some 43,000 people within the extent of the present local-government boundaries. In Newcastle buildings crowded along the river bank and the steep approaches to the low stone bridge, rebuilt since the 1771 floods had swept away its predecessor. In central Newcastle gardens, orchards, and the extensive grounds of Anderson Place survived within the walls, and open country began almost immediately outside. The annexe outside Sandgate where the keelmen lived had grown considerably, and, across the Ouse burn, Byker was a growing industrial suburb ; but expansion beyond the walls on the north and west sides had scarcely begun. Within the walls town improvement was actively in progress. Work had begun on removal of the gates, different quarters had recently been knit together by the construction of Mosley Street and Dean Street, and fine new buildings, such as the Assembly Rooms, had been erected. On the opposite bank of the Tyne the growth of Gateshead had been concentrated along the main road as it approached the bridge, and along the river bank. Gateshead Fell was still undivided common, where there were small groups of cottages inhabited by the workers at Carr's Hill pottery and the quarrymen who worked the grindstones. Another clustering of industrial works supported a second urban concentration on the Tyne just within the river mouth, where North and South Shields, each containing about 11,000 inhabitants, faced each other. Both were essentially river-bank settlements with linear plans, confined to narrow strips along the waterfront and backed by the steep valley-sides.

Between these main groups and also on upper Tyneside there were other industrial works and pits, with dependent colonies of workers, for example at Howdon, Lemington, Blaydon, and Swalwell. Their industries by later standards were on a small scale, however, and they were still only small separate groups, between which the green fields came right to the water's edge. Some at least of the nuclear cells of modern Tyneside had appeared, but Tyneside was by no means yet a single conurbation. That process of multiplication and expansion, which led to the coalescing of the riparian settlements, belongs to the second half of the nineteenth century.

Whereas on the Tyne collieries and miners' rows intermingled with other industrial works and dwellings, geology caused the two to be separated on the Wear. Colonies of keelmen [1] on the river banks just below its great bend at Chester-le-Street, and the straggling pit villages attached to them by wagonways, formed an industrial district quite clearly distinct from the river-mouth concentration (Fig. 35). Begin-

---

[1] In 1799 there were 520 keels plying on the Wear, as compared with about 320 on the Tyne, where the shift of mining from upper to lower Tyneside had reduced their rôle.

ning with potteries and boat-building yards at North and South Hylton, industrialisation was intensified down-stream from Southwick and Pallion (Fig. 48). Shipyards, glass houses, limekilns, saltpans, roperies, and copperas works lined the river, with housing behind. About two-

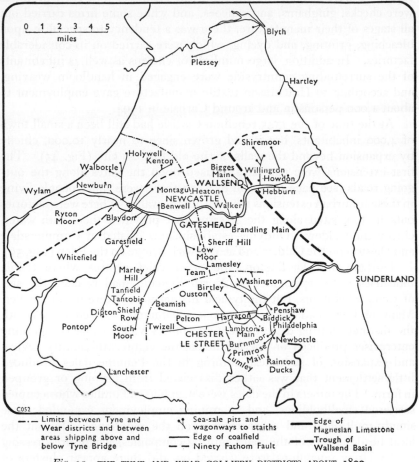

Fig. 35   THE TYNE AND WEAR COLLIERY DISTRICTS ABOUT 1800.

thirds of the 25,000 inhabitants of this Wearmouth cluster lived on the south bank, and only since 1796 had the two components been connected by a bridge. In Northumberland, Blyth and Hartley were small outlying centres of industry and coal shipment, but on the Tees, well beyond the southern edge of the coalfield, there was no iron industry yet, and at Stockton coal was a small import, not an export.

Except on Tyneside and at the mouth of the Wear no urban clusters in North England had more than 10,000 inhabitants, though Carlisle had almost reached that figure, thanks especially to the recent considerable growth of textile manufacturing. This remained the mainstay of its growing population until the coming of the railways. In 1761 calico printing had been introduced with such success that other capitalists were attracted to engage in the business. The chief products were checks, ginghams, and calicoes, and while some firms carried out all stages of their manufacture, there was a tendency to specialise upon bleaching, printing, and dyeing, which were carried on in considerable factories. In addition, large numbers of citizens as well as inhabitants of the surrounding countryside were engaged in handloom weaving, and according to Hutchinson textile manufacture gave employment to about 1,000 persons in and around Carlisle in 1794.

At the time of the 1745 rebellion Carlisle had still been a small town of 4,000 inhabitants, but it had grown since to nearly 10,000, chiefly by expansion beyond the walls of the old fortress city (Fig. 45). The first extensions were naturally focused upon the gates along the outgoing roads (see page 122), and by 1800 there were more people living in these suburban extensions than within the walls. There were factories outside, too, sited along the streams that provided them with water, chiefly the Caldew. Outlying establishments existed at Cummersdale and Dalston on the Caldew and at Warwick Bridge on the Eden (Fig. 56).

Durham and Darlington, the other chief centres where textile industries were represented in North England, had reached the size of 5,000 inhabitants, but the typical market towns were much smaller. Many of them had fewer than 2,000 inhabitants. As compared with the distinct clotting of settlement in colliery villages that coal-mining enterprises produced on the coalfields, the eighteenth-century revival and expansion of silver-lead mining in the Pennine dales produced little settlement that was either dissociated from farming or grouped in form. The miners in the dales were members of families who occupied scattered smallholdings, and as mining employment expanded these simply multiplied and encroached upon the moorland. Only at the local headquarters of the dales mining companies, where ore-dressing and smelting operations were carried on, did there appear clusters of dwellings that can be described as industrial settlements—Nenthead, Allenheads, Rookhope, and Middleton were eighteenth-century creations of this kind. Middleton, for example, had become the focus for the industry in Teesdale, which was experiencing especially great development at the beginning of the nineteenth century. It had grown rapidly to a population of 1,800, and the farmsteads higher up the dale were chiefly occupied by miners, employed at no fewer than 38 active mines.

The lead-mining industry was flourishing and yielding returns commensurate with the outlay of large amounts of capital on providing more efficient and large-scale methods of mining and ore-extraction. Smeaton's drainage level (1776), extending for $3\frac{1}{4}$ miles under Nentdale above its entrance at Nentforce, was demonstrating how access to ore supplies over large areas could be greatly improved by a comprehensive drainage scheme.[1] To the numerous mills that had been built earlier in the eighteenth century, Allen mill and Egglestone mill had recently been added, and Stanhope, Dufton, and Hilton mills followed in 1801 (Fig. 62). New landmarks were making their appearance on the high moorland ridges between the dales. They were the chimney-stacks to which flues led from the smelt-mills to provide for removal of the noxious fumes, and at the same time allow recovery of additional valuable metal by condensation.

In 1800 the prevailing countryside of the lowlands of North England, up to the limit of the farmland, the moorland edge, was a landscape of enclosures bounded by quick hedges and, at the higher levels, stone walls. Except towards its moorland edge, this enclosed countryside was not a new creation. Little enclosure of common arable fields, as distinct from moorland or rough pasture, remained to be carried out anywhere in the north during the great period of Parliamentary enclosure in the later eighteenth and early nineteenth centuries. Fragments of unenclosed arable land were sometimes dealt with by Acts that were chiefly concerned with the enclosure of common grazing land, but less than two per cent of Northumberland and Cumberland, and less than one per cent of Durham and Westmorland were covered by Acts for enclosing common fields. The reporters to the Board of Agriculture in 1794 observed that the Glendale district in north Northumberland, then being enclosed, was the only exception to the generally enclosed character of the farmlands of Northumberland. Of the process of enclosure in its early stages, however, there is little or no contemporary evidence. When documentary evidence of enclosure agreements begins to become less scanty, in the seventeenth century, it points to the last stages of a process that had long been going on. In the bishopric of Durham in 1726 it was estimated that already nine parts in ten were enclosed. The fact is that the type of agricultural economy generally practised in North England had lent itself to the early accomplishment of enclosure because of its pastoral emphasis and its flexible system of working, unlike the three-field system with its rigid, customary constraints. Roger Dion [2] has emphasised the importance of pasture requirements in the open fields as a

---

[1] In the 1850s Sopwith provided for the drainage of the mines in East Allendale by the even bigger Blackett level, which extends 5 miles up the dale from its mouth at Allendale Town.

[2] R. Dion, *Essai sur la formation du paysage rural français* (Tours, 1934).

11

factor delaying enclosure in the open-field areas of northeast France ; but in northern England the arable land was not needed to contribute to the common grazing.

Early enclosure in turn contributed to produce a higher degree of scattering of rural settlement. Some of the rural settlement, pastoral in character, was no doubt dispersed from the first, and the groups of clustered settlement (Fig. 24) were generally smaller than the villages of the Midland area of three-field agriculture. The net result of early enclosure of the common fields that had existed was to bring about further dispersion, of a secondary or intercalated type between the original clusters, as farmsteads were established on their compacted holdings. This has blurred the distinction between the areas of originally grouped settlement and those of primary dispersion.

Nevertheless, although the patchwork of enclosures and the fairly dispersed arrangement of settlements that characterised the long cultivated lowlands of the North Country were well established before the nineteenth century, in other respects extensive changes both in the economy and the face of the countryside had recently taken place or were still in progress. The northern counties had not long emerged from the protracted period of unsettled political conditions, with Border warfare and pillage, which had held up the full development of the agricultural resources and kept the area poor and backward. At the end of the eighteenth century the countryside was at last enjoying prosperity under the newly-found peace and the local stimuli of growing urban markets and prosperous dales mining. Agriculture was advancing as never before. This development was evident both in increased production from long-farmed areas and in extension of the improved farmlands. If there was little open common field left to be dealt with by Parliamentary enclosure, this did not mean that there was nothing for Enclosure Acts to carry out. Parliamentary enclosures were here concerned mainly with large tracts of rough pasture that had formerly been held in common, and, by a succession of measures during the century before 1850, large areas were divided, allotted, and enclosed as a preliminary to their development. This extension of the farmland was well under way when the nineteenth century dawned. On the allotments thus created new farmsteads were established, so that agricultural settlement spread. The plateau areas of the western part of the coalfield in Durham were in this manner enclosed and colonised by farmers during the course of the eighteenth century, that is shortly before the large-scale mining development of these districts. Hutchinson described the extensive division of the common lands of Lanchester parish in 1773 : ' This vast tract of country which was barren, desert, and dreary, where the perplexed traveller wandered in

the ambiguous tracks with anxiety, is now inclosed, much of it cultivated and intersected with direct roads, made in turnpike manner, fit
for the reception of any carriage ; innumerable buildings are scattered
over the prospect ; and the inhabitants are greatly multiplied, are
cheerful and prosperous.'

The enclosure and colonisation carried out by Acts were on a large
scale, different from the haphazard squatting that had already been
going on for centuries. They gave rise to a rapid multiplication of
upland farmsteads beyond the confines of the previously occupied area.
Nowhere were the results more striking than in the northern Pennines,
where the Parliamentary enclosure movement, coinciding with considerable expansion of mining, effected division and colonisation of
large areas of moorland. Acts were passed for the division of Hexhamshire and Allendale Common in 1792, Weardale Common in 1799, and
Alston and Garrigill Common in 1803. Large tracts of new farmland
were carved out of the moorland and occupied by the growing number
of farmer-miner families. This sudden outward stride of the margins
of the occupied areas was quite different from the age-long piecemeal
enclosure, which had produced the irregular patchwork of small fields
on the floors and lower slopes of the dales. In the landscape of later
times the large rectangular intakes of these systematic enclosure schemes,
running up the dale-sides into the crown of moorland, are often clearly
distinguishable from the old irregular farmlands. The remaining tracts
of unenclosed moorland were left as stinted pastures, and are still used
thus by the dales farmers.

Similar contrasts are widely recognisable in the townships of North
England. There are striking differences in appearance between the
small, irregular, and often hedge-bounded enclosures and the larger,
regular enclosures, often bounded by stone walls, of later addition.
Narrow, winding lanes are typical of the former, while straight,
regularly laid out country roads, often with wide grass verges between
the bounding enclosures, date from the period of Parliamentary
enclosure of the commons. The newer settlement, invariably scattered,
emphasises, without radically altering, the already dispersed pattern of
farms.

To provide smallholdings for miners and accommodate the increasing dales population of miner-farmers, the limits of farmland were
pushed exceptionally high in the north Pennine dales by the beginning
of the nineteenth century. Elsewhere, too, owing to the pressure on
food supplies during the Napoleonic Wars, cultivation, especially of
corn, was pushed up to limits which had never been reached before
and from which it again receded later. These extreme limits were not
even regained under the repeated stringency of blockade conditions

during the wars of this century. Cultivation terraces on the Border hills that belong to the Napoleonic period superficially resemble, and have often been mistaken for, prehistoric lynchets.

Apart from the extension of farmland by enclosure of commons that was in full progress at the beginning of the nineteenth century, entailing the construction of many miles of dry stone-walling, the countryside showed other manifest signs of prosperity and ' improvement ' at the hands of enlightened landlords and thrifty, hardworking tenants and yeomen. Much naturally ill-drained and acid land, in which the north country with its prevalent clayey drift soils abounds, was being upgraded by draining and liming. These improvements were enhancing the value alike of old farmland and new enclosures. Enclosure itself was a beneficial measure, since the unenclosed commons had undoubtedly been suffering from overstocking with sheep ; but enclosure was usually the prelude to other measures of improvement. Paring, burning, and liming were recognised techniques of treatment, and the extensive operations carried out by some landlords excited the admiration of visitors such as Arthur Young. As compared with his praise for the large farms of the Northumberland coastal districts, however, Young had only uncomplimentary comments to make about much of the upland farming in 1770 ; but already the necessary improvements were being initiated by pioneers. By the time of his death in 1782 the Reverend John Graham had transformed his Netherby estate near the Scottish border north of Carlisle, and in west Cumberland J. C. Curwen (1786–1828) spent large sums on enclosure and draining and experimented with manuring. When Bailey, Culley, and Pringle were writing their accounts of the agriculture of the northern counties at the end of the eighteenth century, improvements along these lines were well forward, and they were steadily extended and developed during the next half-century.

It was in north Northumberland that the crops and practices of the new farming were first established in North England. Turnips and green fodder crops, sown with the improved drill, were introduced in the latter part of the eighteenth century, and the Northumberland rotation, a five-course modification of the Norfolk four-course, was developed. The adoption of the new crops and methods was facilitated in this district by the large size of the farms and the long leases on which they were held, and also by the favourable light soils and the availability of plenty of cheap lime. By the time of Bailey's report the turnip was being widely cultivated on light soils, chiefly derived from fluvio-glacial sands, in northeast England, and Bailey drew special attention to the distribution of these ' turnip soils ', as he called them.

Cumberland lagged behind, a county of small farms and often

insecure tenancies, where improvement was left to the large land-owners on their estate farms. The fact that the conjunction of coal and limestone was much less widespread restricted the practice of lime burning and the availability of lime as an improver. According to Young, the Penrith district was the best-farmed part of the county in 1770, and the new farming with rotations was being practised here ; but elsewhere the farmers ' know little of clover and cultivate few turnips '. Even in 1794 Bailey and Culley noted patches of turnips in only a few scattered localities, and this in spite of the widespread occurrence of sandy loams that would have admirably suited their cultivation. Pringle also referred to the generally primitive methods in use, commenting that turnips and artificial grasses were little culti-vated, and that wheat was a new crop, far from widely grown.

It was, of course, natural that wheat should be less cultivated in the wetter western districts than in the drier coastal lowlands of the east ; but in fact throughout the north country oats and bigg (barley) were the chief grain crops grown, barley being much cultivated as a bread cereal. They appeared in the Northumberland rotation, with a turnip crop between, followed by two years of clover and other green crops. On heavier soils, fallow was retained and wheat was preferred to barley as the succeeding crop, with beans and peas important instead of turnips. The vale of Tees in particular was wheat and bean land. As the practice of liming had increased, wheat had largely superseded rye in Northumberland, but maslin (mixed wheat and rye) was still grown in some districts, especially on the claylands of southeast Northumberland.

In the lowlands of the vale of Eden and the Solway basin, where old practices still prevailed with little change, it was usual to grow a succession of three or four corn crops (oats and barley) and then to leave the ground to recover for a period of seven to twelve years. But on farms where wheat had recently been introduced, with it had come the practice of preparatory summer fallowing, and the system was modified.

In most districts the bread of the poor was still made chiefly with bigg, but to an even greater extent oatmeal was the staple food, as in Scotland. Potatoes were widely grown for human food, though rarely for animals, and they provided an important addition to the diet. They were cultivated by almost every farmer in Cumberland, but often by the lazy-bed method. A local feature of the cropping round Durham city was the importance of mustard.

Alike in districts of large farms and small farms, in the lowlands arable fields usually amounted to half or more of the total area. In Northumberland, where the new, progressive farming methods were well represented by the beginning of the nineteenth century, many estates had trebled in value during the previous forty years. Nowhere was the transformation more striking than in Glendale, where enclosure had previously been delayed. The Till valley, with its flats of lacustrine alluvium and fringing terraces, was transformed under the stimulus of high war-time prices from a wilderness of gorse into an area of advanced farming carried on by such men as the Culley brothers and John Grey, ready to apply new ideas and themselves contributing considerably to the new techniques.

It was especially in the breeding of improved livestock, however, that north country farmers made a great reputation about the end of the eighteenth century and in the early nineteenth century. The improved Leicester sheep was introduced on the turnip and clover farms of Northumberland, while improvement of the Cheviot and other local breeds had begun; but the chief improvement of native hill breeds for the lowland farms by crossing with the larger breeds came later. The famous Border Leicester was being established by the Culleys on their extensive farms by crossing the local sheep with Bakewell's Leicesters.

Among cattle, that most widely used of modern breeds, the Shorthorn, was evolved by inbreeding the shorthorned Teeswater cattle (themselves probably of Dutch origin) by the brothers Colling who farmed in the vale of Tees near Darlington towards the end of the eighteenth and at the beginning of the nineteenth century. The Durham Ox, a prototype of the modern herds of Shorthorn cattle the world over, was a wonder of the contemporary farming world, an animal of legendary fame, still commemorated in the names of several inns in the county. It toured the country for exhibition during the first decade of the nineteenth century in a specially constructed carriage. Shorthorn animals were being widely used for stocking farms in Northumberland and Durham at the beginning of the nineteenth century, and some of the more progressive farmers in Cumberland, such as Curwen, had also adopted the breed; but in the northwest Longhorns were still most widespread, with Scottish breeds such as Galloways more in evidence near the Solway.

In addition to the new homesteads in many districts on allotments enclosed from commons, there was much other building in the countryside. The increased agricultural prosperity was reflected in the modification of grim old fortresses to make them more comfortable residences for their owners, and in the erection of new 'halls' and substantial farmhouses for the county landowners and large tenant-farmers. Among the new residences were those of the old landowning aristocracy, some of whom were enriched by mining royalties as well as by increased farm rentals ; others were for the *nouveaux riches*, who made fortunes from the coal trade or from mining and other industrial enterprises, and applied their wealth to country estates. For the Delaval family who created Seaton Sluice, Vanburgh had built the great mansion at Seaton Delaval in southeast Northumberland early in the eighteenth century, and he later carried out extensive improvements at Lumley Castle on the Wear. At Wallington Hall, built about 1700 for Sir Hugh Blackett, a magnate of the Newcastle coal trade, ' Capability ' Brown later served his apprenticeship in landscaping. His landscape compositions, however, are not widely represented in his native county. While Brown was landscaping the parks of the English lowland, however, George Bowes, one of the coal owners of northwest Durham who formed the Grand Alliance, was creating a new landscape around his Jacobean mansion at Gibside in the Derwent valley. In 1800 the country seats of the gentry were genuine, if modified, medieval castles (e.g. Lumley, Alnwick, and Raby), or new halls built in classical style (e.g. Seaton Delaval). But soon afterwards there were added some brand new ' castles ', such as Lambton (from 1796) and Ravensworth (1808), in the romantic style of the Gothic revival.[1] Similarly Brancepeth Castle was rebuilt in grandiose style after 1817. Alnwick Castle as it stands today is largely the product of another rebuilding in the middle of the nineteenth century, following that by Adam a century earlier (Pl. 25).

Even the small farmers, proprietors and tenants, were often rehoused in substantial if unpretentious stone dwellings, with the addition of other farm buildings of similar material for byres. Lead-mining companies, as well as other landlords, were active in building cottages for their tenants. Two planned settlements of eighteenth-century construction in the north, at Blanchland and Lowther, are among the most attractive hamlets in the country. The Board of Agriculture reporters about 1800 wrote generally of farmhouses well built of stone, though Pringle made an exception of northeast Cumberland, where hovels of mud or clay were still typical. The railways, however, had not yet come to spread the use of mass-produced bricks and slates, and the numerous new buildings of the period still made use of local materials. The north of England is rich in a variety of freestones, which occur in the widespread Carboniferous and Triassic rocks, and wherever building stone was needed these were quarried fairly locally.

[1] As more fortunes were made during the nineteenth century, the countryside became more thickly studded with mansions, chiefly in the Gothic baronial style, though the Classical revival has a few late representatives, notably Windlestone Hall and Wynyard, built in 1822 by Wyatt for the Marquis of Londonderry who created Seaham Harbour. In Cumberland there were fewer new mansions, but Lowther Castle, rebuilt in 1809, is testimony to the fortune the Cumberland coal trade had brought to the Lowther family.

Throughout the north country the walls of buildings in town and country were of stone, though their colour varied according to their origin—reddish in the Triassic sandstone country, buff, weathering grey, in areas of the older rocks. There were greater contrasts, however, in roofing materials. On the east side in the coastal lowlands, pantiles (Pls. 23, 31), introduced about the middle of the eighteenth century, were increasingly used for roofing in place of thatch, but gave way inland to heavy stone slates. On the west side, in the Lake District, finely laminated green slates quarried from the Borrowdale Volcanic series (Fig. 28) were used for roofing, and even for weatherproofing walls, but in the Cumbrian lowlands the use of thatching (turf, heather, or rushes) continued. Pantiles, an eastern style, did not here spread into the west. In Cumberland, especially, the farmhouses were whitewashed, a practice that Wordsworth deplored; and this was also a feature of Teesdale, but not of the dales farther north.

The steadings of the smaller farms were often long, low buildings like the Scottish ' butt and ben ', accommodating human beings at one end and animals at the other, under a continuous roof. The larger farms had more commodious buildings, and the strong emphasis upon livestock husbandry throughout the farming districts was reflected in the extensive provision of byres, with hay lofts and barns above (Pl. 24). Arrangement of byres in the form of an ⌐ or a ⊔ is very characteristic, with the dwelling house in close proximity, but detached—all the buildings alike made of local stone.

Unlike the districts farther south, the northern counties in 1800 remained unaffected by canal construction,[1] but great improvement in communications had recently been taking place. New and better roads and bridges had been built. The main roads, including the Great North Road, had been turnpiked about the middle of the eighteenth century, and the second half of the century had witnessed a general improvement in the roads. It was not until the eighteen-twenties, however, that new turnpike roads penetrated the lead-mining dales, and whereas the coal-mining districts that produced for shipment were served by wagonways, transport of lead ore from mines to smelting mills and thence to the ports was still by panniers slung across the backs of dale ponies. Carts were gradually introduced, first on turnpike roads, and later on other country roads as these were improved, especially under the implementation of Enclosure Acts. Carrier-cart services plied between the towns and stage-coaches sped along the main roads.

---

[1] North England has had only one canal within its borders, that built between 1819 and 1823 from Carlisle to the Solway at Port Carlisle, which was later superseded by the railway that is laid along its bed. In 1819 also the Lancaster-Kendal Canal was opened.

Bridges, including the Tyne bridge at Newcastle, had been renewed after the great storm of 1771, which swept away almost all the old bridges over the Tyne, Wear, and Tees. Additional new bridges had been provided, notably at Sunderland, where the settlements on opposite sides of the Wear estuary were first connected by a bridge (made of iron) in 1796, and at Stockton, where the Tees was first bridged in 1760.

These improvements in accessibility greatly benefited the towns, enabling their trade to expand with the general economic development of the areas they served. Although still small by modern standards, they were prosperous and growing. Some of them were especially well placed to profit from the growing needs of the concentrations of miners and industrial workers. Thus the markets at Hexham and Morpeth were growing rapidly to supply the butchers on Tyneside. Livestock changed hands and wool was sold chiefly at the great seasonal fairs, and, although these were important features of the life of the towns, they were not confined to them. The July fair at Stagshaw Bank, near Corbridge in Northumberland, remained one of the greatest sheep fairs in the north of England, and although Brough was enjoying prosperity as a coaching stage at the foot of Stainmore on the main road, its urban character and size in no degree matched the importance of its fair, at which large numbers of Scottish cattle were sold to local farmers and for droving southwards.

Variations in the size of market towns in 1801, at the time of the first Census, however, reflected chiefly the varying degrees of development in them of small manufacturing industries, based upon agricultural products. Small woollen mills and tanneries were usually present in these centres, and in some a special development of manufacturing had taken place during the eighteenth century and had become responsible for most of the employment. At Darlington linen manufacture employed most of the working population throughout the eighteenth century, and after 1750 the worsted industry also grew rapidly. Carpet manufacture was important at Durham and Barnard Castle, glove making at Hexham, and felt-hat manufacture at Cockermouth. Tributary rural areas of domestic workers were associated with the towns, while Wigton and Brampton were themselves largely occupied in handloom weaving of checks and ginghams for the Carlisle factories. The knitting and handloom weaving of woollen articles were the mainstay or at least important activities in other market centres and their surroundings, for example Keswick, Appleby, and Kirkby Stephen, and at Kendal in 1801 on the average 2,400 pairs of stockings were supplied weekly to the market. Carlisle was the principal seat of the cotton industry in the north, but other sites were being explored for new cotton factories, as for example Bishop Auckland. Nor were they all confined to market-town settings; besides outlying factories round Carlisle, there were a few shortlived enterprises about the end of the eighteenth century at new and scattered rural sites, for example Castle Eden, Netherwitton, and Corby, but they did not persist long enough or grow sufficiently to create new industrial towns.

The measures of improvement and development characteristic of the latter part of the eighteenth century are epitomised in the account given by Arthur Young of the enterprises of Abraham Dickson at Belford on the Great North Road in the heart of the north Northumberland district of high farming. To Dickson's efforts Young attributed not only the agricultural improvement of the surrounding country by the draining of waterlogged land, hedging with holly, laying down to grass, the cultivation of cabbages for fodder, the development of coal pits and limekilns to provide fertiliser, the establishment of plantations, and the building of a mansion and seven new farmhouses, but also the development of the town so that its population had increased from 100 to 600 within thirteen years. Young noted especially the building of a new inn and improvement of road access, the development of the market and fairs, and the erection of a woollen mill and a tannery.

The benefits of economic development were not reaped indiscriminately, however, or enjoyed by every established centre. The notable general expansion of trade was accompanied by changes in the relative fortunes of towns. This is well illustrated on the lower Tees (Fig. 36). Darlington, with its flourishing textile industries, was much the most important centre in the vale, but it had never been a port. During the seventeenth century Yarm, some miles to the east, had been the lowest bridging-point on the Tees, and prospered as a centre of boat building and a port for the export of agricultural products and lead. But its continued growth was arrested by the rise of Stockton, lower down the river. When Stockton's charter was granted in 1666, it was inhabited by only 120 families and shipping was not mentioned. Thereafter it began to grow at the expense of Yarm. Its town hall, like that of Darlington, dates from the early eighteenth century. The erection of the stone bridge over the Tees at Stockton in 1760, opening easy communication with Cleveland to the south, together with road improvement in the district, increased its importance as a market centre, and at the same time sealed the fate of Yarm as a port. By 1801 Stockton was a busy town with 4,000 inhabitants. It had grown along its axis, the High Street, and between it and the river bank, which was lined with quays, granaries, warehouses, breweries, roperies, sail-cloth workshops, lead works, shipbuilding and timber yards. Navigation of the excessively meandering, silt-choked river channel

was still difficult, however, and much of the loading and unloading
of sea-going vessels was done farther downstream, where small hamlets
had appeared by 1800 at the outports, Newport and Cargo Fleet.
Meantime Yarm, in decline, had a population of only 1,300 in 1801,
and has few more today. It remains as a fossil town, a relic of pre-
nineteenth century construction, without the addition of the typical
features of later phases that have so profoundly transformed the urban

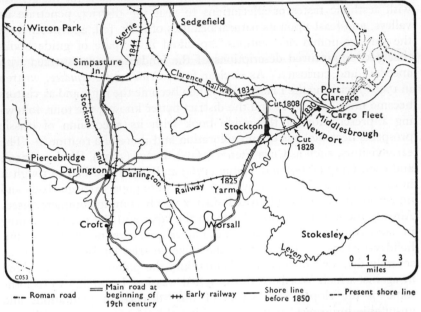

| ▬▬ Roman road | ══ Main road at beginning of 19th century | ┿┿┿ Early railway | ▬▬ Shore line before 1850 | --- Present shore line |

Fig. 36   THE LOWER TEES BASIN EARLY IN THE NINETEENTH CENTURY.

scene elsewhere in the north. The old port of Hartlepool was even
more moribund than Yarm in 1800. Lacking the advantages of a
central situation for handling the trade of the Tees basin, it had stagnated during the seventeenth and eighteenth centuries, and although
for a time it retained some importance for the coal fleets as a harbour
of refuge in bad weather, by 1800 it had relapsed into little more
than a small fishing village. Unlike Yarm, however, a new phase
of development was to follow later in the nineteenth century, adding
to old Hartlepool, within its walled peninsular site, the modern port
and industrial town of West Hartlepool (Fig. 50).

Already in the pre-railway age the several parts of North England
were beginning to be knit together as never before, and their isolation
was steadily being broken down. Even the Lake District, its long-
secluded valleys still inhabited by a distinctive class of 'statesmen',

159

small farmers who owned their land, was becoming known and even famous to the outside world. The grandeur of its hills and lakes had been discovered and appreciated by poets and artists of the ' picturesque' and romantic. It was in 1799 that Wordsworth settled at Grasmere to draw his poetic inspiration from the communion with nature he could there enjoy, and about the same time Turner began to depict the wild scenery in romantic visions of storm and sunshine. From about 1760 it had become increasingly fashionable for the genteel with aesthetic tastes or affectations to visit the district, penetrate its valleys, and feast upon its natural beauties of rock, fell, and water from the vantage-points or ' stations' specified in a spate of guide books that gave enraptured descriptions of the landscape, interspersed with anecdote and curiosity. As is clear from *Pride and Prejudice*, written in 1796–7, visiting the Lakes had by then become the rage, and as visitors became more numerous and the district better known, the tour, following a prescription of the guide book with its succession of classic prospects became ' less of an exploration and more of a routine '.[1] The early visitors, such as Celia Fienes (1698), Defoe (1725), Wesley (1759), and even Gray (1769) and Young (1769 and 1772) had had to rough it in the absence of inns, but by 1800 there were good carriage-roads and numerous inns, and the tourist industry was becoming commercialised. Already there were pleasure-boats on the lakes and the tourists coming in increasing numbers ' were no longer pioneers or explorers, but holiday-makers '.[2] By this time the Lake District landscapes had been severely denuded of their woodlands, and the planting with larch and fir against which Wordsworth inveighed was just beginning to reclothe some of the slopes. He wrote of the ' discordant plantations and unsuitable buildings' that were making their appearance in a district which he conceived as ' a sort of national property in which every man has a right and interest who has an eye to perceive and a heart to enjoy '.[3] This incipient idea of a national trust was conceived only by the sensitive spirit of a Wordsworth. It was certainly not held, much less applied, generally in North England. At the beginning of the nineteenth century archaeological work on the Roman Wall had not begun, and the attitude of the local inhabitants to this ancient monument was essentially utilitarian. For the new steadings that were springing up north of the Tyne valley as the commons were enclosed, the Wall provided a most convenient stone-quarry, and it probably suffered more systematic destruction then than at any time previously.

[1] Norman Nicholson, *The Lakers*. [2] ibid.
[3] *Guide to the Lakes*, ed. W. M. Marchant (London, 1951), p. 127.

CHAPTER 10

THE MODERN INDUSTRIAL AND URBAN DEVELOPMENT

To the old-established seats of industrial activity and the restricted areas of earlier intensive mining operations in North England were added during the course of the nineteenth century large tracts of country that became transformed by mining, industry, and urbanisation. The accelerated process of mining and industrial colonisation produced a succession of fleeting geographical patterns. They were individually hardly more than dissolving views, but their cumulative effects have been of major importance for the present-day regional differentiation. In the course of this period of rapid change many elements of the older dispositions were adapted for continued activity, though others were discarded. Their residues, however, were not always cleared away or effaced. In its present-day complexity, therefore, the geography in large measure reflects the sequent phases of the nineteenth century, each of which, though it added much that was new, was also conditioned by the pattern out of which it emerged. The industrial landscape as we see it today presents an accumulation of these deposits, some of them still functioning, others fossilised.

In the areas affected by development not only was the natural increase of a remarkably fecund population absorbed, large-scale immigration took place, both from the rural districts of North England and from much farther afield. By the eighteen-eighties, however, a net outflow of migrants from North England was already setting in, and this has continued with little interruption since, but vigorous growth of population continued until the First World War. Whenever intense development spent itself in one locality, the retardation or halt was more than offset by new or renewed activity elsewhere. With local and regional shifts that corresponded to changing opportunities of employment, population grew apace as the economy expanded. The population resident in what became the mining and industrial area of the Northeast Coast as it is known today increased tenfold during the course of the nineteenth century from 200,000 to two millions. From having less than half the population of North England this area came to contain over eighty per cent.

Though the industrial and urban colonisation of northeast England was rapid and continuous between 1800 and 1914, three distinct phases may be distinguished. Their approximate date-spans were 1800-25,

1825–50, and 1850–1914. During the first quarter of the nineteenth century, despite considerable developments, the extensions to the restricted areas affected by mining and industry were comparatively small. In the next twenty-five years, however, a wave of mining colonisation swept over the coalfield as the railway system was provided. After 1850 some new mining areas were added, notable among them the Cleveland iron-ore field, but the outstanding features were consolidation and intensification of activity in areas already occupied by industry, together with the major commercial and industrial development of the port conurbations.

The colliery districts of Northumberland and Durham

(a) 1800–25

During this period mining expanded in both the Tyne and Wear districts, but extensions to the small areas affected were comparatively slight, and the unindustrialised countryside of 1800 for the most part preserved its rural character twenty-five years later. Within the mining areas the transformation proceeded, and was accompanied by a continuance of migration from districts where industry was stagnating or even declining to those where it was in full development. Immigration from outside was not yet very important, however, as the natural increase of the prolific mining communities served to meet the increasing labour requirements.[1]

In the old districts west and southwest of Newcastle, which shipped their coal above the Tyne bridge, development was at a standstill, and miners' families were moving to the newer areas farther east on lower Tyneside and the Wear (Figs. 29, 37). Lower Tyneside was at the flood-tide of its prosperity as a mining area at the beginning of the century, and by 1820 the ebb had already set in. Employment was contracting, and miners were moving north to new mining hamlets that were springing up just north of the Ninety Fathom 'Dyke'. Among these migrants, George Stephenson moved from Willington Quay to Killingworth in 1805. He had come to Willington Quay earlier as engineman from upper Tyneside, where he had been brought up at Wylam.

Meantime the Wear district was prosperous and developing, thanks to the happy coincidence of the opening up of the Hutton seam there with the exhaustion of the High Main seam on Tyneside. The earlier workings had been in the higher seams, but the deeper Hutton seam in this district proved to be one of the finest household coals of the

---

[1] *Poor Law Commissioners' Report, 1834*, App. A., Pt. 1, No. 5, p. 130; No. 11, p. 320.

whole coalfield. With its exploitation the centre of production shifted from the older tracts near the staiths to newer areas farther south and southeast, where there was more scope for new enterprise. Some slight extension of the limits of the producing area took place on this side, but although the first winning through the Magnesian Limestone was made at Hetton as early as 1822, conditions on the east Durham plateau altered very little before 1830. It remained a rural area, with farming the mainstay of its inhabitants.

The growing employment in trade and manufacturing that was taking place on Tyneside was shared chiefly between the two main concentrations that already existed there in 1800, one focused upon the bridge, the other at the river mouth. The chief expanding industries of this period were wooden shipbuilding, especially at South Shields, ironworking, especially at Gateshead and Newcastle, and glass making. At Newcastle much of the increase of population could still be accommodated by crowding within the limits of the old city walls, but middle-class suburbs were extending outside at Westgate and Jesmond,[1] and the industrial annexes of Byker and Gateshead were also growing considerably. At the mouth of the Tyne buildings were spreading back from the already congested waterfront on to the higher ground behind, in Tynemouth and Westoe. Some of the new collieries on Tyneside were so close to the river that their workers lived practically on the river banks, where other industries were also carried on. These settlements grew in size and more were added, but they were still far from forming a continuous urban tract.

North of the Tyne, the ports of Hartley and Blyth were in a moribund condition owing to the decline of the salt industry and their poor shipping facilities, but at the mouth of the Wear the flourishing coal trade, and even more the growing employment in shipbuilding and ancillary trades and at glassworks, copperas works, potteries, lime kilns, and an ironworks at Bishopwearmouth, were responsible for significant extension of the urban area, chiefly on the south side.

(b) 1825-50

In this quarter of the century new and expanding markets for coal provided the incentive, and new transport facilities the means, for a great extension of mining. Population leapt from 300,000 in 1831 to half a million in 1851, an amount far in excess of the natural increase. This was the period when mining colonisation was at its height, and a new feature appeared—a large balance of inward migration entering the coalfield from outside. Immigration was given an early impetus by the demand for labour occasioned by the great miners' strike of 1832.

---

[1] Localities on Tyneside referred to in this chapter are shown on Figure 46.

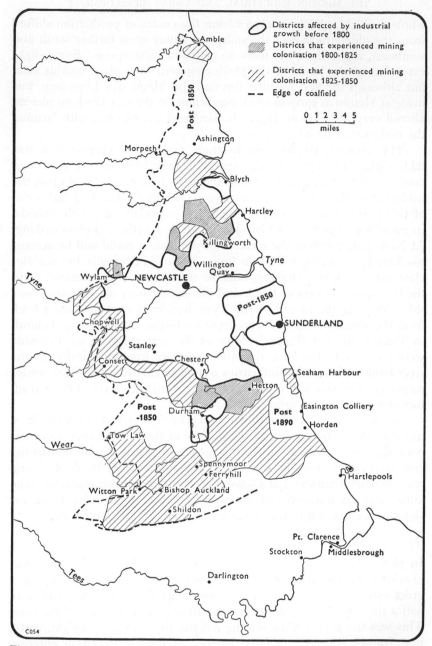

Legend:
- Districts affected by industrial growth before 1800
- Districts that experienced mining colonisation 1800-1825
- Districts that experienced mining colonisation 1825-1850
- Edge of coalfield

0 1 2 3 4 5 miles

Fig. 37 THE NORTHUMBERLAND AND DURHAM COALFIELD: MINING COLONISATION DURING THE NINETEENTH CENTURY.

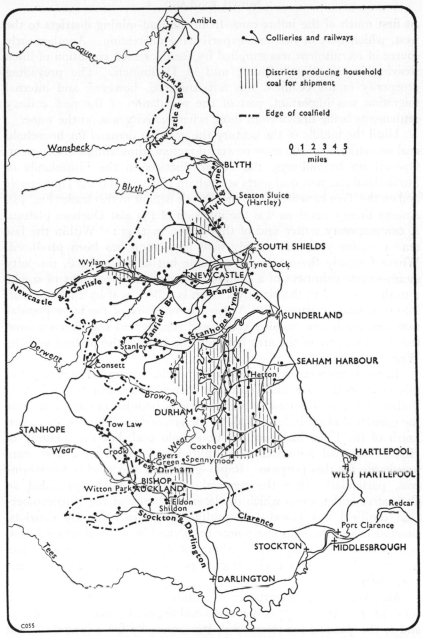

Amble

Colieries and railways

Districts producing household
coal for shipment

Edge of coalfield

0 1 2 3 4 5
miles

Coquet

Newcastle & Berwick

Wansbeck

BLYTH

Blyth

Blyth & Tyne

Seaton Sluice
(Hartley)

SOUTH SHIELDS

Wylam

Tyne Dock

NEWCASTLE

Newcastle & Carlisle

Brandling Jn.

Tanfield Bch.

Stanhope & Tyne Jn.

SUNDERLAND

Derwent

Stanley

Consett

SEAHAM HARBOUR

Hetton

Browney

DURHAM

STANHOPE

Tow Law

Wear

Wear

Crook

Coxhoe

HARTLEPOOL

Byers
Green Spennymoor

West
Durham

WEST HARTLEPOOL

BISHOP

Witton Park AUCKLAND

Eldon
Shildon

Redcar

Stockton & Darlington

Clarence

Port Clarence

Tees

STOCKTON

MIDDLESBROUGH

DARLINGTON

C055

Fig. 38   THE NORTHUMBERLAND AND DURHAM COALFIELD : COLLIERIES AND RAILWAYS
IN 1850.

12

At first much of the influx came from the lead-mining districts to the west, which were at the time experiencing depression. Another early source of recruitment was supplied by the depressed condition of linen weaving in the North Riding and at Darlington. The prevailing prosperity in the coalfield was not universal, however, and internal migration was important, part of the population of the new colliery settlements being drawn from those where activity was on the wane.

Until the middle of the century the growing demand for household coal was still one of the most powerful factors stimulating development. Opened up by railways, the newer districts in the hinterlands of Sunderland and new coal ports at Seaham Harbour and the Hartlepools and on the Tees benefited from the Tyne's default in this trade (Fig. 38). Among these extensions was the invasion of the east Durham plateau. A contemporary writer said of this region in 1841 : ' Within the last ten or twelve years an entirely new population has been produced. Where formerly there was not a single hut of a shepherd, the lofty steam-engine chimneys of a colliery now send their columns of smoke into the sky, and in the vicinity a town is called, as if by enchantment, into immediate existence.' [1] At least some share of the large population increase in the parishes concerned represented transference from the northern part of the area between the edge of the plateau and the Wear.

In the Census returns for lower Tyneside, northward movement of miners from the now almost exhausted coalfield south of the Ninety Fathom Dyke is obscured by the increase of population attendant upon the growth of other industries along the riverside. The first extension north of the Dyke had been for household coal, but the quantity of High Main coal here was very limited and the lower seams were unsuitable for this purpose. Rapid growth of the market for steam-coal, particularly after the removal of export duties, provided an alternative outlet, upon which the later prosperity of the Northumberland coalfield was based. Naturally, the more southerly districts, situated nearer the shipping points on Tyneside, were developed first, especially as the unimproved harbour of Blyth was of little use. But there was also a small outlying tract of new development in the extreme north near Amble.

Meantime some resuscitation of mining in northwest Durham and south of the river on upper Tyneside had begun, thanks to the railways and to the demand for steam-coal, but especially for coking-coal, that was provided by growing industries on Tyneside and at Consett. The margins of the mining area were pushed out to the south and west, and new colliery settlements appeared.

[1] *Report of Child Employment Commission, 1841.* Appendix 1, p. 143.

In the southwest corner of the coalfield a new era had dawned in 1825 with the opening of the Stockton and Darlington Railway, which was built with the direct object of developing the small landsale pits of this district to enable them to produce for shipment. Up to 1830 the development was confined to the area south of the Wear that was traversed by the main line and the Eldon branch, but, once the practicability of developing the coal trade had thus been demonstrated, other projects for opening up new districts lying south and southeast of Durham city were carried out forthwith. New mining ventures, accompanied by large-scale immigration, took place, first in the small but intensively worked tract of good household coal ('Tees Wallsend') that lay just east of Bishop Auckland, and in the area southwest of that town. In the eighteen-forties, however, the principal scene of new operations and most rapid colonisation was on the north side of the Wear valley, northwest of Bishop Auckland.[1]

How cumulative were the stimulating effects of railway development is illustrated by the rise of the iron industry. Its sudden expansion was largely to meet growing demands for railway material, and it played an important part in providing employment directly at works that were set up on the western edge of the coalfield at Wylam, Consett, Tow Law and Witton Park, as well as by stimulating in turn the local production of coking-coal. Until 1850 the location of blast-furnaces (Fig. 39) was governed by the availability not only of specially suitable coking-coal but also of local or easily accessible supplies of ore from the dales to the west. It soon became evident that these supplies were inadequate, and they were supplemented by Whitby ironstone. Of blast-furnaces erected before 1850, however, only those at Walker-on-Tyne were built specifically to use this ore.

On Tyneside the first iron ships were built before 1850, and Armstrong established his engineering works at Elswick in 1847; but neither of these developments, far-reaching though they were to prove, was of much immediate importance. The factors of current importance were the continued decline of coal mining near the river as the coal there was worked out, the continued development of the coal trade as railway connections with the natural hinterland were multiplied and extended, and the steady growth of the chemical, wooden shipbuilding, iron, and engineering industries.

The birth of the modern alkali trade in Britain dates from 1806, when Losh set up his works on the Tyne at Walker. The new industry

---

[1] This district was first penetrated by a railway in 1840, when the Byers Green branch of the Clarence Railway was extended across the Wear. Soon afterwards the Stockton and Darlington Railway entered this new field by means of the Shildon tunnel (Fig. 38).

was greatly helped by repeal of the salt duty in 1823, and by 1830 it was established at Walker, Bill Quay, Felling Shore, and Friars Goose, where it provided steadily increasing employment during the next two decades. There were copperas works at most of the small industrial settlements along the river, as well as a variety of other industries. The salt industry had declined, but the manufacture of glass was still

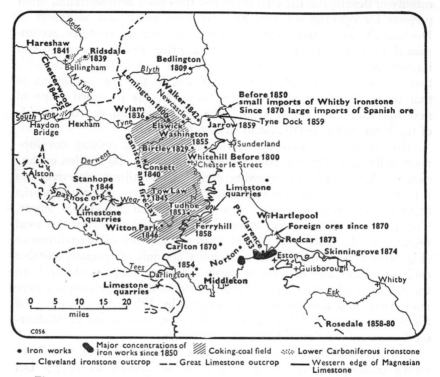

Fig. 39 NORTHEAST ENGLAND : THE NINETEENTH-CENTURY IRON INDUSTRY.

important at Gateshead, Byker, and South Shields, and the output of wooden ships, especially from the Shields, continued to increase, chiefly to meet the ever-growing needs of the coal trade. In 1829 a shipyard with a patent slipway was set up at Jarrow, together with a sail factory. The workers lived at Dunkirk Place, which had come into existence with the opening of Jarrow colliery.

Most of the industrial development of the period, however, was in that group of industries which marked the growing importance of iron and steam in the new age. Such were the manufacture of steam-engines, especially for colliery use, of railway materials, and of parts for the new iron bridges. Marine engineering was also developing, as

168

steam was beginning to be applied to the propulsion of vessels. Iron was the raw material of all these industries and ironfounding and mill-work flourished. The firms on Tyneside that were in the forefront of these developments had been established before 1830, and experienced great expansion during the next two decades. At the Forth Bank works (Newcastle) of Hawthorn, which had been established in 1817 with fewer than a dozen employees, more than 200 were employed in 1830, more than 400 in 1840, and 900 by 1850.

Most of the industrial establishments of Tyneside remained concentrated near the bridge and near the river mouth, and the increase of population was therefore mainly in Newcastle-Gateshead and the Shields. Here the nuclear areas had reached their population limit, and further increase involved extensions of the built-up areas. At Newcastle the municipal boundaries were extended in 1835 to include the outer zone of buildings which by then surrounded the old city. Within the walls, the work of Grainger and Dobson was at is height in the 'thirties and 'forties, transforming the plan and townscape to develop and adapt the city to fulfil its modern function as the great commercial capital of the region.

Beginning with the re-development of sites made available by the recent demolition of the city's northern wall, Grainger and his associates carried through a vast scheme of street development. In the middle 'thirties 2,000 workmen were engaged in preparing the ground and erecting whole new streets of massive stone buildings with classical façades. Such architectural distinction and coherent design are possessed by the core areas of few cities, and they are quite unique in industrial Britain. Not only was much of Newcastle within the line of the walls rebuilt at this time, its plan underwent some radical changes and reorganisation (Figs. 25, 26). Blackett Street, along the line of the north wall, was approached from the south by Grey Street (Pl. 42), which doubled the older line of Pilgrim Street. But Grainger Street and Clayton Street, entering it from the southwest, were new lines that intersected the curving course of the main thoroughfare of old Newcastle as it led from St Nicholas' church to Newgate, providing the market street. Immediately to the north, the Anderson Place estate, where a nunnery had once stood, was acquired for development, an undertaking that involved filling in the dene of the Lort burn ; and new covered markets were provided between the parallel new streets here. When the railways came, the completion of the High Level bridge (1849), which spans the Tyne valley 112 feet above the river, provided the railway approach from the south, and accommodation was provided in the southwest for the great Central Station (1850) by clearing a site that lay across part of the west wall. Grainger Street naturally became the chief shopping street of Newcastle for the next century. It led from the Central Station, across Westgate Road and Newgate Street, past the markets, to the hub of the reorganised city at the junction with Blackett Street and Grey Street, where the columnar monument to the champion of parliamentary reform dominates the modern townscape.

Over much of Tyneside, however, industrial expansion during the 'thirties and 'forties was barely enough to balance the decline of mining and the consequent migration of families from the mining settlements near the river. Wallsend parish was able to show a small net increase of 200 persons between 1831 and 1851 only because of the growth of an industrial community at Willington Quay; from other parts of the parish an exodus of miners was taking place. In his *History of Wallsend* Richardson refers, for example, to the virtual disappearance of the village of Battle Hill, where workers at the Bigge pit had lived, and which had a Methodist Chapel that could seat more than 400 people. The parishes of Whitley, Monkseaton, and Chirton all experienced actual decreases of population, and in Hedworth on the south bank the total remained practically stationary. Above the Tyne bridge, too, this was a period when the population near the river changed very little, though new mining settlements appeared in the parishes that stretched back from the south bank.

At Wearmouth growth continued. This was the great period of the Wear household-coal trade—the supply from the Tyne was declining and railways had not yet enabled other coalfields to capture the London market. Moreover the Hetton wagonway and the Durham and Sunderland Railway (1836) strengthened the connections of Sunderland with its developing hinterland (Fig. 38). They contributed to the decline of older shipping points farther upstream and concentrated the benefits of the prosperity of the growing trade at Sunderland itself. Other railways diverted the trade of some districts to the Tyne and to Seaham Harbour, but these losses of territory were amply compensated by the developments in the rich area still left to Sunderland. The coal trade needed more and more vessels to transport the coal, and this was also the heyday of wooden shipbuilding on the Wear, which shared also in the building of emigrant ships. The glass industry was also approaching its zenith. In the urban extension associated with this economic expansion the most important spread was west of Bridge Street (Fig. 48). South of the river, the vicinity of the river bank was largely built up, and although some growth of population continued in Sunderland proper, the chief developments were farther west. North of the Wear, however, most of the growth of population was still in the area east of Bridge Street, though the new Monkwearmouth colliery was responsible for the beginning of considerable building extension westwards.

Still farther west, Southwick, an industrial satellite, was growing steadily, but had not yet coalesced with the main cluster.

On the Tees improvements by deepening the channel and making cuts through meander necks east of Stockton had been carried out after 1808 (Fig. 36), and the port and town of Stockton were growing even before the railway was opened in 1825. The railway allowed the Tees to enter the coal trade, and marked a period of active railway-building by means of which the resources of the south and southeast of the

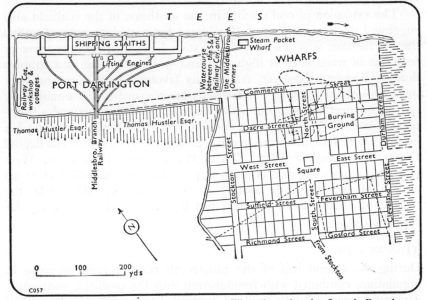

Fig. 40 THE NUCLEUS OF MIDDLESBROUGH. The 1830 plan for Joseph Pease's new town, prepared by Richard Otley, surveyor. This is now St Hilda's Ward. In building, extra streets were inserted between the lots, thus increasing the building density considerably.

coalfield were exploited in conjunction with the ports of the Tees and the Hartlepools (Fig. 38). The first coal shipments from the Tees were made at the old port of Stockton, but the railway company soon began to look for a more convenient shipping point farther east, and chose Middlesbrough as the site of a new port, opening an extension of the railway in 1830. A town had been planned adjoining the new staiths, and a company was formed to develop the estate. A square of 32 acres was laid out as the site of the new town, and the first house was built here in 1830—the nucleus of modern Middlesbrough (Fig. 40).[1] The great expansion of coal shipments followed, and by 1851 the new

[1] In 1808 J. Graves had written in his *History of Cleveland*: ' In the northern extremity of Acklam parish lies the township of Middlesbrough, which consists of four farmhouses situated on the south bank of the Tees ' (p. 471).

171

town already had a population of 7,600. Seaham Harbour and Middles-brough share the distinction of being the first towns created by railways. The Marquess of Londonderry had decided to construct a port to serve as outlet for his extensive collieries in the Hutton seam district to the west of Seaham. Harbour works were begun in 1828, a railway was built between the pits and the port, and the first coal was shipped in 1831. At the same time a town was being built on a regular plan furnished by a Newcastle architect, and by 1850 the new port of Seaham Harbour was a thriving community of 3,500 people.

The extension of coal mining in the southeast of the coalfield also suggested the development of Hartlepool for coal shipments. In 1830 the old harbour was in a dilapidated state. It contained only three or four feet of water even at high tide and was being used as a rubbish dump. Tennant, however, realised its favourable situation and took up a project for carrying out harbour improvements and establishing railway connections with the collieries in its natural hinterland. Shipment of coal was begun in 1835, and five years later the import of timber began. Port facilities were greatly enhanced when West Hartlepool Dock was opened in 1847. Thereafter the new component, West Hartlepool, grew rapidly both as a port for the coalfield and as an outlier of the Tees-side industrial area near by. Alongside the dock another new town was laid out by Ward Jackson in a regular grid (Fig. 50).

(c) Since 1850

During the second half of the nineteenth century rapid increase in population, combined with immigration into the coalfield, continued. The rural areas of North England continued to contribute to the flood of immigrants, but districts much farther afield were also drawn upon. Many labourers came from the depressed rural areas of Wales, Ireland, Scotland, and East Anglia, as well as the Cornish mining settlements. Between 1850 and 1880 mining made further encroachments upon districts previously rural, but intensification of mining activity in existing areas, with rejuvenation of their population cycles, was even more important. The boom in the coking-coal trade that accompanied the establishment and immediate remarkable expansion of the iron industry on Tees-side was reflected by a renewed burst of mining activity in the southwest corner of the coalfield. Vigorous development meanwhile proceeded in the somewhat younger area northwest of Bishop Auckland, and still farther north a more remote and hitherto untouched tract lying west of Durham city was added to the mining area (Fig. 37). At the same time a swing from production of household coal to that of coking coal allowed rapid development to continue in the district east of Bishop Auckland. The Stockton and Darlington Railway Company's engineering works at Shildon also provided increasing employment here, and iron smelting, begun at Tudhoe (Fig. 39) in 1853, combined with coal mining to bring about rapid increase of population at and near Spennymoor.

In the old district of northwest Durham mining was in full revival during the second half of the century. Possessing excellent coals of coking, steam, and gas types, this district benefited from the expansion of all these markets, and a general and rapid increase in population was in progress. The rise of the iron industry at Consett was responsible for a spectacular local growth of population there.

In Northumberland mining activity was also being intensified. Detailed investigation of the colliery history and course of population change in individual parishes shows that development here was somewhat spasmodic. The opening of a new colliery, or sinking operations to a new seam at an existing colliery, would cause an influx of workers and create a new settlement or add some pitmen's rows to an older village ; then, until another such development took place, the population would remain more or less stable. Developments were rather sporadic in occurrence as well as spasmodic in character. Over the period since 1850 the field of production has been considerably enlarged by the opening up of new tracts, especially north of the river Blyth, but clear zones of contemporaneous development and mining colonisation cannot be recognised.

In east Durham household coal did not remain for very long the basis of this area's prosperity. Already by 1850 the new railways were allowing this coalfield to be supplanted in the markets of London and southern England by the Midland coalfields. Production did not decline, however, for an outlet for increased output was found in the demand for gas coal. Indeed, in some of the northern parishes in this area, where population had for some time been decreasing, a new cycle of growth began after 1850. On the east Durham plateau the second half of the nineteenth century was characterised by the intermittent growth of previously established mining settlements, rather than by the creation of new ones, of which only four sprang up between 1850 and 1900. New mining settlements appeared, however, in northeast Durham (Fig. 37) in an important extension of the field, where mining had been held up earlier because the Hutton seam was rather too soft and friable for household use. On the other hand, that part of mid-Durham lying immediately east and southeast of Durham city, after its relatively short period of prosperity as a household-coal district, has had little share in later developments. Since 1850 the number of inhabitants there has shown little change.

By 1880 little scope was left for further extension of the mining area. The principal later additions (Fig. 37) have been in the north, where improvement of the port of Blyth encouraged large-scale development in the Ashington district in the decades before the First World War ; and in the southeast, where the appearance of large new colliery-settlements since 1900 is attributable to progress in the technique of sinking and to the building of a railway along the coast. In many districts, however, deep mining has provided the means of further expansion. In northwest Durham, for example, in spite of long and vigorous exploitation, the wide range of valuable seams allowed continued development, witness the rapid growth of such settlements as Stanley and Chopwell. There was also further intensification of activity in the gas-coal district, with revival of older areas near the Wear and acceleration of population growth on the plateau. In the southwest of the plateau, within the coking-coal region, the Ferryhill district also showed a rapid increase of population, but for the most part the rest of the coking-coal region was no longer experiencing immigration.

Thus the history of settlement is seen to be far from uniform over the coalfield. There have been pronounced regional variations in the date of commencement of the industrial cycle, as well as in the number of cycles experienced and their relationship to each other. These differences are ultimately related to the geological structure as it has affected the coal resources and their accessibility, to the distribution of different types of coal and the development of their respective markets, and to the situation in relation to transport facilities.

The port conurbations

In the colliery districts the most rapid and striking transformation and colonisation was experienced during the early railway period. By 1850 the railway network was substantially complete (Fig. 38), and the chief feature of the latter half of the century was steady intensification of industrialisation behind a front that had become fairly stable. The territorial position attained by the early wave of mining extension in the railway period was consolidated ; some further extensions took place, but after the middle of the century the encroaching front of mining made less spectacular advances. It was different at the ports. Here the major development of industry and urbanisation did not reach its maximum intensity until after 1850, when it was greatly accelerated. If this was especially true on Tees-side, where development was so closely related to the iron and steel industry, which was established there only after 1850, it also applied at the other ports.

The decades preceding 1850 had provided railway links between the ports and their mining hinterlands. For the realisation of the full possibilities of their situation, however, improvement of shipping facilities was very necessary. In this respect the 'fifties were years of special significance for the commercial and industrial development of the Northeast Coast, for they marked the beginnings of a new phase in port development. In 1850 the Tyne Improvement Commission was set up and began its great work of improving the navigability and shipping accommodation of the river. The bar was removed, dredging of the channel was undertaken, the construction of piers at the river mouth was begun in 1856, and coal-shipping facilities were increased by the construction of Northumberland Dock in 1857 and of Tyne Dock in 1859. At Sunderland, the opening of South Dock in 1850 and its extension and the completion of a direct outlet to the sea in 1856 greatly improved the capacity of the port (Fig. 49 and Pl. 37). At Seaham Harbour and at the Hartlepools important extensions to the docks were carried out, and in 1852 control of the Tees was vested in the Tees Conservancy Commission, which took over the work of the Tees Navigation Company and greatly extended its scope. Thus the way was prepared both for the further and accelerated expansion of the coal trade and for the rise of the modern shipbuilding industry.

Coal production in Northumberland and Durham had increased from less than 3 million tons to more than 10 million tons during the first half of the century, and the number of pitmen rose from perhaps 12,000 or 13,000 to 40,000. There are fuller and more reliable statistics that tell of the growth of coal shipments. From about 2 million tons in 1800 they had doubled by 1830, and they doubled again during the next twenty years. New ports had shared in this expansion of the coal trade, and the Tyne accounted for considerably less than half the total in 1850 as compared with two-thirds 50 years earlier.

From 1854 official mineral statistics are available. They show that during the next 60 years coal production increased from 15 million to 56 million tons, with a corresponding increase in employment to over 200,000 in 1913. Shipments increased meantime from 8½ million tons to nearly 35 million, largely as a result of the great expansion of the export trade, which was chiefly in steam-coal. Coastwise shipments, amounting to 8 million tons in 1913, were little more than they had been half a century earlier, but exports had grown from 2 million tons to 26 million (including coal leaving in ships' bunkers). Of the latter figure, the lion's share (more than 15 million tons) was shipped from the Tyne, with Blyth also assuming importance from the 'eighties. Of the 22 million tons not sent away by sea, and mostly consumed by local industries, and at the collieries and on the railways, 9 million tons were converted into coke for iron smelting.

Shipbuilding entered upon a new epoch as wood was replaced first by iron and then by steel. A few iron vessels had been launched during the 'forties, but little progress was made until 1852, when Palmer produced his iron screw collier *John Bowes*. So vastly more efficient than its predecessors did the new type prove that a new industry rapidly sprang up. Following hard upon the appearance of the first iron collier came that of the first iron battleship—also built at Palmer's new yard at Jarrow. Henceforward there was an established demand for metal armour-plates for naval vessels, and, under the stimulus of the Crimean War, Palmer's forged ahead. The Crimean War also played an important part in the rise of another great concern on Tyneside, at Elswick (Fig. 46), where Armstrong had bought two fields on the river bank in 1847 to set up a factory for making hydraulic machinery. The Crimean War turned his inventive genius to ordnance, and in 1859 the Elswick ordnance works were established to exploit his inventions.

On the Tees, the 'fifties saw even more spectacular change, associated with the foundation of the iron-smelting industry. The first blast-furnaces were built at Middlesbrough in 1852; by 1856 no fewer than 23 had been erected and 21 were in blast. In the train of smelting there followed the establishment of works to carry out the secondary processes and of iron-shipbuilding yards.

The foundations having thus been laid in the 'fifties, the next sixty years were a period of almost uninterrupted industrial development on Tyne, Wear, and Tees. Some of the older industries, however, failed to maintain their earlier prosperity. For a time the chemical industry continued to expand on Tyneside and Wearside, but its peak had been reached by the early 'seventies, when it employed nearly 7,000 workers. When the British Association met at Newcastle in 1863 it was noted that nearly half the chemical industry of the United Kingdom was concentrated on Tyneside; but in that same year Solvay began the ammonia process of alkali manufacture, and the British alkali trade was never again so prosperous.

Glass making, which employed more than 4,000 workers on Tyneside and Wearside in 1871, also declined during the latter part of the century. The expansion of the new riverside industries, however, more than balanced the decline of the old industries that they replaced. Indeed, their expansion and prosperity contributed to hasten the decline of the older industries by ousting them from some of their sites. Such was the value of river-bank sites that the chemical and glass manufacturers were induced to abandon their none-too-prosperous undertakings for the high prices that shipbuilders were prepared to offer for the sites so as to extend their shipyards. At Wallsend in 1883 and later, Swan, Hunter and Co. extended by taking over Allen's Chemical Works. In 1894 Parson's Marine Steam Turbine Co. bought the derelict site of the Carrville Chemical Works. In 1902 Doxford's shipyard extended at Deptford on the Wear by buying and clearing away the chemical works that had existed on the site since 1772.

From the middle of the century more and more of the strips of level land lining the river banks of lower Tyneside were required for the needs of shipbuilding, and were taken over for shipbuilding yards, slipways, pontoons, graving docks, and marine engineering shops. These sites were partly natural terrace land, partly ballast dumps of the earlier coal trade, and partly the products of reclamation with material dredged from the river. By expansion and amalgamation great concerns such as Palmer's at Jarrow, Leslie's at Hebburn, Swan Hunter's at Wallsend, and Wigham Richardson's and Armstrong's at Walker came into being. Somewhat later the shipbuilding industry was also established above the Tyne bridge, a development rendered possible by the substitution of the swing bridge (Pl. 41) in 1876 for the low stone bridge that had previously spanned the river at Newcastle. Its construction, together with the work of the Tyne Improvement Commission in deepening the channel, allowed fuller development of the river banks above the bridge both for the shipment of coal and for industrial undertakings. Among the most notable results were the establishment of naval shipbuilding at Elswick and the construction of the Derwenthaugh and Dunston staiths.

While marine engineering accounted for a large share of the development of the engineering industries on Tyneside, other branches also showed remarkable growth. General engineering continued to expand, especially at Newcastle and Gateshead. The large locomotive works of the North Eastern Railway Co. at Gateshead employed about 2,000 in 1902, and the carriage and wagon works at Walker Gate more than 300. From its beginnings in the 'eighties electrical engineering grew with remarkable rapidity at Heaton and Hebburn (Fig. 45).

Accompanying the industrial development, population increased on Tyneside from about 200,000 at the middle of last century to three-quarters of a million by 1914. This huge additional population was accommodated mainly in terrace housing that spread over land behind the river-side industrial strip and swallowed up the earlier industrial settlements, parts of which nearest the river were replaced by works. The growth of Wallsend is typical of the extension of the shipbuilding towns of lower Tyneside. At the peak period of its growth at the turn of the century more than 1,200 houses were added in three years.

Since most of the new employment that was responsible for crowding workers on Tyneside was provided alongside the river itself, the spread of housing to north and south was limited compared with lateral extension and filling in of gaps between the individual clusters. The settlements of Tyneside coalesced into a single conurbation (Fig. 47), but a large measure of municipal independence was preserved, and nowhere in Britain has the fragmented state of local-government areas remained more out of keeping with the geographical reality that has emerged.

In this elongated conurbation strung out along the tidal estuary, outward swelling of the urban area away from the river that is its life-blood has been most pronounced around the old-established nuclei at the bridge and the river mouth. North of Tynemouth a fine stretch of sea-front and excellent communications with Newcastle have favoured dormitory and resort development at Cullercoats, Whitley Bay, and Monkseaton. On the other hand, immediately west of the river-mouth concentrations, on the south side Jarrow Slake with Tyne Dock lies opposite the coal docks and river-side shipping staiths at Whitehill Point. With their approaching railway lines, these maintained more open areas. Since 1849, when Robert Stephenson's High Level bridge was opened, just west of the old Tyne bridge, which was soon afterwards removed and replaced by the swing bridge, the connections across the river between Newcastle and Gateshead have multiplied (Fig. 26 and Pl. 41); but even now the bridges remain concentrated within a stretch of three-quarters of a mile, and there is none below Newcastle.

Newcastle took the railway to its very heart, and in the capital of the region that gave it birth the railway has claimed primacy of place in a way that is exceptional in old cities. Railways were built alongside the castle, traversing the oldest part of the city between the line of the Roman Wall and the river (Fig. 26). Here elevated tracks of road and railway bridge approaches now occupy most of the area and enmesh the old Norman keep (Pl. 41). The construction of the great Central Station (1850), immediately to the west, involved demolishing part of the west wall. The great fire of 1854 conveniently cleared much of the property in the especially congested area of steep, narrow ' chares ' that climb the river bank above the quayside, where the river-side wall had been removed a century earlier. As trade has grown the quay has been extended east for about a mile and a half below the bridges, till it stretches beyond the mouth of the Ouse burn (Fig. 45). Farther north connections between central Newcastle and its growing industrial annexes to the east, across the denes of the Pandon and Ouse burns, were greatly improved in the 'eighties by the construction of New Bridge Street.

The smaller concentration of population at the mouth of the Wear grew from 70,000 in 1851 to 170,000 in 1911. Neither the causes of this growth nor the form it took were complex. An almost uninterrupted expansion of the coal trade and of shipbuilding and associated industries was accompanied by a compact swelling of the urban area (Fig. 49). This was chiefly to the southwest, within easy access of the riverside works, and in the process the village of Bishopwearmouth was engulfed (Pl. 37). More shipyards on the north bank were responsible for the growth of Southwick as an industrial annexe, but Monkwearmouth colliery separated it from the main urban area, and it was not incorporated within the borough until after the First World War.

For both the Tyneside and Wearside conurbations the great period of growth lay between 1850 and 1914, and this is clearly reflected by the drab uniformity of the major extensions of the urban areas that belong to this period of high-density terrace building in brick and slate.

At Blyth and Seaton Sluice the old salt and chemical industries hardly lingered into the nineteenth century, and by 1850 the development of railways in southeast Northumberland, in particular the Blyth and Tyne Railway, had allowed the Tyne to invade the hinterlands of their unimproved ports. Seaton Sluice ceased to exist as a port, but at Blyth some improvements were undertaken after 1854 by the Blyth Harbour Company. They proved quite inadequate once steam colliers were introduced, and the increased shipments were not maintained. The major development of Blyth awaited the setting up of the Blyth Harbour Commission in 1882. Improvement of the entry was undertaken by the construction of piers, a new channel was dredged and by successive stages the accommodation and equipment of the port were extended to enable it to share in the growing steam-coal trade from the Northumberland pits. Shipments increased rapidly from 150,000 tons in 1883 to 4,730,000 tons in 1913, and the development of local marine industries was also stimulated. But employment at local collieries continued to contribute significantly to the growth of the amalgam of settlements that came to be incorporated as the borough of Blyth.

After 1850 Tees-side experienced an industrial expansion of a suddenness and magnitude as great as any in British industrial history. It began when, immediately after the discovery of ironstone at Eston, blast-furnaces were set up on the Tees to smelt the local ore with coking-coal from Durham. The Tees had previously been importing pig-iron from Scotland, but the tables were turned at once, and the riverside location of the blast-furnaces greatly facilitated the distribution of pig-iron. Already by 1855 there were 35 furnaces in the district, and production of pig-iron that year exceeded 80,000 tons. The chief concentrations of blast-furnaces sprang up in the river-peninsula between Middlesbrough dock and Newport, and along the line of the railway east of Middlesbrough (Fig. 39), on flat land close to supplies of ore and already in contact with supplies of coal and limestone by means of the railway. At Middlesbrough the tract between the railway and the river was occupied by the industrial works and the pre-1850 town, so that the new town extended south of the railway towards Linthorpe over the plain of glacial clay (Fig. 51). Beyond its advancing front of buildings, the surface of the plain was pitted with numerous brick-fields that provided the material with which the town was being built. To the east, separated from the main urban mass by the alluvial valley of a tributary (Ormesby) beck, which was followed by the Guisborough Railway (1852), a succession of satellites sprang up along the Redcar Railway (Pl. 38). Such were North Ormesby, South Bank, and Grangetown, all dependent on iron works. Whereas the works extended over reclaimed foreshore to the north of the railway, the housing spread south of the railway line on the slightly higher, firmer ground of the drift plain (Fig. 53a).

So rapid was the increase of population that, within ten years of the establishment of the iron industry, the population of Middlesbrough had overtaken that of the Stockton-Thornaby group, from which it remained physically separated by the open marshy tract of the old meander loops. Between 1860 and 1880, however, the industrial expansion of Tees-side was shared almost equally between the two groups. Following in the wake of iron smelting, large numbers of puddling furnaces were set up, especially after 1860. Between 1864 and 1872 they increased in number from fewer than 200 to more than 1,000, and in the latter year Tees-side supplied more than one-third of the country's wrought iron. Most of this large output was iron rails. There were also many foundries, which, like the puddling furnaces, were established along the railways. Although waterside sites gave an added advantage for engaging in the export trade and for coastwise distribution of products, the iron industry was not limited to such sites during this period, as all its raw materials were received by rail. There were outlying units on the railways some distance to the north and west, at Darlington, Norton, and Carlton ironworks (Fig. 39), and the Stockton-Thornaby area was quite as important as Middlesbrough. Using materials provided by the primary industries, engineering shops and shipbuilding yards also grew at both centres.

The demands of the growing iron industry were at first met entirely by expansion in local ore production, which proceeded apace as the ironstone field was feverishly opened up to feed the Tees-side furnaces. By 1856 the annual output of local Cleveland ore had reached a million tons. The number of mines was increasing every year, and railway companies vied with each other in providing the necessary transport facilities to handle the lucrative freight. The first workings had been along the outcrop of the Main seam on the northern outliers at Eston, Normanby, and Upleatham, and on the main escarpment south of Guisborough (Fig. 6). But shaft mining soon became necessary as the most easily accessible tracts were developed, and by the 'seventies shaft mining was being extensively carried on in the basin of deeply buried ore between Guisborough and the coast (Figs. 6, 53). Nearly 10,000 miners were employed at about 40 mines. By 1880, when the production had reached 6 million tons per annum, the Skelton-Loftus area had become the main centre of mining, although the Eston and Upleatham mines were still the most important individual workings. New settlements, unrelated to the older villages of the area, sprang up as the mining was extended southeastwards (Fig. 54). Mangrove Park, Boosbeck, New Skelton, North Skelton, and Lingdale all appeared at this time. At the same time the mining industry swelled the population of communities such as Guisborough, Loftus, and Eston. The total population of the mining district, which in 1850 had been less than 7,000, reached 30,000 by 1881, a figure within 5,000 of the maximum recorded at the 1921 Census, and larger than the present population of the district.

Steel production began on Tees-side in 1876, and by 1880 steel was ousting wrought iron, and the import of high-grade foreign ores was becoming important. The growing ascendancy of steel over iron and the increasing use of imported ore were the outstanding features of the subsequent period up to the outbreak of the First World War. The 'seventies had already seen the victory of the steel rail, and between 1872 and 1878 the number of puddling furnaces on Tees-side was reduced by half. In 1872 300,000 tons of rails were turned out in a total output of wrought iron that amounted to 640,000 tons. In 1878 the corresponding figures had fallen to less than 7,000 and 300,000 tons respectively, and by 1903 wrought-iron output was only 119,000 tons. Although production of wrought iron declined, and that of pig-iron failed to show any significant further increase, the production of steel was greatly expanded. From an average of 316,000 tons per annum in the early 'eighties it had risen to an average of 1,632,000 tons between 1906 and 1910. Production of local ore reached its peak of $6\frac{3}{4}$ million tons in the early 'eighties, but thereafter fell off as supplies were steadily exhausted. On the other hand, consumption of foreign ore increased rapidly in its place. Not until 1877 did imports exceed 100,000 tons, but by 1893 they were more than a million tons, and in 1913 exceeded two million tons, a figure again reached in 1936 and 1937. That was an amount greater than the production of Cleveland, and very much greater in terms of metal content.

The increased rôle of imported ore made the advantage of tidewater sites for the blast-furnaces more and more decisive. When new furnaces were set up, sites were chosen in immediate proximity to the water-front, with facilities for unloading ore at jetties. The inland works, at a serious disadvantage, progressively dropped out of production as their plant became obsolete. An outlying smelting centre at Skinningrove, close to the remaining ore mines, has survived to the present (Fig. 54 and Pl. 35).

Another expanding industry, which by its nature was even more definitely tied to the river, was shipbuilding. The output of the ship-yards varied much from year to year, but over the sixty years before 1914 showed a very substantial increase. During this period employment in the shipyards on the Northeast Coast increased from 5,000 to nearly 50,000. Salt production was another new feature of the economy of Tees-side that appeared during this period. It began in 1875, but was still only 3,000 tons in 1883. By the middle 'nineties, however, over 300,000 tons were being produced. Between 80 and 85 per cent of this was derived from brine wells located on the north shore of the estuary, and the remainder from Middlesbrough and the south shore farther east (Fig. 6). Most of it (200,000 tons) was exported, and chemical industries remained undeveloped. By 1900 salt production had diminished considerably, and from then until 1914 oscillated at about 200,000 tons per annum, about half of which was exported.

Thus the lion's share of the late nineteenth- and early twentieth-century expansion of Tees-side industry went to Middlesbrough and its satellites on the estuary to the east, and while the relative proportions of the Tees-side population in the Stockton-Thornaby and Middlesbrough groups had remained constant and approximately equal between the 1861 and 1881 Censuses, thereafter Middlesbrough's share increased to 60 per cent in 1911, while that of Stockton-Thornaby fell to 32 per cent.

The Hartlepools and Darlington, each about eleven miles distant from Stockton, derived advantages from their proximity to the great developments alike on the coalfield and on Tees-side, but retained their distinctiveness and independent character.

The Hartlepools grew rapidly as a port for the coalfield, as their equipment for handling coal and timber was augmented and as the southeastern corner of the coalfield was opened up by deep mines. West Hartlepool grew also as an industrial outlier of Tees-side, with iron and steel works as well as ship-building and -repairing and marine engineering industries. The scope for urban expansion on the flat land behind and south of the dock at West Hartlepool, as compared with the cramped peninsular site of old Hartlepool, enabled the new town rapidly to become much the larger element of the conurbation (Fig. 50). In 1831 there were the settlements of old Hartlepool, with 1,400 people, on the headland, and the village of Stranton, with fewer than 400 inhabitants, clustered round an open green. Seventy years later more than 20,000 were crowded into the Hartlepool peninsula, and more than 60,000 in the new town of West Hartlepool, which had engulfed the village of Stranton.

Darlington, though never a port, was already a prosperous town of 5,000 inhabitants at the beginning of the nineteenth century (Fig. 52). It retained its importance as an agricultural market and service centre in the vale of Tees, but changed its industrial character. Its old linen industry, with outwork in the surrounding rural area, faded out, but the wealth of its Quaker families was applied to new enterprises. In particular it became a railway town. The linen industry was in a depressed condition by 1830, but already its new character was taking shape as headquarters of the Stockton and Darlington Railway, the first public railway. As new lines were opened in quick succession, it became a hub in the developing railway system of the northeast, and when the North Eastern Railway Company emerged in the 'fifties and 'sixties by amalgamation of earlier independent railways, Darlington, on its main line, became firmly established as one of the major railway centres of the country. A large body of workers, employed both in operating and maintaining the company's system and in its local engineering works, gathered in the growing town. The population, which had already reached 12,000 by 1851 in spite of the decline of linen manufacture, trebled in the next thirty years, and thereafter continued to grow steadily.

Outside the Northeast Coast the manifestations of nineteenth-century industrialisation and urbanisation, with few exceptions, have been local and sporadic. In their occurrence they, too, have been especially related to minerals and railways.

West Cumberland

In West Cumberland, for some time after 1800 increased production and shipment of coal was achieved by colliery development in the immediate vicinity of the ports. Following the unsuccessful attempts in the latter part of the eighteenth century to establish iron smelting, no more was done for some time. Ore from Cleator Moor was shipped to Scotland for the Carron ironworks, and about 1825 South Wales ironmasters took out leases in the ore field ; but large-scale development really began only after 1840. Blast-furnaces were then set up locally (Fig. 34), but the local coal made such poor coke that for some time longer most of the rapidly increasing output of ore was shipped away. It went chiefly to South Wales, with smaller quantities to Staffordshire and Scotland, though some was sent east by rail to Tyneside. The first trans-Pennine railway, from Newcastle to Carlisle, had been built in 1838. In the early 'forties the Maryport–Carlisle railway was built, and in 1847 it was extended to Whitehaven. Durham coke thus became available for West Cumberland ironworks, and Cleator Moor ore could be sent to the Durham coalfield. The invention of the Bessemer process of steel making greatly increased demand for the specially suitable West Coast haematite and stimulated improvement of railway connections with the Northeast Coast. Reciprocal traffic was greatly increased by construction of the South Durham–Furness Railway (1861) across Stainmore to Tebay Junction, built specifically for this purpose. The Furness deposits had meantime been developed, following the construction of the Furness Railway and creation of the port of Barrow. By 1860 this railway had been extended to the Lancaster and Carlisle Railway, the Park ore mine had been opened, and both ironworks and shipbuilding yards had been established at Barrow, which was growing as rapidly as contemporary Middlesbrough. An increasing quantity of West Coast ore was smelted locally, especially when Durham coke became more readily available. By 1870 the proportion smelted locally was more than half, and in the next few years there was considerable expansion of local smelting capacity and an increasing demand from the local shipyards. During the 'seventies several new furnaces came into blast in Cumberland (Fig. 34), some at Workington and other established centres, but others at Maryport, Whitehaven, and Millom, where the famous Hodbarrow ' flat ' deposit had been discovered in 1863. Ore production in the Cleator Moor-Egremont area reached its peak in 1870, when thirty mines were working. Continued development at Hodbarrow staved off decline in the Cumbrian production of ore until the middle 'eighties, but by then miners were emigrating in considerable numbers from the northern area.

The unsuitability of the local coal for coking restricted the stimulus that iron smelting could give to local coal mining, but the secondary metal-working industries, including shipbuilding, took increasing quantities of coal, and as the ports were improved to handle the traffic larger quantities were shipped away. The introduction of the method of longwall working after 1870 was an important factor, for it made possible the exploitation of a bigger range of thin seams below the Main seam. Railways had prepared the way for more intensive development of the inland margins of the coalfield, including the northeastward extension from Maryport, and new mining settlements sprang up. The chief pits, however, remained along the coast, where a considerable proportion of the output was actually won from under the sea (Fig. 4). Coal production had exceeded one million tons per annum before 1860, and by the end of the century it was more than two million tons. Employment in mining increased from between 3,000 and 4,000 to more than 8,000, and mining settlements spread in straggling fashion over the coalfield and the adjacent ore-field. The chief concentrations of miners, as of other industrial workers, were in the three ports. Whitehaven, Workington, and Maryport were mining and iron-smelting towns as well as ports. Already in 1801 more than half the 30,000 inhabitants of West Cumberland lived in these three towns,[1] and the total population increased to more than 50,000 by 1851, and more than 100,000 by 1901. Since then the total has remained fairly stationary, slight growth in the three main centres having been offset by considerable migration from the derelict ore-mining settlements. Although the ports were shipbuilding centres, too, and Maryport and Workington had considerable tanning industries during most of the nineteenth century, the industrial prosperity of the area was narrowly based upon coal, iron-ore, and iron smelting.

At Carlisle the coming of the railways in and after 1838 opened a new phase in the growth of the old Border city. It thenceforward assumed its modern rôle as a great railway centre, while market and other service functions for an extending area were increasingly concentrated in it. Although the handloom weaving that had provided the livelihood of many of its inhabitants at the beginning of the nineteenth century quickly disappeared, Carlisle continued to be an outlying centre of cotton manufacture and its industrial basis was widened by new developments. The subsequent increase of population, from 20,000 to 70,000, has been accommodated entirely by outward spread of the built-up area (Fig. 57).

Between Carlisle and Newcastle the Tyne Corridor, traversed by a railway (1838) from the very outset of the railway period and itself possessing some coal and other mineral resources, was able to experience a considerable measure of industrial development and with it the appearance of urban, or at least industrial, settlement.

In the Pennine dales and also, though not on so great a scale, in

---

[1] In 1801 Whitehaven with nearly 9,000 inhabitants was the largest, followed by Workington (5,700) and Maryport (3,000), but it was outstripped by Workington during the latter half of the century, as Workington became the chief iron-smelting centre. In 1901 Workington had 26,000, Whitehaven barely 20,000, and Maryport 12,000.

the Lake District, the last phase of vigorous activity in lead mining was at its height about the middle of the century. The occupation tables of the 1851 Census enumerated nearly 4,000 miners in the dales and another 400 workers were employed in smelting and other associated occupations. The old copper mine at Coniston also enjoyed a last outburst of activity, employing between 500 and 600 workmen and producing between 3,000 and 4,000 tons of ore per annum during the eighteen-fifties; the old lead mines of the Keswick district were also revived for a period, but the newer Greenside mine on the east side of Helvellyn became the chief lead mine and employed 300 in 1860 (Fig. 28).[1] By this time the Borrowdale wad mine, which had reached the peak period of its activity in the early years of the century, was already moribund, having begun to fail after 1833. The Coniston mine declined after 1874, and was finally abandoned in 1889, and although some of the lead mines have worked intermittently since then, both in the Lake District and the northern Pennines ore mining has declined since the eighteen-seventies to the point of virtual extinction, leaving its scars in the landscape, a modified farming economy, and a residual population.

The irregular working of coal seams on a small scale for local use, unsuccessful attempts to develop mining on a larger scale in North Tynedale at Plashetts (Fig. 59), and extensive, but shortlived working of iron ore about the middle of the century in Redesdale, were all responsible for marked oscillations in the population of some parishes during the course of the nineteenth century.

With modern industry represented only by scattered mining and quarrying operations, urban development has been restricted to the market towns, some though not all of which have assumed increasing importance as service centres. As such they have experienced modest growth, though the industries that arose from the farming of their surroundings and employed large proportions of their inhabitants in the early nineteenth century have since declined to the point of extinction. The rural countryside has also been denuded of the domestic industries that flourished, but after a period of depression that followed the end of the Napoleonic Wars farming continued to prosper until the eighteen-seventies. Nor did it subsequently experience the same degree of depression as affected corn-growing counties. The rural areas have since been increasingly affected by the needs of the nearby urban populations for food, water, and recreation. They have felt the impact in other ways, too. Their surplus population has been drained off into urban and industrial employment, but the movement has not remained entirely in one direction. In the population of the

[1] It was then producing about 900 tons of ore per annum.

rural areas an adventitious element has appeared, no longer confined to the monied classes as they acquired country estates, but coming to include workers settling in retirement or commuting daily to their urban employment. Catering for holiday-makers has now become the mainstay of the Lake District. Earlier attempts to develop spa resorts, for example Gilsland and Croft, met with little success, but some of the dale centres and a few places on the coasts have felt the benefits of the tourist trade in considerable degree.

These developments have been very uneven in their incidence over the rural areas, and still more does this apply to the modern large-scale quarrying operations that cater for the needs of the industrial centres for raw materials such as flux. The scenes of such developments have been governed by the occurrence of the required materials in accessible situations, and here again the railway system provided during the nineteenth century is fundamental to an interpretation of the distribution of the new features.

More detailed reference to changes in those parts of North England that lie outside the major tracts of industrial transformation may conveniently be left to the succeeding chapters in which the present-day character of its constituent regions is considered.

THE INDUSTRIAL AREAS

CHAPTER 11

THE NORTHEAST COAST—I

THE economic core of North England is the mining and industrial area known as the Northeast Coast. It is aptly named, for it extends along more than 70 miles of the North Sea coast from a little north of Whitby to the mouth of the Coquet at Amble (Fig. 41). Where the coalfield is widest, in southwest Durham, its western border is only about 30 miles from the sea, and, thanks to the penetration of tidewater up the re-entrant estuaries, the most distant collieries are little more than 20 miles from shipping points. The major urban and industrial development is concentrated on the banks of the estuaries; among individual towns with more than 50,000 inhabitants only Darlington is neither a port nor on the coalfield.

This coastal area, rendered distinctive by the presence of intense mining and industrial activity and concomitant dense settlement, consists of the geographically distinct though juxtaposed or closely connected regions of coalfield, Tees-side, ironstone field, and Darlington. The coalfield, largest of these constituent elements, is far from uniform. Within its area of 900 square miles there are considerable physical differences, and despite the heavy overlay of mining and industry, persisting agricultural differences. Besides these elements of diversity, there are others that have now assumed major importance. They depend upon the age, intensity, and texture of the industrial occupance. Others again concern the employment structure, current trends and future prospects, and the orientation of social and economic relations of different portions. Many individual characteristics contribute in important ways to the geographical differentiation of the coalfield, which could be variously divided on the basis of homogeneity in respect of each of several aspects. But the complex associations of numerous elements, which are themselves in varying degrees discrete and which display different distributional systems, means that reality would be distorted by presentation within the necessarily arbitrary frame of a division that properly applies to only one aspect of the geography. Perhaps the most general and far-reaching distinction within the coalfield area, however, arises from the development of the industrial port-conurbations. They are especially distinctive tracts where the scale and completeness of urbanisation, as well as its bases, differ from those which obtain elsewhere in what are still essentially mining districts. Other differences within the coalfield are real enough, but their bases do not all make concordant patterns, while those that do are not by any means coincident.

Mining does not everywhere extend to the western edge of the coalfield as this is shown on the official geological map. Beneath the Brockwell seam the lower Coal Measures form a narrow marginal out-crop of practically barren strata (Fig. 41). Only in part of Durham, between Consett and Tow Law, is the zone more than a mile or two wide, but in Northumberland the edge of the mining area also lies appreciably east of the coalfield margin. North of the river Blyth, indeed, there are few collieries west of the main railway line.

Elsewhere the manifestations of mining and industry are ubiquitous features of the scene, though they do not occupy the whole terrain. Most of the countryside in fact is still farmed. Farmland has been seriously encroached upon by buildings and spoil heaps, farm units have been disrupted, and the farm economy is throughout dominated now by the needs of the industrial communities. Yet many features of the agricultural countryside and its rural settlement pattern that belong to an earlier age show through the texture of the heavy, but not uniformly heavy, overlay.

The emphasis of the farming throughout is now upon dairying. Nearly all farms maintain a dairy herd, the local breed of Shorthorns being by far the most popular, and many farmers are producer-retailers of milk. Those farms that are not mainly concerned with milk pro-duction are grazing farms which buy store cattle in spring to fatten during the summer. Some also maintain a flock of cross-bred sheep. Most farms keep pigs and practically all keep poultry.

The drift soils vary in origin and texture, and the chief regional contrasts related to this are in the proportion of arable land. This is greatest on the light soils of outwash sand and gravel, and on the light brashy soils of the western part of the east Durham plateau ; but it is still considerable on the heavy clay-loams with boulder-clay subsoils in the coastal tracts of Northumberland and east Durham. Indeed, except in the higher western districts of the Durham coalfield, all farms have some ploughed fields. A basic four-course rotation of roots, corn, seeds, and corn is practised. Of corn crops oats is the most generally grown, and wheat is usually represented, but barley seldom. Swedes are the principal root-crop, and nearly all farms grow some potatoes. In the chief arable tracts the farms sell considerable quantities of corn and chipping potatoes. There are practically no orchards and few market-gardens. Considerable quantities of vegetables, however,

189

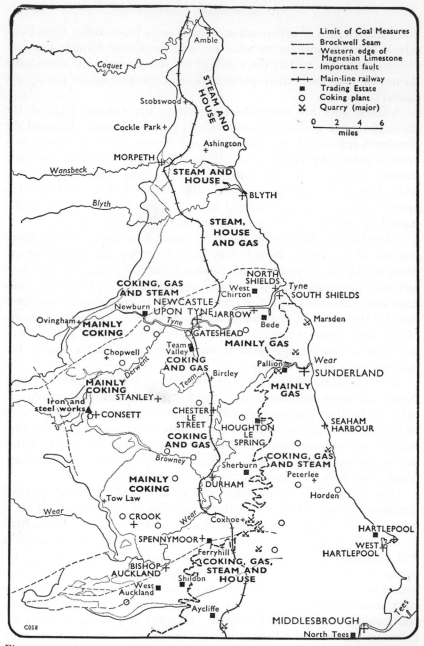

Fig. 41 THE NORTHUMBERLAND AND DURHAM COALFIELD. The principal types of coal produced in different districts are indicated. Apart from regional variation, different seams in a given locality may vary.

are produced locally on the allotments that are a common feature of the colliery settlements. In the past the miners were extensively engaged in pig-keeping. Some poultry are still kept, but the unkempt sheds 'crees' among the allotments and near the colliery rows (Pl. 29) are especially associated with the miners' hobbies of pigeon fancying and whippet racing. During the inter-war period of depression poultry keeping and vegetable production were fostered by schemes of small-holdings, especially in southwest Durham.

Medium or small farms are usual, and the stone byres that are notable features of all the farmsteads emphasise the importance of cattle. The traditional importance of corn is still reflected in the survival of several gin-houses, circular stone outbuildings where corn was formerly threshed by a horse-gin. Whereas in the dales stone walls divide the fields, on the coalfield as in other lowland districts the fields are enclosed chiefly by hawthorn hedges. Little woodland survives in the landscape. There are fragmentary strips of mixed deciduous woodland along the steep sides of the deep-cut denes, where relics of forges are found along some of the streams. Small plantations of conifers, interspersed with rough grazing as well as with farmland, fleck the hills of the western part of the Durham coalfield, and larger blocks are now maintained by the Forestry Commission, especially in the Derwent valley around Chopwell. Farther east, except for a certain amount of park timber around some country mansions, the landscape is singularly bare of trees, its scanty woodland hidden in the Wear valley and in the denes of the east Durham plateau.

Within the coalfield both the intensity of urbanisation and its character vary. Along the banks of the Tyne from its mouth to beyond the bridge-head nucleus at Newcastle-Gateshead and reaching almost to the western edge of the coalfield at Ovingham, the riparian settlements have now coalesced to form one of the seven major conurbations of Britain, containing nearly 900,000 people (Fig. 47). Only slightly separate, a few miles to the southeast, at the mouth of the Wear, is a compact, smaller conurbation of another 180,000 inhabitants (Fig. 49). In the extreme southeastern corner of the coalfield, the Hartlepools are another port-conurbation with a population of 90,000 (Fig. 50).

The other individual nuclei are much smaller. They include old-established urban centres such as Durham, Bishop Auckland, Chester-le-Street, and Morpeth, that have grown with accretions of mining settlement and enhancement of their functions as service centres. There are also minor and highly specialised ports—Blyth and Seaham Harbour. Until very recently, apart from a few ironworks, industry other than mining was almost entirely concentrated in the ports. But the mining settlement itself differs in texture, reflecting the differing course of mining colonisation and development.

Some of the oldest mining settlements on upper Tyneside have been swallowed up in the modern conurbation, as have others that date from the eastward shift of mining to the deeper basin of coal on lower Tyneside at the end of the eighteenth and beginning of the nineteenth centuries. In some parts of northwest Durham and along the middle Wear, however, where the history of mining presents a long and changing pattern of activity, this is reflected in a highly complex accumulation of landscape features.

In those districts, notably northwest Durham and Northumberland, where outcropping or shallow seams were exploited relatively early and by a large number of pits, many of them shortlived, a straggling, sprawling settlement pattern has resulted (Fig. 42a). In contrast, the colliery settlements of east Durham are compact, distinct, and more widely spaced (Fig. 42b). They are associated with large, deep collieries that work extensive areas from a single pit-head. Large, concentrated settlements, however, are not confined to east Durham. The later phases of mining development have produced them in some other parts of the coalfield, for example at Ashington (Fig. 42c) and in northwest Durham, where they have been added to the earlier, scattered settlements. Such large-scale enterprises, however, have never affected some localities near the western edge of the coalfield. Small, shallow pits and drift workings remain characteristic, and mining has often simply multiplied the units of an essentially dispersed pattern of settlement (Fig. 42d).

In some places miners' rows have been added to the old villages, which in time have been enveloped and transformed; in others the two may persist side by side. On the high ground of northwest Durham the older settlement consisted of hamlets and scattered farmsteads, rather than villages, and the agricultural colonisation hardly preceded that brought about by mining. The earliest grouped settlements were confined to the valleys, but mining settlement shows no such limitation of siting. On the contrary, the high ground that rises between the valleys offered the most complete range of coal seams and the greatest resources of buried wealth, and some of the chief scenes of revived mining activity and the largest concentrations of mining settlement now crown bleak tracts of summit plateau towards a height of 1,000 feet. In the lowlying coastal plain, on the other hand, the older

Fig. 42 (*Opposite*) TYPES OF SETTLEMENT PATTERN IN THE NORTHUMBERLAND AND DURHAM COALFIELD. (*a*) The Stanley district in northwest Durham. (*b*) The Easington-Horden district in southeast Durham. (*c*) The Ashington district in Northumberland. (*d*) The Gaunless valley district in southwest Durham.

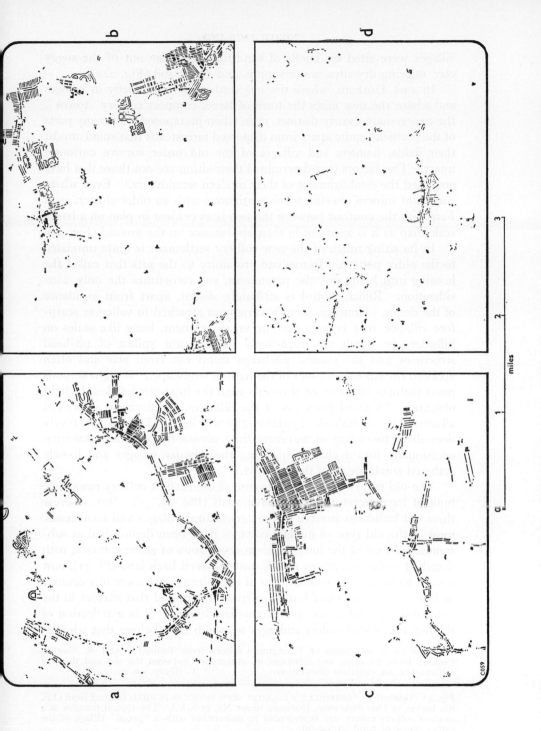

villages were sited on knolls of sandstone that rise out of the soggy clay, offering dry sites, water supply, and arable soil (Fig. 22*a*).

In east Durham, where the old settlement was chiefly in villages and where the new takes the form of large, compact colliery ' towns ', the two remain clearly distinct, even when juxtaposed. In many parts of the coalfield, quite apart from dispersed farmsteads that stand amidst their fields, hamlets and villages of the old order survive curiously intact. The factors that determined their siting are not those that have governed the establishment of their modern neighbours.[1] Even where masses of miners' dwellings are contiguous with an older cluster, as at Ferryhill, the contrast between the two is as evident in plan on a large-scale map as it is apparent in their appearance on the ground (Fig. 43).

In its siting much of the new colliery settlement is quite unrelated to the older pattern. Immediate proximity to the pits that called the housing into being was the paramount, and sometimes the only, consideration. Relief control is strikingly absent, apart from avoidance of the denes. Housing, though sometimes attached to valley or scarp-foot villages, may equally hachure an escarpment, hang like scales on hillsides, or perch on ridge-tops. The gaunt spikes of pit-head structures and the conical pit-heaps stand out from afar and often accident the smooth outlines of the natural landscape.. If night shrouds many features of the scene it reveals what the intricate detail of daylight obscures. ' Viewed from any of the hillsides, the darkness is pricked all around with hundreds of twinkling pins of light. They look strangely dreamlike, threading in wavering lines across the darkness, knotting occasionally into a cluster, mapping the angular villages and loosely gathered small towns of the coalfield.' [2]

The old rural settlement and some of the earliest colliery rows were built of local freestone with pantile roofs (Pls. 23, 31). But, whereas these old buildings survive in the agricultural villages and farmsteads, most of the old type of miners' cottages have been demolished as substandard. Few of the low, single-storeyed rows of stone cottages, with detached outhouses across a wide and unpaved back lane (Pl. 31), now remain to show the characteristics of the mining settlement of a century or more ago. The chief buildings from this period that survive in the older mining settlements are Methodist chapels. It is a reflection of the different social orders and ages to which they belong that whereas

[1] The clear separation of Easington Colliery from Easington and of Shotton Colliery from Shotton, and contrasts in appearance between the old and the new settlements, are excellent illustrations.   [2] T. Sharp, *op. cit.* p. 17.

Fig. 43 (*Opposite*) FERRYHILL: A COLLIERY SETTLEMENT IN DURHAM (extract from O.S. Six Inches to One Mile map, Durham, Sheet NZ 23 S.E.). The typical features of a modern colliery colony are represented in association with a ' green ' village of the earlier phase of rural settlement.

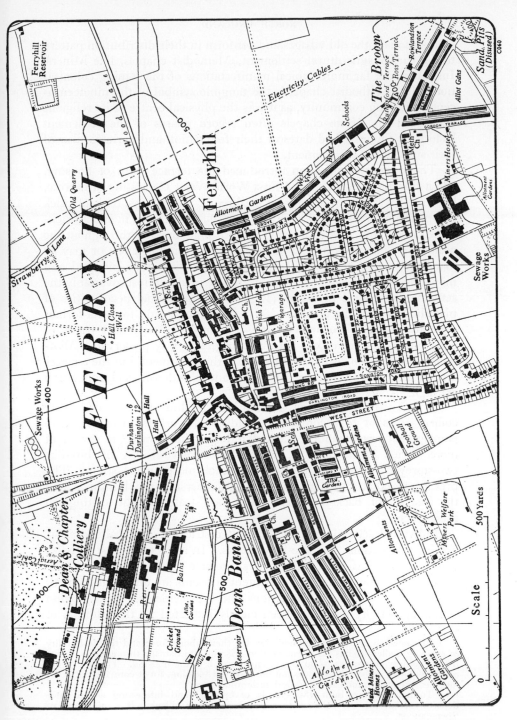

FERRYHILL

Ferryhill Reservoir

Wood Lane

Old Quarry

Strawberry Lane

Electricity Cables

The Broom

Lumford Terrace
Ross Terrace
Rowlandson Terrace

Sand. Pits (Disused)

Gordon Terrace

Allot Gdns

Schools

Brad. Ter.

Miners Houses

Meth. Ch.

Allotment Gardens

Allotment Gardens

Sewage Works

Hall Close Well

Hall

Sewage Works 400

Durham..6
Darlington 12

Parish Hall

Vicarage

Ch.

WEST STREET

Football Ground

Allotment Gardens

DARLINGTON ROAD

Allot. Gardens

Dean & Chapter Colliery

Baths

Allot. Gardens

Dean Bank

Reservoir

Cricket Ground

Low Hill House

Ch.

Aged Miners Homes

Allotment Gardens

Allotments

Miners Welfare Park

Allotment Gardens

Scale

500 Yards

churches mark the old villages and conform in their distribution pattern to the earlier agricultural settlement, Methodist chapels, like Miners' Institutes, are far more typical manifestations of the mining colonisation. The Methodist chapel is the tangible symbol of the nineteenth-century mining community, as it was the physical centre of its religious and social life. The chapels often record phases of the settlement history by the inscribed dates of their foundation and perhaps also of their subsequent enlargement.

The mining colonisation introduced the terrace form of housing, and it prevailed until after the First World War. Consisting of narrow, but usually two-storeyed cottages of three or four rooms, built of brick and roofed with slate, and with their outhouses enclosed in small brick-walled backyards, terrace housing (Pl. 30) predominates throughout the coalfield.[1] The rows may straggle along old country-lanes, or may be marshalled in serried ranks beneath the overshadowing pit-head and mountainous spoil-heap (Pl. 28). Large or small, almost invariably the settlement is ragged in outline (Fig. 42), its individual peculiarities of plan the result of the conditions of acquisition of land from its former agricultural use. The irregularities of outline often reflect traces of earlier field-patterns or old lanes with rights of way preserved. Allotments are common, as blocks attached to the settlement, but the terraces are not interspersed with garden space, and plot densities of population are high.

Since 1919 large tracts of Council housing, built to replace obsolete colliery rows or to accommodate additional workers in areas where employment has expanded, have abandoned the terrace [2] in favour of more varied estate layouts, where the small groups of box-like two-storeyed houses are arranged in much more open fashion. The prevalence of attached garden-plots interspersing the buildings and the absence of back-yards are other new features that distinguish these tracts.

Individual settlements and different districts of the coalfield show varying proportions of these ingredients. In areas of longest activity, where mining has passed through successive cycles, not only is the pattern most amorphous, its constituent elements are often most varied, the products of successive additions and replacements. Rejuvenation of mining activity has often been clearly indicated by the addition of

[1] The need to provide accommodation for their labour force and the desirability of avoiding endless claims for compensation arising from damage through subsidence led the colliery companies to build or acquire much of the housing. The institution of the rent-free colliery house was not an unmixed blessing, for it contributed to the long persistence of much sub-standard accommodation.

[2] Tudhoe Grange, built 1865–70, is exceptional and interesting as an early departure from the terrace form in a planned mining village. It is now part of Spennymoor.

what are obviously later accretions of different construction and layout alongside the older part of the settlement. Settlements of more recent origin, especially if they were the product of a sudden burst of large-scale activity, display more homogeneous as well as more compact housing (Pl. 28). Their buildings are architecturally uniform and have been planned and built *en masse*. The colliery settlements often consist well-nigh exclusively of housing. Their other buildings rarely consist of more than a few food shops, typically including a co-operative store, some public houses, schools, one or two chapels, and perhaps an assembly hall or institute.

The larger concentrations in the texture of the coalfield settlement have become, by virtue of size or nodality, fairly important shopping and entertainment centres, and now show the pretentious façades of multiple stores and cinemas. As mentioned earlier, some are the enlarged nuclei of old-established centres, but others are entirely the creation of the mining and industrial colonisation. Among such, Consett and Stanley are major examples, while Crook, Houghton le Spring, and Spennymoor are others of less well-developed status. Centralised institutions, such as secondary schools and hospitals, show less relations in their locations to the focal points of the economic life than in other parts of the country where settlement is more nucleated or sparser. Here the foci of social services correspond less consistently with those of economic services. A remarkably close network of bus routes, with frequent services, links the coalfield communities with each other and with the great port-cities, and the various currents of regular movement that are represented by journeys to work, to school, and for shopping and entertainment present complex patterns of criss-crossing associations. Instead of highly crystallised all-purpose foci and clearly defined fields, the pattern of major centres is interspersed with numerous auxiliary or specialised centres, and there is complicated overlapping of spheres of influence.

In the heart of the coalfield the ancient city of Durham is the most striking reminder of the earlier phases of the life of the county palatine, but it is now encased by the accretions of the nineteenth and twentieth centuries, when a new economy and society has transformed the old order.

The original nucleus, sited on a meander core of the Wear, survives as a peaceful enclave, the ecclesiastical and university quarter (Fig. 44 and Pl. 46). Immediately to the north, just outside the line of the wall that spanned the neck of the peninsula, old and new Durham meet in the market square. From here the modern town straggles out along the Sunderland road and sprawls across the bridge beyond the old borough of Elvet; but especially does it extend west, beyond the old

Framwellgate bridge, where the main railway station is situated, and farther, to the modern diversion of the Great North Road that by-passes the city through Neville's Cross. Even so, the outward spread has been modest. The population is still less than 20,000, compared with 4,000

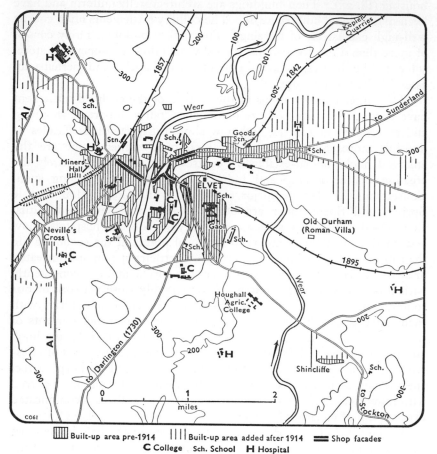

Fig. 44   DURHAM: THE MODERN CITY (cf. Peakes, 40 and 46).

in 1801. The population of the county has increased tenfold in the intervening period, and Durham city is now less populous than several of the mining towns.

Its special functions relate to its administrative importance as the county centre. It is the headquarters both of county government and of numerous other county organisations, such as the Miners' Union, that have been attracted by its central position and established status. It is an important educational and medical centre, but for shopping and entertainment it serves a somewhat limited area. Its immediate environs are one of the portions of the coalfield where mining activity is less intense. Quite apart from restriction of its influence by the greater facilities offered near at hand by Newcastle, Sunderland, Darlington, and Stockton, neighbouring mining towns such as Chester-le-Street, Bishop Auckland, and Stanley command within their immediate vicinity larger concentrations of population than Durham, and offer comparable shopping and entertainment facilities.

The textural differences in settlement just noted are especially responsible for the regional contrasts in the coalfield today, but other differences that also arise from the particular history of development play their part. The older mining areas are characterised by a greater density of pits, and, if they have experienced a later recrudescence of mining, there is also a greater variety of pit size represented. The scars of abandoned workings are more widespread, and there is a more complex mingling of residual and functioning features. Besides the dense network of active railways, which in all areas are an important element of the coalfield landscape, abandoned wagonways have left their trace in the form of grimy tracks, in varying degree overgrown with weeds. Some stretches are variously distinguished by their use as footpaths, by retention of their boundary fences, or, most clearly and permanently, by their embankments. Naturally they are especially typical of the old mining districts of Tyneside, northwest Durham, and the Wear near Chester-le-Street. Since 1943 extensive new disfigurements that mark the mechanised open-cast workings have appeared in the parts of the coalfield where seams outcrop.

The coking-coal area in west Durham, however, in addition to possessing the features that belong to the outcrop coalfield, has others peculiar to itself. Among these are the sites of nineteenth-century ironworks (Fig. 39) and of old beehive coke-ovens and modern by-product works. Of the ironworks only those at Consett remain active, but the others have left their marks of dereliction. Since 1900 the pit-head batteries of beehive ovens have been superseded by retort ovens and by-product works,[1] and an increasing proportion of the coking has become concentrated at the iron and steel works. Except for Consett the latter are not on the coalfield, but there are also some large coking plants on the coalfield (Fig. 41), though they are far more concentrated in location than were the old beehive ovens. They are conspicuous features, especially at night, in the coking-coal districts.

Although the type of coal changes gradually eastwards (Fig. 41) there is general correspondence of the area that produces coal of

[1] Only at Rowlands Gill in the Derwent valley are there beehive ovens still in action, but at many pits elsewhere their ruins have never been cleared away.

coking type with that of outcropping seams. Both lie west of the main south–north route, in west Durham, but the correspondence is not exact. The coal of east Durham is soft and unsuitable for metallurgical coke, but the southeast is exceptional in this respect, and at some of the large modern collieries by-product works have been established, for example at Horden. In the Northumberland coalfield, with outcropping and shallow seams, many features of west Durham, including a high density of pits, much variety of pit size, and recent open-cast workings are present, but the coal is unsuited for coking, and consequently other features that are very characteristic of west Durham are missing.

More locally the exploitation of other minerals is responsible for other distinguishing activities (Fig. 41). Valuable fireclays and ganisters that occur in the lower part of the Coal Measures are worked for the manufacture of refractory materials on the western edge of the coalfield, especially at Crook, Consett, and Stobswood (near Morpeth). Dolomite is quarried on a large scale in the Magnesian Limestone escarpment, especially near Sunderland and near Coxhoe, where it most nearly approaches the Tees-side steel works. Dolomite is also worked on the coast at Marsden and south of Seaham Harbour ; and the glacial drift is worked for building-bricks, especially at Birtley. These activities locally relieve the general dependence upon coal mining, but are nowhere as important in this respect as the large iron and steel works at Consett, descended from the Derwent Ironworks that were established there in 1840.

In important respects, the broad, simple associations that have been noted between the human geography and aspects of the geology are greatly complicated by other and quite discordant distributions. It will be remembered that access to tidewater and occurrence of good household types of coal have been shown to be as important as ease of winning coal in determining the progressive development of the coalfield (Fig. 37). Both the present trends of the mining industry and its future prospects especially reflect the past history of mining, but it is quite fallacious to conceive a progressive zonal development of the coalfield. The earliest large-scale working of coal was on upper Tyneside, but the middle Wear valley, in front of the Magnesian Limestone escarpment, was also an early scene of mining and came to the fore in the seventeenth century. Moreover, the seams here, though not deep, are not outcropping. The first sinking through the limestone in 1822 predated extension of mining over much of west Durham ; and a district west of Durham city, the part of the coalfield most remote from shipping points, was not opened up till after 1850. The most recently developed district of all, however, is the southeastern corner, and the scenes of most recent expansion and of greatest remaining reserves are here and in Northumberland north of the Wansbeck. Between the mouths of the Tyne and Wear there are also considerable reserves under the northernmost portion of the Magnesian Limestone. In the coalfield as a whole a conservative estimate of the remaining reserves of coal workable under present conditions is 5,000 million tons, about two-thirds of which is in Durham. At the present rate of output this would give the coalfield a life of more than another hundred years. Long before this, however, considerable tracts that are already in an advanced stage of depletion will have been completely worked out. Considerable tracts of the southwest, where the resources were already severely depleted, were flooded while their pits lay idle during the years of depression between the wars. Their remaining resources, estimated at about 400 million tons, could not justify the enormous expense of draining the old workings. The tracts that are still being worked here and in the old districts of northwest Durham can have only a limited life. The remaining reserves are in thin seams and water presents a serious problem. The National Coal Board expects that by 1965 production in northwest Durham will be about 18 per cent less than what it was in 1950, and nearly one-third of the industry's personnel there will have become redundant.

The colliery districts of west Durham were especially hard hit during the inter-war years. In most communities two-thirds of the insured population were miners, and by 1932 half of these were unemployed. That these same districts are prosperous again today reflects full employment in the mining industry. The menfolk in the mining settlements are scarcely less dependent upon the pits. But some alleviation of the traditional lack of occupational balance has been achieved by provision of more industrial work for women and girls. Not only does modern transport extend the availability of employment in factories and offices in the port conurbations, factories are now less exclusively concentrated there.

Owing to its especially desperate plight in the nineteen-thirties the southwest corner of the coalfield was given priority in the application of measures to relieve the distress, and some light industries, including clothing, were introduced before the War, especially in the trading estate opened at West Auckland in 1939 (Fig. 41). As these have expanded and new firms, making a variety of consumer goods, have settled at a variety of sites in the district, the southwest has come to offer greater variety of employment than most parts of the coalfield. Many workers were recruited from some of the mining settlements here when Royal Ordnance factories were set up at Spennymoor and Aycliffe (Fig. 41), and considerable numbers of workers still travel to the post-war trading estates that have succeeded them. Some travel as far as Darlington. In northwest Durham, however, during the five years after the Second World War only seven new firms were established, employing about 700 workers, nearly all girls, and many who seek factory or office work travel considerable distances to the Team Valley Trading Estate and Newcastle.

In Northumberland and east Durham the long-term prospects of mining are brighter, but dependence upon the single industry is extreme. Many mining communities, however, now find themselves within range of the employment provided at new factories on Tyneside and Wearside, and in shops and offices there. At Peterlee (Fig. 41) in the southeast of the coalfield a new town is being established as a measure of re-grouping the mining population and providing a service centre. It is intended that its ultimate population should be 30,000. It will not be a single-industry town, for at this early stage, before much housing has been built, manufacturing industry in the form of a large worsted-spinning factory has been attracted.

In most parts of the coalfield, while the last twenty years have seen a great increase in the employment available for women and girls, the dependence of the men upon mining has been only slightly reduced. Lack of occupational variety is a persisting problem, aggravated in west Durham by the looming inevitability of redundancy as the mining industry shrinks. It would be idle to pretend that the degree of development of new industries has as yet substantially reduced the dependence upon the basic industries, or provided an adequate solution for the near future in those districts where impending exhaustion of the coal will bring about severe reduction in mining employment.

Expanding exports of coal played a large part in the nineteenth-century development of the coalfield, and when production was at its peak, in the years before the First World War, 40 per cent of the annual output of over 50 million tons was shipped to foreign countries. The loss of overseas markets contributed seriously to the fall in production and to the unemployment in the industry between the wars, and painful adjustments of the economy were necessitated. Although at present there is full employment and prosperity in the coalfield, production is considerably less than it was forty years ago, and the labour force has been reduced by more than a quarter. The export trade in coal is a mere shadow of what it was, but coastwise shipments to gasworks and electric power stations on Thames-side and at other places on the east and south coasts are still important. This coalfield still supplies half of London's needs. Iron ore and timber remain the chief imports,[1] and only the Tyne at Newcastle Quay has considerable imports of

[1] Mineral oil is becoming increasingly important.

foodstuffs and general cargoes. Although considerable quantities of fish are landed at North Shields and Hartlepool, the other ports are extremely specialised industrial ports.

Among them Blyth, with 97 per cent of its total trade accounted for by coal, has greatly enhanced its relative status and now ranks after the Tyne for coal shipments. Its port equipment was further improved between the wars, and shipments, which had already reached 4·75 million tons in 1913, were considerably increased. The export trade has since collapsed, but coastwise shipments have continued to grow. Total shipments in 1954 amounted to 5·4 million tons, as compared with 8·5 million tons from the Tyne and 3·25 million tons from the Wear.

The communities that have gathered at the ports created by the coal trade have, in the case of those situated on the coalfield itself, always been mining settlements as well as ports. Amble and Seaham Harbour are primarily communities of miners, but Blyth also has a significant ship-building and -repairing industry. On Tyneside colliery hamlets near the river banks were the germs of several of the municipalities, but the local coal resources are now worked out. Mining is thus no longer an important source of employment on Tyneside, but it is still active on Wearside, where there are large collieries within and on the outskirts of Sunderland borough (Fig. 49).

Both on Tyneside and Wearside ship-building and -repairing and marine engineering are the leading industries. Tyneside accounts for more than half and Wearside for nearly one-quarter of the employment in these industries on the Northeast Coast.[1] The other basic industries of the region, iron and steel and heavy chemicals, are concentrated much more on Tees-side. Tyneside has a significant subsidiary share of the chemical industry, but there is no primary metallurgy either on Tyneside or Wearside. The great shipbuilding concern of Palmer's at Jarrow and Hebburn included blast-furnaces in its integrated undertaking, but since the firm failed after the First World War the iron and steel industry has not been represented on Tyneside. Except for outlying works at Consett on the coalfield and at Skinningrove on the ironstone field, smelting is now confined to Tees-side (Fig. 51).

Other types of engineering are also important, though locomotive engineering left Gateshead in 1932 and is now chiefly concentrated at Darlington. Tyneside has been in the forefront of development in electrical engineering, and heavy branches of this industry have risen to prominence as a major activity on Tyneside, at Hebburn and Heaton (Fig. 45). The linkage with older industries is illustrated by the recent emphasis upon the production of electrically operated shipdeck equip-

[1] Ancillary industries, such as rope making and the manufacture of paint and anti-fouling compositions, are also important.

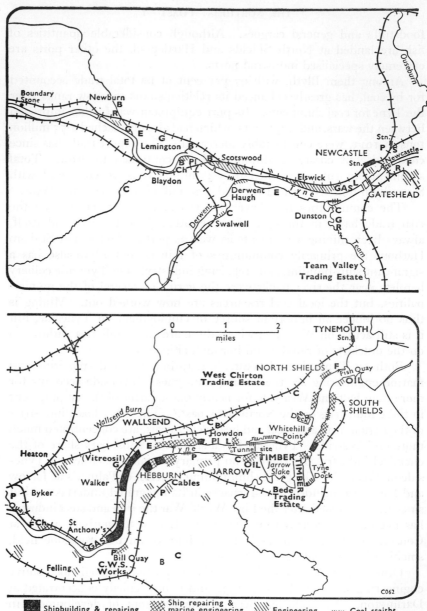

Fig. 45 TYNESIDE : INDUSTRIES. The boundary stone marks the limit of jurisdiction
of the Tyne Improvement Commission—the tidal estuary.

ment by the firm of Clarke, Chapman and Co. of Gateshead, who have
made machinery for ships and collieries since 1864. Recently, light
electrical trades have assumed increasing importance, and have also
become represented on the Wear by an electric-valve factory.

The establishment of trading estates,[1] the exertions of the North
Eastern Development Board, and government assistance through the
Distribution of Industry Act, 1945, have brought a welcome addition
of new light industries, but the industrial structure is still dominated
by a narrow range of heavy industries concerned with capital goods.
It has been pointed out that the narrowness of the basis of the industrial
structure was in no small measure induced by the boom conditions
enjoyed by these industries in the past. Older industries yielded riverside sites to these expanding industries as they sought more and more
space for extension. The pottery, paper, glass, and chemical industries,
however, are still represented by residual units, some of which have
adapted themselves by specialisation. Such for example are the
Lemington works, producing electric-lamp bulbs, and the Wear glass
works, which have achieved renown for oven glassware (Pyrex). At
Wallsend the Thermal Syndicate manufactures a highly specialised
product, Vitreosil (fused silica ware). A local firm of soap manufacturers,
Thomas Hedley and Co., established more than a century ago in east
Newcastle, is now engaged there in large-scale production of detergents,
and on upper Tyneside at Blaydon and Prudhoe (Pl. 20) there are works
that produce fertilisers and other chemicals. The modern plastics
industry is also represented on Tyneside by one of its largest units,
a new factory at West Chirton alongside the Newcastle–Tynemouth
road, which produces laminated plastics (Formica).

On both Tyneside and Wearside the basic heavy industries and their
ancillary trades line the river banks. Shipbuilding has in the past been
carried on above the Newcastle bridges at Elswick, but the shipyards
that remain on Tyneside are chiefly grouped some distance below the
bridges at Walker and Wallsend on the north side and at Hebburn
and Jarrow on the south side (Pl. 39). Here the channel is more spacious
for launching and there is lowlying ground along the river banks. The
stretches along the river on lower Tyneside and within the mouth of the
Wear that are occupied by shipyards present a most distinctive waterfront of gargantuan proportions (Pl. 33). The berths with gaunt staging
and skeletal hulls, backed by vast prefabricating sheds, are overshadowed
by giant cranes, some of them rising from protruding gantries. The
ship-repairing yards, equipped with dry docks, slipways, pontoons, and

---

[1] Figure 41 shows the locations of trading estates with five or more tenants.
There are also several other group sites and single factories scattered over the
area.

floating cranes, also contribute, with their occupants, to the forest of steel that rises from the river.

Another distinctive and long-established feature of the waterfront are the staiths, jutting piers of open construction, once made of timber but now of steel, that enable coal-wagons to discharge their loads into the collier vessels berthed below in river or dock (Pl. 34). On the Northumberland side of the Tyne coal-shipping facilities are now concentrated a short distance within the river mouth, where there are docks and extensive facilities for direct loading on the river at Whitehill Point.[1] On the south bank, directly opposite, Tyne Dock is most important, though there are other staiths ranged at intervals as far as the mouth of the Derwent.[2] With shrinkage of coal shipments the coal-handling facilities are far in excess of present needs, and old staiths are going out of use, shipments being concentrated upon those that have been modernised, as at Tyne Dock.

Elsewhere, engineering sheds and other factories, together with storage and marshalling yards, occupy the river-banks, but the occupation of river frontages by active industry is much less continuous than at the beginning of this century. Since the great depression, when so many works closed down, many riverside sites have been unoccupied. Shipyards that were considered redundant were systematically scrapped by the captains of the industry as a measure of rationalisation to meet the difficulties of the period that followed the First World War. The cleared sites, available for industry, have been slow to find new occupants. The new industries that might have been attracted do not specially need the river and have found sites elsewhere. An increasing number of factories are found in the hinterland, along the roads and railways that connect the various Tyneside towns some distance back from the river and those that converge upon the crossing at Newcastle-Gateshead.

Along the riverside industry occupies at most only a narrow strip behind which terrace housing immediately begins (Pl. 39). Intermixed with housing are other factories, less dependent upon river transport, and groups of new factories, provided on rentals in trading estates. Some of the new light industries are dispersed along the railways away from the river, but most occupy sites in the trading estates. The earliest (1936) and largest of these estates lies alongside the main railway line as it approaches the Tyne crossing from the south along the Team valley below the Gateshead cuesta. Two others are on lower Tyneside, west of North Shields at West Chirton, and alongside Jarrow Slake

[1] It is proposed, however, to fill in Northumberland Dock here to provide accommodation for installations needed to develop the Tyne as an oil-receiving port.

[2] At Dunston, on the haughs between the confluences of the Derwent and the Team with the Tyne, is the major electric power station of the Northeast (Fig. 45).

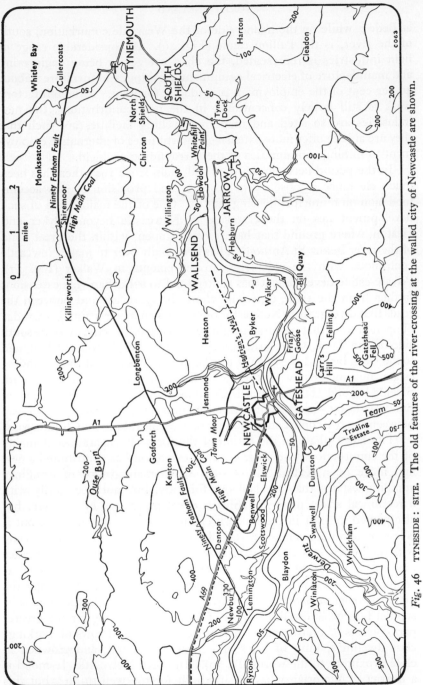
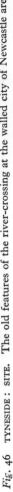

Fig. 46 TYNESIDE : SITE. The old features of the river-crossing at the walled city of Newcastle are shown.

207

at Bede ; while on the inland side of the Wearside conurbation, south of the river, is the Pallion estate (Fig. 49). A considerable range of light industries is represented, the chief categories being engineering and manufacture of electrical equipment, clothing, and furniture ; about 40 per cent of the employment provided is for men. Although factory work is still largely concentrated in the port-conurbations, the new industries are so sited and modern travelling facilities are such that they are able to offer more extensive opportunities of alternative employment to mining communities of the surrounding coalfield.

In the period between the wars and again since 1945 there has been much clearance of obsolescent property and provision of new accommodation on municipal housing estates. One of the major areas of such development lies on the east side of Newcastle beyond Byker and Heaton, where ground that had remained open, within the great bend of the river below St Anthony's, has been built over to make Newcastle continuous with the older riparian settlements in Walker (Fig. 47). Private estate development has contributed to suburban villa extensions farther from the river, especially along the sea-coast and between the roads that diverge from Newcastle, but the Town Moor maintains a wedge of open ground that penetrates right to the core of the city. On the south side of the Tyne, Gateshead has spread out over Gateshead Fell, and to the west, beyond the floor of the Team valley occupied by the trading estate, housing is now spreading. The southward extension of South Shields beyond Harton towards Cleadon, combined with the swelling of Sunderland by suburban growth on its outskirts, has narrowed the gap between the two conurbations to a mere two miles along the Cleadon road.

The latest phase in the fusion of the formerly separate settlements of the conurbations and their outward extension has contributed a new and more open texture of housing, with small groups of dwellings studding estates that are laid out formally, but not necessarily with a rectilineal street pattern. Ribbon development, as everywhere, has also played its part in the modern extension of the urban areas, but it is less evident than in many parts of England. The new tracts of housing with their open, studded texture, surround more compact areas of terrace property. The ribbed expanses of the latter, produced by nineteenth-century urban growth, predominate in the townscape, enveloping the heterogeneous nuclear areas. The terrace housing includes some substantial bourgeois dwellings built of local stone, but by far the greater part consists of drab tracts of narrow, closely packed rows of working-class dwellings, built of brick and invariably slated, and crowded in close proximity to the works (Pl. 39). In north Newcastle, Jesmond is a district of Victorian villa housing built for the well-to-do ; but this type, though represented elsewhere, is an unimportant constituent.

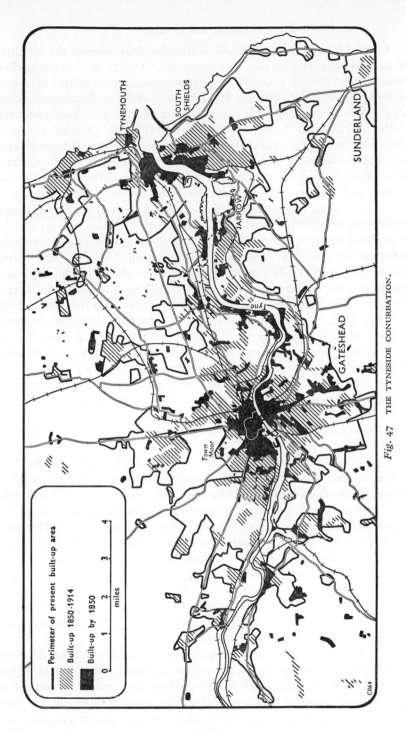

Fig. 47 THE TYNESIDE CONURBATION.

Perimeter of present built-up area

Built-up 1850-1914

Built-up by 1850

miles
0   1   2   3   4

TYNEMOUTH

SOUTH SHIELDS

SUNDERLAND

JARROW

Tyne

GATESHEAD

Town Moor

C064

Central Newcastle is especially distinctive by reason of the maturity of its development as a city core (Fig. 26). Unlike the corresponding areas of most British provincial cities, moreover, most of this area possesses architectural distinction, for it consists of the re-developed central area within the old city walls that Grainger and his associates produced in the 'thirties and 'forties of last century (Pl. 42). Within this area there are now few residents. In the south, near the Quayside, in an area adjacent to the castle and the cathedral, a specialised financial quarter of banks and offices has emerged in the streets between the Central Station and Pilgrim Street. Leading from the new road bridge that was opened in 1928, Pilgrim Street now carries most of the through road traffic that crosses the river. The continuation of this axis in Northumberland Street [1] has developed into a shopping street that rivals or outstrips the older axis from the Central Station along Grainger Street into Blackett Street. It has extended the major shopping thoroughfare, which is now continuous from the Central Station north to Barras Bridge. The heterogeneous buildings and irregular cornices of its northern part, in Northumberland Street, contrast with the uniform façades of Grainger's streets. Away from the steep descent to the river, central Newcastle shows little obvious sign of the original diversity of terrain that was provided by the denes of the Lort and Pandon burns. Rising from the north bank of the river, with its closely grouped but strongly contrasted bridges, central Newcastle (Pls. 41, 42) has a highly individual profile in which the ancient Norman keep, the towers of the old parish churches, and the monumental column to Grey are prominent landmarks.

The commercial cores of other towns of Tyneside are far less developed and are merely local shopping and entertainment centres, subsidiary to Newcastle. Sunderland, however, has a central core which, although of nondescript appearance, competes as a shopping centre with Newcastle over an extensive area of central and east Durham. On Saturdays in winter, combined football match, shopping, and cinema or theatre trips, and in summer shopping and seaside outings, are very popular to Sunderland from the colliery settlements of all but the most outlying parts of the Durham coalfield. Even so, Newcastle is the undoubted metropolis of the coalfield and of a much wider rural area beyond. It exerts a more limited and specialised influence even in the Tees basin and west of the Pennines.

The scale, form, and wider regional importance of urban development on the estuary of the Wear present contrasts with those of Tyneside (cf. Figs. 47, 49). They spring from significant differences in their physical settings. Site conditions are notably different (cf. Figs.

[1] J. W. House and B. Fullerton, ' City Street ', *Planning Outlook* 3 (1956), 3–25.

46, 48). To reach the sea the lower Wear passes through a post-glacial gorge cut across the limestone plateau of east Durham, but the Tyne occupies a pre-glacial valley plugged with drift, and only occasionally does it transgress from the drift floor to engage the rock sides of the valley. The pre-glacial valley is constricted and steep-sided where it

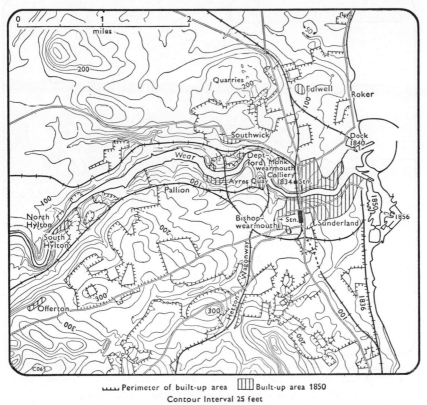

ᴜᴜᴜ Perimeter of built-up area   ⦀⦀⦀ Built-up area 1850
Contour Interval 25 feet

Fig. 48   WEARSIDE : SITE.

crosses the resistant sandstones that overlie the High Main coal in Newcastle and Gateshead ; here are the bridges, the modern ones spanning the valley high above the river. The municipalities that lie opposite each other on lower Tyneside are still linked effectively only through Newcastle ; below the Newcastle bridges there are only ferries and the uncompleted Jarrow–Wallsend tunnel project.

Tyneside is a conurbation that has developed from two main clusters, one at the bridge, the other at the river mouth several miles farther east. But they are connected by a tidal waterway, and as they have swollen, the intervening stretches along the river banks have also been filled in with the settlements associated with riverside industries. In comparison, the smaller conurbation on Wearside is a much more compact development. It remains essentially a river-mouth concentration, within two miles of the sea, and there is no counterpart of the

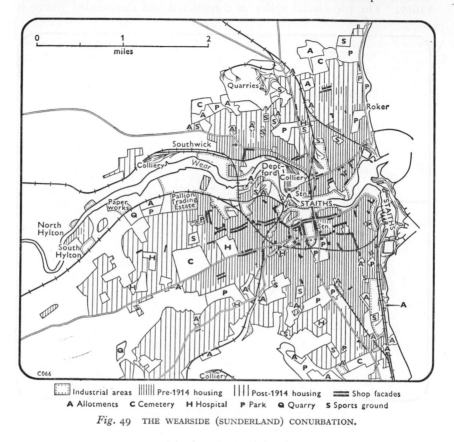

Industrial areas ▦ Pre-1914 housing ▥ Post-1914 housing ▬ Shop facades
A Allotments C Cemetery H Hospital P Park Q Quarry S Sports ground

Fig. 49 THE WEARSIDE (SUNDERLAND) CONURBATION.

Newcastle-Gateshead component of Tyneside. Wearside corresponds only with the Shields component of the latter, and in the contrast between its morphology and the more complex morphology of Tyneside are reflected further differences in their functional development.

On Tyneside the position of the bridge that carries the major south-north route across the river at a point ten miles inland, yet where the river is still navigable, was the earliest and has always been the dominant factor. There was no bridge, however, across the navigable portion of the Wear until the very end of the eighteenth century, and the importance of the bridge even now remains local. It has served to knit together the originally independent small communities at the river mouth. As on Tyneside, industries are strung out along the river banks, with attached masses of housing behind (Fig. 49 and Pl. 37). Thanks to the bridge they are now bound into a compact municipality, the larger portion on the south side of the river where, too, at the junction of the High Street of old Sunderland with Bridge Street and its southern prolongation, Fawcett Street, is the hub of the town. The south side of the river mouth has naturally been the scene of the main provision of coal-shipping facilities in the extensive docks that serve the southern and major part of the port's hinterland. On the north side, Monkwearmouth dock occupies only a small area, actually within the river mouth, and to the north the Roker sea-front has offered more scope for amenity development.

CHAPTER 12

THE NORTHEAST COAST—II

BOTH the setting and the pattern of industry and towns in the lower basin of the Tees are different again. The Tees-side conurbation begins only at Stockton and Thornaby. Darlington is separated from it by a belt of farming country and lies more than ten miles to the west, and much farther along the tortuous course of the river (Fig. 36). In one of the meander loops between is Yarm, its port dead but its stone warehouses still standing alongside the river as reminders of its former trade. The tidal limit is now at Worsall, a little above Yarm, but far below Darlington. The Great North Road and the main south–north railway cross the Tees near Darlington, and the major crossings have always been west of contact with tidewater.

Before additional bridges were built at Middlesbrough in this century, the lowest crossing was at Stockton. The bridge built there in 1760 established connections, chiefly of local importance, between south Durham and Cleveland, and at the same time killed the older port of Yarm. But in spite of the straightening and dredging of the channel up to Stockton, the port has shifted eastwards to the estuary itself. Just below the site of Middlesbrough dock the Tees opens out at Cargo Fleet into a shallow basin of tidal mud flats, the opposite shores of which are widely separate and isolated (Pl. 38). This area, with an indefinite extension south, is the saltfield that has been discovered within the last century. The saltfield, however, does not extend west of Middlesbrough dock and Billingham, nor does it reach the Hartlepools on the north side of the estuary (Fig. 6).[1]

The forces that produced urban settlement operated to disperse rather than concentrate the town pattern. Apart from the loosely grouped major aggregation between Stockton and the coast at Redcar, Darlington and the Hartlepools are large distinct clusters. Close networks of main roads, railway lines, and high-tension electric cables connect these urban centres with each other, with the coalfield and the ironstone field, and with the main south-north trunk routes, but there are still extensive lacunae in which it is difficult to appreciate the near presence of such an intense development of modern industry.

Between the built-up tracts the rural countryside is of fairly uniform character. The Durham plateau slopes very gradually towards the

[1] Anhydrite, worked since 1923 at Billingham, is less restricted in its inland extension, but the limits of the workable beds have not yet been determined.

Tees, but in Yorkshire the Cleveland plateau dominates the lowlying ground by an imposing escarpment, with great embayments and out-lying hill masses. West of it, however, the watershed between Tees and Ouse drainage in the Northallerton gate is an inconspicuous feature of the drift surface. Throughout the vale of Tees a coating of drift that largely consists of boulder-clay conceals the more varied sub-structure, and there are few rock exposures. The subdued but un-dulating relief of the drift flattens out eastwards, where the lowland part of Cleveland is featureless country of laminated clays. Locally, patches of fluvio-glacial sands and gravels relieve the continuous expanse of distinctly heavy clay soils, and, together with knolls of limestone that protrude through the thinner drift towards the west and north-west, have provided sites for several of the old villages.

Away from the salt marshes and reclaimed silt of the estuary itself, strips of alluvial meadowland extend up the main valley and along the courses of tributary becks. In the upper Skerne basin, Bradbury and Morden carrs are flat tracts of peaty silt, only partially reclaimed, which provide nothing but rough grazing. West of Stokesley and Seamer, the Leven is liable to flood over considerable areas, but the appreciable trenching of the Tees above Yarm restricts river flooding and allows drainage in the adjacent parts of the vale to be distinctly better than the close texture of the soils might lead one to expect.

On the drift soils, the farmlands everywhere present a mixed pattern of arable and grass fields, though in varying proportions. In the central tract about one-quarter to one-third is arable, but the proportion increases slightly to the west and considerably, to nearly one-half, in Cleveland. In modern times there has been a general increase in grass on land that was traditionally devoted to wheat and beans, though the grassland can seldom be of very high quality. In Cleveland, however, wheat retains considerable importance, and in the west barley is more important than is usual in North England. In spite of the urban markets near by, very little land is used for market-gardening, though potatoes are an important sale crop from farms. Throughout there is increasing emphasis on fluid-milk production, which is usually supple-mented by production of fat stock, including considerable numbers of pigs, and on some farms fattening is still the mainstay.

Steep slopes and really infertile soils are rare, and except for the encroachments of industry, communications, and housing, practically all the surface is farmland. There is an abundance of hedgerow timber, but little woodland apart from the plantations on the Wynyard estate north of Stockton. After the Anglian colonisation, the area was devastated at the time of the Norman Conquest, and its subsequent recolonisation from the west has left a legacy of Scandinavian place-names and strong traces in the local dialect. The rural settlement is also distinctive in having developed in association with an agricultural system more nearly akin to that of the English Midlands than obtained in any other part of North England, and enclosure of the open fields was later in being completed than in most of the lowlands of the north country. Village clusters are still conspicuous in the texture of rural settlement, though many farmsteads have sprung up between, and villages that are grouped round open greens are especially typical.

Some of the old villages have been swallowed up by the urban extensions of the last century, and others have recently been affected by an influx of urban workers, but most retain a profoundly rural character. There is little extractive industry. At a few places along the Cleveland Dyke (Fig. 6), which traverses the area in a straight line from west to east, crossing the Tees at Egglescliffe and reaching the Cleveland hills south of Roseberry Topping, there are quarries to provide roadstone. Towards Barnard Castle, approaching the mouth of Teesdale, there are limestone quarries at Forcett and Barton, but most of the flux for the Tees-side smelting industry comes from farther afield in Weardale, or from east Durham.

Although the iron industry has withdrawn from its earlier scattered sites along the railways (Fig. 39), there are occasional outlying industrial works in the countryside between the major concentrations of housing and industry, as at Greatham Station and along the Stockton and Darlington Railway. An industrial estate, intended to be the basis of the New Town of Aycliffe, has made its appearance since the war on the main route north of Darlington.

The Hartlepools, situated on the very edge of the coalfield, where the buried course of the lowest seam is intersected by the coastline and the limestone cliffs of Durham end in a promontory north of the flats and marshes of the Tees estuary, are physically distinct from both the colliery settlements of the southeastern corner of the coalfield and the Teesmouth conurbation.

The modern port, created and developed by railway companies to serve as an additional outlet for the Durham coalfield, has remained highly specialised. Its outward shipments are almost exclusively coal and coke, for coastwise distribution. Now that the export trade has faded out, the coal dock within the newer west harbour has become redundant, and coal is loaded only from the staiths in the old harbour and its extension, Victoria Dock (Fig. 50). After North Shields, Hartlepool is the second fishing port of the northeast coast, north of the Humber, and the fish quay is also in old Hartlepool, alongside the Victoria Dock.

The railway company, as owner of the port, developed water areas amounting to more than 180 acres from the large tidal slake behind the headland. Arising from these exceptional facilities, the most distinctive feature of the port is its timber trade. The Hartlepools receive nearly half the timber imports arriving at the Northeast Coast

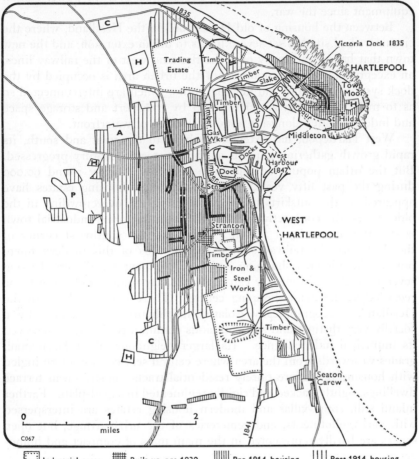

Fig. 50 THE HARTLEPOOLS.

ports. Most of this consists of pit-props, but timber is also imported to be prepared for shipfitting and other local trades. A large area of land is devoted to open timber storage and woodworking industries, and although this includes some yards in the industrial district on the south side of the town, it is mostly adjacent to the docks. Other manufacturing industries, notably shipbuilding and marine engineer-

217

ing, have also availed themselves of the local advantages. In ship-building employment the Hartlepools are far behind Tyneside and Wearside, but much less so in marine engineering. In the employment it provides this is now the leading industry of the Hartlepools, although one of the main firms concerned has turned over to power-station equipment since the war.

Between the housing of old Hartlepool on the Headland, where the circumscribed site has set severe limits to urban extension, and the new town that has spread easily over the flat land west of the railway lines, an exceptionally large proportion of the urban area is occupied by the dock system of the old and new harbours, which are interconnected so as to make Middleton an island, and by transport and storage space and industrial sites alongside about five miles of waterfront.

West Hartlepool has extended behind to the west and south, its rapid growth gathering impetus as the nineteenth century progressed. But the urban population has been almost stationary round 90,000 during the past fifty years, and although new housing estates have appeared on the outskirts to relieve some of the overcrowding in the older parts, the compactly and rapidly built Victorian industrial town is still the predominant feature. Adjoining the southwest corner of the docks are the railway station and nucleus of this modern town, but within this area shopping and entertainment are dispersed along several streets. No locality can at present lay undisputed claim to be regarded as the main shopping centre. There are also shops in the Headland, a geographically isolated neighbourhood, occupied by a socially very distinct and self-conscious community that has preserved its municipal independence. Its larger neighbour, West Hartlepool, grades westwards from the area where central services are intermingled with housing into more purely residential tracts, mostly mean terrace dwellings, tightly packed and rigidly regimented in a grid-plan. Farther inland still, some villas and modern housing estates are interspersed with parks, allotments, and cemeteries of the urban fringe, but open spaces are hardly represented in the main mass of compact and homogeneous townscape.

The occupation of a large area on the south side of the mid-nineteenth-century town by industrial works has contained the spread of housing here and has also precluded the amenity development of what could have been an attractive sea-front with a fine beach. Where some residential development has been possible farther south alongside the sandy beach, Seaton Carew, although lying within the modern municipality, is somewhat detached from the rest of the town. In the intervening industrial tract are the great integrated iron and steel works of the South Durham Company with blast-furnaces, steel-melting shops and rolling mills, and associated ore-preparing plant and batteries of coke-ovens. This concern is one of the main steel-producing units of the Northeast Coast, and the current development plans that are being carried out will enable it to retain and strengthen its position. Its huge slag-tip rises to a height of eighty feet, and dominates the flat coastal site of the town.

Just as this outlying establishment of the Tees-side steel industry is naturally situated on the south side of the Hartlepools along the railway as it approaches from Stockton, so the new trading estate, which has been established to attract light industries and to lessen the extreme dependence of the district upon a few basic heavy industries that employ only men, has been deliberately located on the northwest side of the town with a view to drawing labour also from the neighbouring colliery settlements. Most of these workers are women and girls employed in textile and clothing factories, but by no means all the movement of labour is into the Hartlepools. In the reverse direction some miners travel from homes in the Hartlepools, and much larger numbers of workers now travel out of the town south to the Imperial Chemical Industries works at Billingham and to other works on the north side of the Tees estuary.

In the earlier phases of the modern development of Tees-side, the coal trade and shipbuilding played an important rôle. Their relative importance is much less today, and the rationalising activities of National Shipbuilders' Securities Ltd. during the inter-war years have left only two active shipyards, at Haverton Hill and South Bank (Fig. 51). Primary metallurgy, however, has become increasingly concentrated at the mouth of the Tees, and the chemical industry has not only made its appearance, but has undergone a prodigious and continuing development. Thanks to these expanding industries, the population of the Tees-side conurbation has continued to grow [1] while that of Tyneside has for some time past been more or less stationary, and migration from Wearside and the Hartlepools has been so considerable as to bring about a decline there. But, like the other conurbations of the Northeast Coast, Tees-side is narrowly dependent upon a few basic heavy industries.

Market conditions and technical developments have combined to emphasise production of steel, as compared with pig-iron, and at the modern plants pig-iron is converted as hot metal. Wrought iron, the major product of the young and lusty industry a century ago, is no longer made, the last puddling furnace having gone out of action in 1922. For some decades Tees-side has been providing about one-fifth

[1] Between 1931 and 1951 its population increased from approximately 300,000 to 330,000.

of the national output of steel. Most is heavy rolled steel of non-alloy type, and although large quantities are consumed by the great metal-using industries of the Northeast—engineering, shipbuilding, and mining—the production of finished steel is considerably in excess of the regional needs. Much is supplied to other parts of Britain and a considerable quantity is exported.

As the Cleveland orefield nears exhaustion,[1] the dependence upon foreign ore has been becoming more and more definite, in spite of increased use of scrap metal. Three-quarters of the ore used, and an even higher proportion in terms of metal content, is now imported, and in the steel furnaces of the district the ratio of pig-iron to scrap, already considerably above the national average, has increased in recent years. Inevitably the industry is being drawn to the coast, production being increasingly concentrated at newer, up-to-date plants on the south side of the Tees estuary (Pl. 38), leaving sites that are less suitably located when their equipment becomes obsolescent.

After its scattered distribution a century ago, the industry at an early stage abandoned the inland sites on the coalfield and along the railways leading to it. Within the Tees-side conurbation itself an east-ward shift has since been taking place, and there are no longer any active blast-furnaces, steel furnaces, or rolling mills at Stockton. The process is now being carried a stage further, and the post-war capital development of the industry to modernise its equipment has concentrated upon units east of Middlesbrough, and on the coast at West Hartlepool. The new melting-shop at Lackenby, opened in 1953, has replaced an old one at the Britannia Works in Middlesbrough. Although the Lackenby works mark a further stage in the eastward migration of the industry, they are not the easternmost works on Tees-side, for there was already an outlier at the mouth of the estuary on Tod Point, north of Redcar. The great modern iron and steel works of south Tees-side, as an essential feature of their equipment, have their own jetties for un-loading ore on the shipping channel in the estuary. The Imperial Chemical Industries works at Billingham also have direct shipping facilities, and recently special facilities for unloading oil have been provided at Teesport[2] on the south side of the estuary. Middlesbrough dock, so long the essential feature of the port, and successor to Stockton, has receded in importance. It is still, however, the shipping point for coal, the trade for which it was originally built. The Ironmasters' District, adjacent to it in north Middlesbrough, although retaining

---

[1] Production has fallen below 600,000 tons since 1956, compared with over 6 million tons per annum for thirty years before 1914. Till 1920 the Cleveland deposits were the main home source of ore ; they still provided 2 million tons per annum in the late 'thirties.   [2] In operation since 1950.

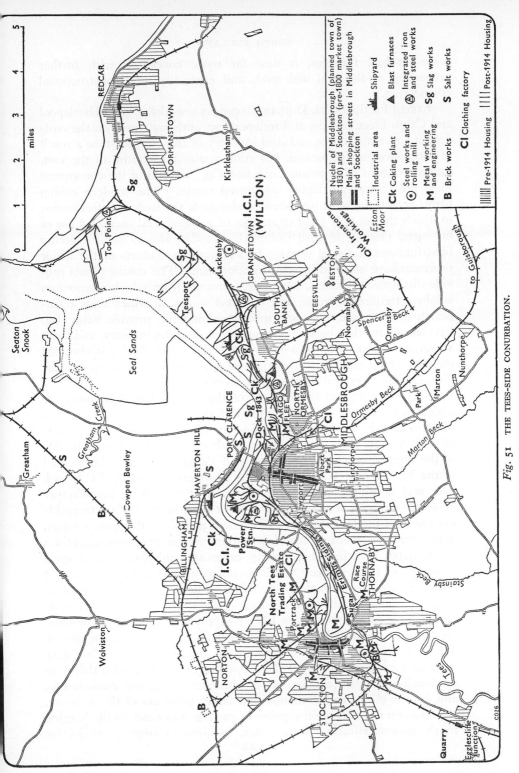

Fig. 51 THE TEES-SIDE CONURBATION.

Nuclei of Middlesbrough (planned town of 1830) and Stockton (pre-1800 market town)

Main shopping streets in Middlesbrough and Stockton

Industrial area

Ck Coking plant
⊙ Steel works and rolling mill
M Metal working and engineering
B Brick works

⊶ Shipyard
▲ Blast furnaces
Ⓐ Integrated iron and steel works
Sg Slag works
S Salt works

Cl Clothing factory

Pre-1914 Housing   Post-1914 Housing

221

some residual furnaces, is now far more concerned with further processing of the iron and steel, and especially with constructional engineering.

Except for the South Durham Company's works at West Hartlepool and Cargo Fleet and the still independent outlying works on the coalfield at Consett, the iron and steel industry of the Northeast, as a result of successive amalgamations, has come under the control of the vast, unified concern of Dorman, Long and Co. Several of the constituent units are themselves highly integrated works. The modern coking plants are for the most part situated alongside the iron and steel works, to which they supply great quantities of gas fuel, and increased use of hot-metal practice in steel making has tended also to bring together blast-furnaces and steel works. In addition by-products of the major processes have assumed increased importance. The coking plants provide distillation products, including ammonia from which ammonium sulphate fertiliser is made, and the steel works, in which basic openhearth furnaces are more and more predominant, provide basic slag. Fertilisers have thus become a major product of the industry, and there are large slag-crushing mills at several places. Rough slag is also sold for use in road making, so that there is far less waste to dump into the Tees estuary to extend the foreshore than formerly.

To these chemical by-products of the iron and steel industry are added on a yet larger scale the output of fertilisers and organic chemicals of Imperial Chemical Industries, first at Billingham on the north side of the Tees, and since the last few years also at Wilton on the south side of the estuary, east of Grangetown and Eston (Fig. 51). At the end of the First World War the company now represented by I.C.I. took over and developed a war-time government project to manufacture synthetic nitrogen compounds, and from 1923 there was a remarkable expansion of the undertaking. The essential basis of this huge concern is the conjunction of raw materials that are used in enormous quantities —air, water, coal including coking type, and anhydrite. In respect of supply of these primary requirements as well as of other important considerations the Billingham site offered a quite remarkable combination of advantages for the enterprise. Adjacent to the existing conurbation of Tees-side with its large labour supply there was at Billingham, on the north bank opposite Middlesbrough, a spacious open site on flat land, with an extensive frontage on the tidal river. This gave facilities for the cheap import of the few raw materials needed that were not locally available (chiefly potash, phosphate rock, and creosote oil), and for the cheap distribution of the heavy products of the industry, as well as for drawing upon supplies of cooling-water and for discharging much noxious effluent. Pure water, required in large quantities for steam-raising, was available from the Tees Valley Water Board. Within the site itself is the mine-shaft that makes available from below the anhydrite, now used in quantities amounting to one million tons per annum. There were already in existence direct railway connections with the coalfield which, from pits within twenty-five miles, supplies over one and a half million tons of coal per annum to Billingham for its huge electric power station, its great batteries of coke-ovens, and its hydrogenation plant.

The key products of the primary processes in the Gas and Synthesis Plants are ammonia and hydrogen, with Drikold (solid carbon dioxide) an important by-product. The ammonia is applied with local anhydrite and imported potash and phosphate rock to produce ammonium sulphate and other fertilisers, as well as sulphuric acid and nitric acid for other chemical industries, and there is a large output of Portland cement and plasterboard as by-products. In the Hydrogenation Plant, hydrogen produced by passing steam over heated coke is added to imported creosote oil to produce crude petroleum, with calor gas as a by-product, and the petroleum is in turn distilled to provide motor and aviation spirit and a great range of other chemicals.

Since the Second World War a new unit of comparable scale has been equipped on the south side of the estuary at Wilton. It lies on the southeastward extension of the saltfield, but although it is concerned with electrolysis of brine for the production of chlorine and caustic soda, its major activity is the cracking of oil for the production of heavy organic chemicals. It has already become a major centre of the young petro-chemical industry, which has vast prospects. Perspex, terylene, polythene, and ethylene glycol are already among its many products that are becoming increasingly familiar in our everyday life.[1] The northern part of the Wilton estate, where these vast new works are being developed, offers another spacious, smooth site, that lies between the two main west-east roads of the Cleveland plain, and close to the south shore of the estuary and the Redcar railway that runs alongside (Fig. 51). It is connected across the Tees with the Billingham works by pipelines that make the liquid and gas products of the two units inter-available.

Two great private firms thus dominate the industrial employment on Tees-side. They draw labour not only from outside the municipalities in which their works lie but from farther afield. From the Hartlepools, for example, about one thousand I.C.I. employees travel daily to work at Billingham. Outside the control of these firms, the other factories of Tees-side are mainly engaged also in male-employing industries such

[1] Most of Britain's production of titanium metal, at present used mainly for aircraft, also comes from Wilton.

as heavy engineering, foundry work, and shipbuilding. Although in latter years clothing factories have been established with a view to drawing upon the supply of female labour, such light industries are still very much under-represented.

The position in this respect is now much better balanced at Darlington, which since the Second World War has once again become

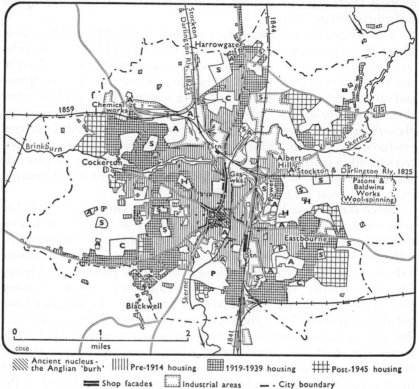

Fig. 52   DARLINGTON (based upon an urban survey carried out by D. Scrafton in 1958).

a considerable textile and clothing manufacturing centre, with more than one-third of its workers engaged in this group of industries. The population is now 85,000, having grown by nearly 18 per cent between 1931 and 1951. The major new enterprise has been the establishment of a large wool-spinning factory on the east side of the town (Fig. 52). The nucleus of Darlington, with its spacious market square, lies west of the river Skerne some distance above its entry into the Tees. The original main line of the Stockton and Darlington Railway approaches the town from the Durham coalfield to cross the Skerne north of this nuclear area. On the east side of the Skerne valley it crosses the main line of the York–Newcastle railway as this passes due north after crossing the Tees at Croft. The main industrial belt of Darlington consists of extensive railway works and other engineering establishments ranged along this axis mainly north of the railway station, and alongside the former sites of the textile mills that were strung out along the Skerne. There are other railway establishments to the northwest where the South Durham and Bishop Auckland lines diverge, and railways and associated works thus divide the urban area into segments. The major extension of housing encloses the original nucleus on the west side of the railway. Harrowgate is a large northward extension along the Great North Road. Another large tract of housing lies east of the main railway line and station, and it is on this eastern side that the latest major industrial development has taken place. Five miles north of Darlington is the group of factories established since 1945 on the site of the Royal Ordnance Factory at Aycliffe. At present these factories draw their labour from older settlements on the coalfield and Darlington, and the New Town, designated in 1947, is still only partly built.

Stockton, the oldest part of the Tees-side conurbation, has a core surrounding the large market-square at the bend of the river, with the High Street leading south to the bridge (Fig. 51). Its nineteenth-century extension included development of an industrial annexe on the other side of the river in Yorkshire. Here the industrial town of Thornaby was appropriately known as South Stockton in the early period of its development. Its modern name is taken from the village that preserves its distinctness on the southern outskirts of the built-up area. Stockton, with Thornaby, is no longer a port of any significance nor a centre of primary metallurgy. It has become first and foremost a centre of heavy engineering, concerned with malleable-steel products and with plant for mines, gasworks, blast-furnaces, and nuclear power stations. As at Darlington, railways and industrial works break up the urban area into a number of residential neighbourhoods, though all depend in large measure upon shops and entertainments in the town centre. The largest modern extension of Stockton has been on the north side, round the old village of Norton, which is sited, like so many others of the vale of Tees, on a patch of sand. Population has increased here especially rapidly since the development of the Billingham chemical works.

The nineteenth-century shift of the port from Stockton to Middlesbrough, combined with conditions of site, have made Tees-side an essentially bi-nuclear conurbation, the Stockton portion separated from the Middlesbrough portion (Fig. 51). Housing avoids the lowlying riverine flats where the Billingham beck makes its way uncertainly to join the Tees, and other watercourses thread the cut-off meander loops from which the Tees was diverted at the beginning of last century. The recent remarkable growth of Billingham and Norton, and the progressive southwestward extension of Middlesbrough towards Thornaby have tended to enclose the intervening belt on its northern and southern sides. Some peripheral portions are also occupied by industrial sites and marshalling yards, notably alongside the river below Stockton bridge and below the new Newport bridge where Billingham chemical works and the Ironmasters' District of Middlesbrough face each other across the river. But the most direct road and rail inter-connections between the Tees-side towns still cross a central area that is largely open ground,[1] and Stockton racecourse occupies the southern meander loop of the old river course.

The railway that created Middlesbrough in 1830 makes its way east from Newport across the base of the last great northern bend of the river towards the dock, which superseded the earlier river staiths a little upstream. The railway sharply demarcates the industrial zone, known as the Ironmasters' District, on what was once the Newport Marshes, from the rest of the town on the drift plain to the south (Fig. 51). The exception to this very clear-cut distinction is the housing of St Hilda's Ward, the original planned town of the Middlesbrough Estate (Fig. 40), built on a slight rise that is outlined by the 25-foot contour line. Embedded in the industrial and port area north of the railway, it is a neighbourhood that possesses a considerable degree of social cohesion, reflecting the combination of poverty and geographical isolation. The modern town-centre, with administrative buildings, shops, and cinemas, has grown up south of the railway station at and near the northern end of Linthorpe Road, the axis of the regularly laid-out town of the period after 1850. In keeping with an urban area that is entirely a product of the past century, growing rapidly south-wards on a uniform site, differences in the townscape are gradations that express the age and social status of the housing. There are slums to the north, suburban villas to the south, the only significant hiatus corresponding to an interrupted belt of open spaces, including cemetery, football ground, and Albert Park (1868). On the east and west margins, beyond flanking, shallow, stream valleys with alluvial floors, new municipal housing estates lie somewhat detached, but the main southward extension of the town over a uniform site has been remarkably compact.

On the east side the valley of Ormesby beck is followed by the

---

[1] A site within this area has recently been developed for the North Tees trading estate, east of Portrack.

Guisborough railway (1852), beyond which North Ormesby is the first of a series of blocks of housing that lie on spurs of drift between strips of alluvium along the valleys of small tributary becks. They have sprung up in association with the great iron and steel works that are ranged alongside the Redcar railway (Pl. 38). This railway, built in 1846, follows the shoreline of that time, but the works extend on to the reclaimed foreshore to the north. Not so the housing, which keeps to the somewhat higher ground of the drift to the south. The typical nineteenth-century 'steel town' was a phalanx of terraces, but the modern housing-estates are as clearly distinguishable on the map by their less rectilineal layout, just as they are on the ground by their house-types. Whereas the older tracts of housing lie north of the modern main road to the coast, the newer estates, such as Teesville, the southward extension of Grangetown, and Dormanstown, lie on its southern side. Farther south another main road, linking Yarm with the coast at Marske, runs near the foot of the hills. Most of the old villages, sited on a strip of sand deposits, lie slightly off this road and have retained their rural character. Such, for example, is Marton, but where the Guisborough railway intersects the road near by, the railway station has become the nucleus of a dormitory suburb of Middlesbrough. To the east Normanby and Eston, on the road and at the scarp foot, became iron-mining settlements after 1850.

The old townships of Cleveland had their village nuclei at the foot of the hills, and their farmlands extended in strips northwards to the estuary shore. In addition to the pronounced zoning of present land-use, in west-east belts between foreshore and hills (Fig. 53a), the south-north pattern of drainage and similarly aligned strips of the old rural landscape are still apparent. It contributed to the physical distinctness of elements of the modern overlay that have been fitted into this older framework. The eastern boundary of Middlesbrough County Borough itself follows the Spencer beck, beyond Cargo Fleet. The industrial settlements farther east are now grouped in Eston and Redcar Urban Districts, which together carve up most of the farmland that is left between estuary, hills, and coast. In one of these gaps of rural land that remained between the two west-east roads is the Wilton estate, where the latest I.C.I. development is taking place. Even so, Redcar still remains an outlier, a coastal resort and industrial offshoot, in origin and subsequent development alike completely bound up with Middlesbrough.

Billingham on the north bank takes its name from the old village that is now enveloped by the housing created between the wars in conjunction with the great chemical works that occupy a riverside site of one thousand acres (Fig. 51). Farther east in Billingham Urban

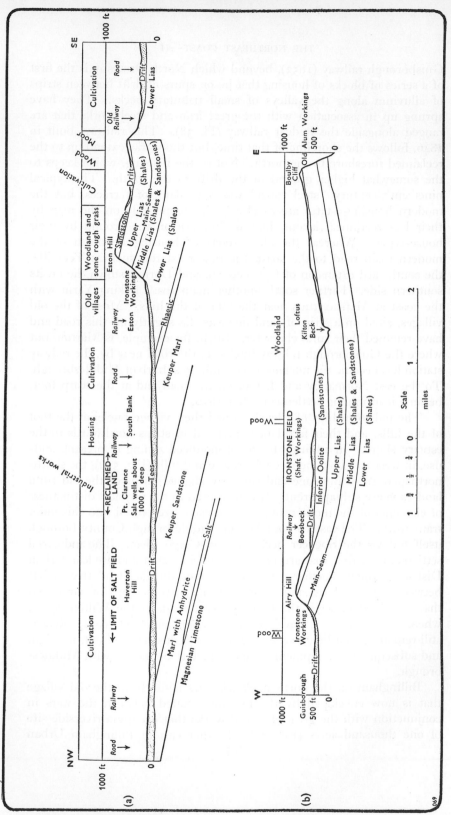

Fig. 53 CLEVELAND AND TEES-SIDE : TRANSECTS.

District are older elements, Haverton Hill and Port Clarence, which date from railway and industrial projects of last century. Between the site of Port Clarence ironworks at the head of the estuary and an isolated zinc works on the coast at Seaton Snook, the north shore of the estuary, separated from the main channel by Seal Sands and Greatham Creek, is well-nigh deserted. The modern main road from the Hartlepools along the old shoreline to the Transporter Bridge, and the railway farther inland, both traverse salt-marshes intersected by a maze of small creeks. This area is now dotted with brine-pumps, from which pipe-lines transport the brine to Haverton Hill and to the Cerebos works at Greatham Station.

During its life of just over a century as an iron-mining field, Cleveland has been badly scarred, but even at the peak of activity the industry employed fewer than 10,000 workers, and the area was never so heavily colonised by mining settlement as the coalfield. Although it is now administered as Urban Districts, it has never lost its predominantly rural aspect. A large measure of its amenity value has been preserved, and the great open spaces of heather moorland, with sweeping views and bracing air, are a priceless boon to the urban industrial communities who live only a few miles away.

In front of the main escarpment, Eston and Upleatham hills (Fig. 54) are outlying masses of the same hard rocks. They present an abrupt face that dominates the plain and estuary from a height of 800 feet at Eston Nab. The dip-slope south is more gentle towards the re-entrant valley in which lies Guisborough. The Slapewath beck enters the eastern end of this vale by a channel that represents a diversion of the drainage since pre-glacial times and provides the railway with an approach to the mining field farther east.

South of Guisborough the main escarpment rises boldly to heights of over 1,000 feet, and the plateau surface beyond has a general height of over 800 feet, and is free from glacial drift. The sandstones and shales give only thin and poor soils that are acid and podsolic, and the high plateau surface is open moorland. Farther east, however, there is a coastal tract of plateau which lies at a distinctly lower level (400–700 feet). The rocks here are coated with drift, and there is more and better soil. Most of this lower plateau surface is farmed (Pl. 35), though the farmland at best is only of moderate quality. The moorland edge often corresponds very closely with the limit of the drift, and the drift-free plateau is almost invariably moorland even where, as on Eston Hill, it lies at a somewhat lower altitude.

From Saltburn southwards the highland reaches the coast, and the fine stretch of sands that extends from the mouth of the Tees past Redcar and Marske is replaced by a rocky and forbidding cliff coast shunned by settlement. Narrow breaches mark the mouths of the becks that dissect the plateau with deep, steep-sided, and usually wooded ravines, called gills. The absence of any coastal plain and the presence of these gills, breaking the smoothness of the plateau surface, make communications along the coastal belt difficult. Railways make some remarkable detours such as between Brotton and Skinningrove round Cliffe, and there are steep road gradients, as at Loftus bank.

The rural settlements, situated on the plateau surface between the

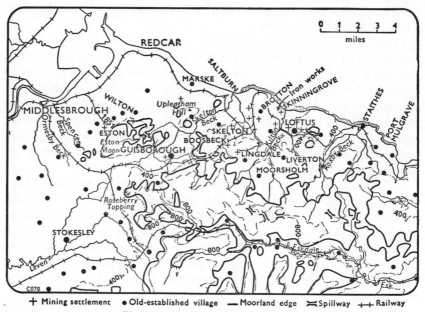

+ Mining settlement   ● Old-established village   — Moorland edge   ⋈ Spillway   ┼┼ Railway

Fig. 54   CLEVELAND : SETTLEMENTS.

heavily wooded gills and below the moorland edge, consist of scattered stone-built farmsteads and a few villages. Straggling hamlets, such as Moorsholm and Liverton, are found near or above 500 feet, but even so lie off the direct moorland road from Guisborough to Whitby. Some of the old-established groups acquired considerable additions of brick-built terrace-housing to accommodate miners. Elsewhere, quite new mining settlements sprang up alongside mines without regard for any other considerations than proximity to the place of work and a cheap plot of ground on which to crowd some houses. Thus drab rows of miners' cottages were herded together in bleak open country on the plateau. They appeared suddenly, like fungi, but have not grown since. The mining population of Cleveland had already reached its maximum by the eighteen-eighties, and withdrawal from the more isolated and remote colonies of sub-standard housing has recently been accentuated.

The ironstone that lay near the extensive outcrops along the escarpments of the main plateau and its northern outliers has been worked out, though the adit mines have left their scars along the wooded, or gorse and bracken covered slopes. Only to the east, in the plateau tract between Guisborough and the coast near Loftus, where the ironstone is buried in a basin structure and needed fairly deep shafts to reach it, is there lingering activity (Fig. 53b). Even here the mining properties were already opened up in the early phase of feverish activity before 1880. The second and final phase, working over the old mines to extract the ironstone left by the earlier pillar-and-stall operations, is in an advanced stage, and production continues from only a few mines where the workings have not yet withdrawn right to the shafts.[1] The single iron and steel works sited within the ore-field, at Skinningrove (Pl. 35), continues to operate and has been modernised since the Second World War. It lies near the mouth of Kilton beck, in its deep-cut gill below the old village of Loftus. Farther south along the coast the southernmost of the former ironstone workings are passed near Port Mulgrave, and the excrescences of extractive industry that are met farther south are those from earlier alum workings.

The growth of large industrial populations in the vale of Tees and the emergence of new urban centres have had important repercussions in the territorial groupings of the social geography of the area. Striking illustrations are provided of the operation of the factors that control the growth or decline of urban functions and that shape the territories commanded by neighbouring and competing centres.

Darlington and Stockton are long-established centres that have maintained and even strengthened their position in modern times. In each a well-developed nodal situation and an entrenched status in the local economy have been aided by the growth of the local population through industry and by the strengthening of external connections by modern methods of transport. On the other hand, the former market centres of Stokesley and Sedgefield have quite failed either to acquire industry or to develop the features of modern townhood, and they have now faded into the rural background. Significantly, they lie off the railway lines upon which urban development depended in the nineteenth century, and on main roads near enough to major centres to fall within their range when motor transport came. They themselves have no *raison d'être* as service centres in the modern scale of urban mesh.

---

[1] Some alternative employment is now provided at the Skelton trading estate, established in 1947, and at a new factory at Guisborough; but the new industries employ chiefly women.

Some of the new concentrations of housing are towns in no other sense than size of population and form of local government; they have never attained urban stature as service centres. At the Hartlepools the local concentration of 90,000 people has naturally called into being a considerable equipment of central services. What is remarkable, however, is that the regional influence of so large a town has remained so restricted. Only a small area beyond the borough boundaries, including the southeasternmost colliery settlements and a few neighbouring rural villages, is oriented towards the Hartlepools.

Middlesbrough, however, is a newcomer that has not only become much the largest urban group on Tees-side but one that has developed for itself an extensive sphere of influence or urban field. For different functions the margins of this field naturally vary, but its core is essentially Cleveland, the area lying to the east, southeast, and south. The inhabitants of the steel-making settlements of south Tees-side and of the mining settlements farther south, as well as of the farms and villages between, look to Middlesbrough for shopping and entertainment. Redcar, Saltburn, Loftus, and even Guisborough, although they are local service centres, in many respects lie definitely within the field of Middlesbrough. Their own inhabitants, as well as those round about, make extensive use of the services provided in or distributed from Middlesbrough.

The rural area south of Middlesbrough, lying in a railwayless tract, has now been integrated with Middlesbrough by the development of motor transport. Just as in Cleveland Middlesbrough's field of influence now extends far along the main roads towards Whitby, so it extends south along the Northallerton road beyond Stokesley. On its southwest side, however, Stockton is a more accessible centre and the influence of Middlesbrough is restricted. Moreover, access to Middlesbrough from the area that lies west of the river Leven is so hampered by the paucity of bridges that the villages and farmsteads here have better contacts with Stockton and Northallerton.

Although it has remained small, Northallerton is well placed as a district centre in the lowland gateway between the vales of Tees and York and enjoys widely ranging administrative importance as the county headquarters of the North Riding. It has also been helped considerably by the existence of the county boundary along the river Tees. This protects its territory by restricting the fields of Durham towns in respect of important services, such as education, that are administered within a county framework. The absence of good bridges across the Tees between Croft and Yarm is a further handicap to Darlington and Stockton that redounds to the benefit of Northallerton as an agricultural market and shopping centre. Where road bridges make connections better across the Tees the fields of these Durham towns encroach effectively into Yorkshire. Thus the influence of Darlington is strongly exerted southwest towards Scotch Corner.

The most important extension of the field of Darlington, however, lies to the west and north, up the Tees basin and into the Wear basin and the coalfield. In these directions Barnard Castle, Bishop Auckland, and Spennymoor are in many respects independent and are themselves well-developed social service centres, but their residents as well as those of the surrounding districts undoubtedly look to Darlington also as a service centre of a higher order of equipment. In the southwestern part of the coalfield Darlington competes with Newcastle as a centre for major shopping. Even in respect of the primary urban fields, that of Darlington extends beyond the half-way distance towards the smaller centres. On the east, however, the extent of its influence is confined by the effective competition of Stockton.

Stockton's own field is restricted both to west and east by the proximity of Darlington and Middlesbrough. It is more freely and extensively developed to the north and south. Immediately across the Tees, the inhabitants of Thornaby and the rural area immediately beyond can find in Stockton facilities as good as those provided at Middlesbrough somewhat farther away, and Thornaby falls within the field of Stockton rather than of Middlesbrough. The field of Stockton also extends into Yorkshire by Yarm into that area west of the Leven where Middlesbrough is much less accessible. But it is especially a large, though mainly rural, area in southeast Durham that Stockton commands, and here modern improvements in transport have enabled it to absorb the urban functions of the old market of Sedgefield.

The hold of Middlesbrough upon the communities of the north bank of the Tees has hitherto been slight and restricted, as Stockton can provide for its own inhabitants and those of nearby places services hardly inferior in any respect to those of its much larger, but less well-established neighbour. Since the Newport bridge was opened in 1934, however, the fields of Middlesbrough and Stockton have overlapped in Billingham, and with this improved access across the Tees the influence of Middlesbrough in Durham may be expected to increase.

Among Darlington, Stockton, and Middlesbrough none enjoys a position of primacy such as that exercised by Newcastle over a large area farther north. Middlesbrough's advantage of size is offset by the established regional relations of the older centres and, at least in comparison with Darlington, by the superior nodal situation of the latter. The rise of Middlesbrough has not affected Darlington and Stockton as agricultural markets. Indeed, Middlesbrough has no market, and it is Guisborough that serves as minor market-centre in Cleveland.

The flourishing produce-markets at Darlington and Stockton, which derive from the long importance of these towns in the rural economy, are important features of the modern trade of the region, and especially attract the families of miners and industrial workers from other towns.

In publishing a daily morning newspaper Darlington provides a service offered by no other centre in North England except Newcastle itself. Through its agency the influence of Darlington permeates the Tees basin and extends north into the Durham coalfield and south into Yorkshire to compete for circulation with Newcastle and Leeds journals. As the full influence of Newcastle as regional capital becomes weaker with increasing distance, its rôle is assumed most nearly in south Durham by Darlington, but farther east Stockton and Middlesbrough and, to a much less extent, the Hartlepools, divide a territory that is largely independent.

CHAPTER 13

WEST CUMBERLAND

THE other industrial area of North England, in west Cumberland, is no less definitely based upon a coastal coalfield with an adjacent iron-ore field (Figs. 4, 5), and until very recently it has been even more dependent upon the employment provided by its extractive industries and the iron smelting arising from them. The extent and resources of the mining area, however, are much less, and the scale of industrial development is correspondingly smaller. In recent years coal output has not been more than one and a half million tons, and that of ore only half a million tons,[1] and the population living in this industrial area is only about 100,000. The output of coal and still more that of iron-ore have declined as the richest and most accessible resources have been worked out, and the population has not increased over the past half-century. Shipbuilding and its ancillary trades, a busy activity of the ports in the days of wooden ships, has been dead since about 1870, and smelting, which was formerly carried on at several sites on both the coalfield and the orefield (Fig. 34), is now confined to Workington. With other industries almost unrepresented, it is not surprising that the depression of the inter-war period affected this district with special severity, and nearly half the working population became unemployed. Considerable migration took place from many settlements, especially from the Cleator Moor district, where the ore was exhausted and the ironworks derelict. Since then a considerable infusion of light industries, the appearance of a large chemical industry at Whitehaven, and the location on the west Cumberland coast of two of the first great projects concerned with nuclear fission, have profoundly altered the general situation, opening up brighter economic prospects.

Physically the area consists of the narrow strip of Carboniferous rocks that lies between the older massif of the Lake District and the Irish Sea. The fells drop steeply along the outer margin of the pre-Carboniferous rocks, but the narrow belt of Carboniferous rocks is an area of heavily faulted structure and broken relief. Slab-like masses of Whitehaven Sandstone, preserved above the productive Coal Measures in troughs, form high ground that reaches 800 feet on Arlecdon Moor (Fig. 55). The latter separates a groove that runs roughly parallel with the coast, drained by the Ehen in the south and

[1] In 1956 production dropped below 400,000 tons.

235

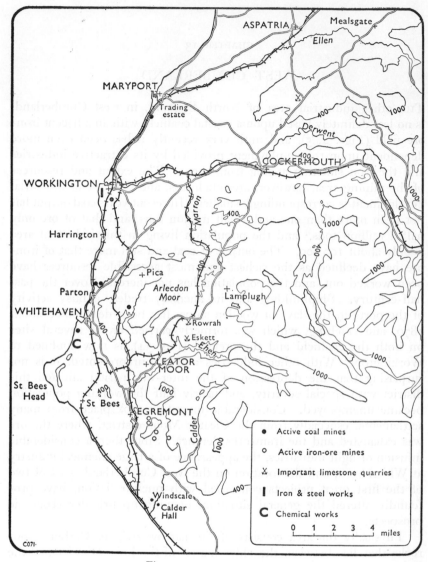

Fig. 55   WEST CUMBERLAND.

by the Marron tributary of the Derwent in the north. No major river
from the Lake District crosses the coalfield south of the Derwent, and
the long line of cliffs is notched only by the mouths of local streams
and by the ice-cut trench of the St Bees valley behind Whitehaven.
The gills are cut into extensive plateau surfaces, among which that at
430 feet is especially well represented. From the Derwent valley

northwards, however, the coalfield is lower, with larger and more open valleys. Southwards from St Bees Head, red Triassic sandstones replace the Coal Measures as the floor of the coastal lowlands in front of the Lake District mountains. The change is noticeable in the colour of the local stone buildings.

On the coalfield the prevalent drift soils are cold, heavy, and compact. Most of the farmland is now under grass, and the fields show widespread evidence of difficult drainage and are often infested with rushes. At lower levels the farmers retain some arable fields, but the higher farms are purely pastoral, and there are considerable patches of rough grazing on the plateaux in front of the steeply-rising fell country that is reached east of the Cockermouth–Egremont road. Some coniferous plantations serve as shelter-belts, and there are streaks of native woodland along the post-glacial gills, but otherwise there is little woodland. Thorn fences, however, are characteristic of the coastal belt and pass gradually inland and upward into the country of stone walls. Considerable tracts of allotments are features of the mining settlements, and some of the miners and quarrymen work smallholdings.

The presence of local urban markets has combined with the heavy soils and damp climate to emphasise dairying. Cattle rearing also remains important, and many of the calves reared are sold as stores, as the grassland is hardly rich enough to fatten cattle. Some lambs, however, the product of crossing half-bred ewes with Suffolk rams, are sold fat. Wheat was once grown in considerable quantities on the heavy soils and provided a considerable shipment from Whitehaven, but it is little grown now. Oats is the predominant cereal, but grass occupies the arable land for three years of the six-course rotation that is commonly practised, and potatoes are the only crop sold off the farms in any quantity. South of St Bees lighter, sandy soils overlie Triassic rocks with good subsoil drainage, and there is a notable increase in the proportion of arable land. Potatoes are important, but the main emphasis is still on the livestock enterprises—milk, store cattle, and fat and store lambs.

From Maryport in the north the coastal railway follows the cliff top to Whitehaven, with the shafts of large modern collieries alongside. It links the three active ports, situated at the mouths of the chief valleys that breach the cliff line, and passes by the former ports of Harrington and Parton at the mouths of smaller valleys. Beyond Whitehaven it leaves the cliffs to by-pass the St Bees headland by taking advantage of the direct passage provided by the St Bees valley. Another railway line, a little distance inland, interconnects the mining settlements of the coastal tract, and, beyond the sandstone ridge, the line from Egremont and Cleator runs along the Ehen–Marron groove. Its southern portion traverses the old iron-ore field, its northern portion, a single track, near the inner margin of the coalfield closely follows the course of the Marron to its confluence with the Derwent. All the railways, and especially the old wagonway tracks leading to the coast, follow sinuous courses as they seek easy gradients through the broken, hilly country.

Most of the population live in the three port towns, Maryport, Workington, and Whitehaven, which are at once mining and manufacturing centres, outlets for the coalfield, whence a considerable proportion of the output is still shipped to Ireland, and service centres for the surrounding areas. In the buildings of their nuclei, adjacent to the artificial harbours, local sandstone is prominent. In the heart of Whitehaven, for example, substantial stone buildings line the streets of the regular grid-plan of Lowther's new town (Pl. 27). The core of Maryport likewise shows the regular plan of Senhouse's new town of the eighteenth century on the south side of the river Ellen. Workington, however, has an irregular core that grew alongside the medieval castle on the south side of the Derwent estuary. Most of the modern built-up areas are quite typical of nineteenth-century extensions elsewhere in North England, consisting of tightly packed rows of brick dwellings with slate roofs. On their outskirts, as well as large pits and modern industrial works, are modern council-housing estates which are conspicuously different.

In other parts of this coalfield of outcropping seams where much of the mining has been carried on from drifts and shallow shafts, the mining settlement, which has accumulated over a lengthy period of sporadic development, resembles that of west Durham rather than of east Durham. It consists of a ragged, sprawling pattern of miners' rows, sometimes clotting to give high-density settlement, as between Workington and Whitehaven or on the old ore-field around Cleator Moor, elsewhere isolated and forlorn as at Pica on the edge of Dean Moor.

Few of the rows of old single-storeyed stone cottages survive, the characteristic type being two-storeyed brick buildings. Pit-head gear and mine dumps form their dreary settings. The ironworks (Fig. 34) that sprang up at several places during the nineteenth century have added other scars to the landscape. But the dislocated structure has not offered such a continuous field for large-scale mining operations as in the Northumberland and Durham coalfield. Rather has mining been carried on here in a number of pockets, bounded by faults or folds, and in spite of the small extent of the total area a larger proportion has preserved an essentially rural character. On the inland margin of the coalfield, where the resources have been largely exhausted and where operations were only small-scale, the economy has now reverted to a rural character and the scars are healing. The ore field in the Carboniferous Limestone between Lamplugh and Egremont (Fig. 5) is also exhausted, but, at least in the southern parts in the Ehen basin around Cleator Moor, the disfigurements are more extensive and there is a more lasting residue of housing and service equipment to which new industries are being brought to provide employment. Cleator Moor, where there was once a large flax-spinning mill, has once again become a centre of textile manufacture and also has clothing factories. A little farther north the chief local source of employment is now provided by the extensive limestone quarries of Rowrah, which provide flux for the Workington blast furnaces.

In the northeastward extension of the coalfield along the Ellen valley inland from Maryport as far as Mealsgate, the imprint of mining and industry during the past century of activity has been localised, and on the whole it has not been heavy. Outlying collieries and nearby terrace-housing punctuate the farmlands that are threaded by the Maryport–Carlisle railway and the Mealsgate mineral line. The largest settlement, Aspatria, straggles for over a mile along the main road.

For long mining clung to the coast in this coalfield, and it is again becoming increasingly localised there, on the very coast, as the centre of production moves seawards from the exhausted tracts behind to the areas of unworked coal remaining under the sea. Undersea working is itself an old feature of this coalfield, and even before the nineteenth century was being pursued more than half a mile beyond the shoreline from Whitehaven colliery. Coal-faces are now being worked as far as 5 miles out to sea, and the principal collieries line the coast from Risehow in the north to Whitehaven in the south. The Solway pit, just south of Workington, is a large new undertaking. Within the range so far penetrated is an undersea extension about as large as the landward portion of the coalfield (Fig. 4). When every allowance has been made for the continuation seaward of the same folded and faulted structure, this undersea zone may be expected to contain another 260 million tons, and if mining can be extended 8 or 9 miles out to sea these probable reserves would be increased by a further 400 million tons.

There are buried extensions of unproved wealth both north and south of the present coalfield (Fig. 4). The northern boundary of the outcrop of Coal Measures is the Maryport Fault, beyond which they are downfaulted beneath the New Red Sandstone. In the centre of the Solway basin these rocks may reach a thickness of 3,000 feet or more and may rest in turn on a considerable thickness of barren upper Coal Measures. The Coal Measures themselves are likely to be folded and faulted, so that only in the synclinal troughs would the full range of seams be present, while from intervening anticlines all of them may have been stripped away. Under such conditions estimates of reserves cannot be reliable. Immediately north of the fault near the coast is a relatively poor area, and probably the most promising tract lies out to sea. Exploratory work into it is being carried out from Risehow colliery. At the southern end of the coalfield a small tract of buried Coal Measures extends under the St Bees headland and is also prolonged out to sea. Its landward portion is already being worked south of Whitehaven.

Thanks to mining development in the northern part of the coalfield after the provision of railways and the exploitation of thin seams by longwall working, Maryport was handling more than half the coal shipments at the beginning of this century. Its ironworks were the farthest from the local ore-field, and it received most of the ore imports. It is now of little importance as a port, however, and has lagged behind in equipment and even in maintenance of its approach channel. Its ironworks and railway-engineering shops abandoned, its pits idle or slack, Maryport had over two-thirds of its population out of work in the early 'thirties. Since then the development of the Solway industrial estate, on the east side of the town, has widened the range of employment and has done much to offset the narrow dependence upon mining, especially by offering a high proportion of jobs for women and girls.

Workington was the scene of the only major development of the inter-war period, the establishment of the United Steel Company's modern plant. The iron and steel industry of Cumberland has become entirely concentrated here, except for the survival of some blast-furnaces at Millom alongside the Hodbarrow deposit, where, however, only pig-iron is made. The United Steel Company undertook improvement of the port, and, since the opening of the Prince of Wales dock in 1927, Workington has taken the lead in coal shipments. By reason of its ore imports, it has also become the chief importing port. The steelworks are equipped with modern coking plant, which consumes about one-third of the Cumberland output of coal. Technical improvements have made possible this use of local coal, although a large quantity of south Durham coal is also brought to mix with it to strengthen the coke.

Whitehaven has remained the outlet for the southern part of the coalfield and there are important undersea workings in its immediate vicinity. Since the war a large chemical industry has sprung up and now employs one-quarter of the industrial workers at Whitehaven. From a concern [1] that engaged in making ingredients of detergents and

[1] Marchon Products Ltd. treat imported phosphate rock with the sulphuric acid to yield phosphoric acid for the manufacture of detergents.

cosmetics there has developed a great new works that exploits the vast resources of anhydrite that underlie the area immediately south of the coalfield. Using as its other raw materials shale that is also available from the hillside on the spot and local coke, the Solway Chemical Works are already producing sulphuric acid at the rate of 100,000 tons per annum, an amount considerably in excess of the local needs of the parent concern. The process yields as clinker an incidental production of 100,000 tons of Portland cement. Whitehaven is also near enough to participate in the employment provided by the atomic energy establishments near the mouth of the Calder. At Sellafield, on the site of a war-time Royal Ordnance Factory, the Windscale plutonium factory produces weapon fuel. For both the present factory and its predecessor, the relative security in the far northwest of England behind the screening Lake District mountains was an important locating factor, and the coastal site allows the radio-active effluent to be discharged by pumping out to sea. The need to discharge, at a height of 400 feet, cooling air that is radio-active is responsible for the two great stacks that rise above the atomic piles. Across the river, at Calder Hall, Britain's first nuclear power station was opened in 1956 (Pl. 36).[1] Electricity is generated for the national grid and plutonium is produced as a by-product.

Between these outlying establishments of industry in its most modern manifestations and the southern part of the old-established industrial area with the new chemical industry on its margin, is the buried ore field (Fig. 5). Most of what remaining reserves of West Coast haematite exist probably lie here in a proved extension of the ore-bearing Carboniferous Limestone south of Egremont. But the limestone itself hardly extends south beyond the Calder. Except for a lingering activity at Hodbarrow (Millom), where deposits associated with the famous ' flat ' are still yielding ore, the only active mines, four in number, all lie in this concealed tract, which is being actively explored by borings. Three of the mines have been working for some time, but the other is new, tapping the recently discovered Haile Moor deposit.

An old industrial area, remote from the major national markets, West Cumberland seemed a singularly unpromising field for new enterprises and was becoming increasingly derelict between the wars. Yet it has emerged in the post-war period with greatly strengthened foundations and promising prospects. It is not only that the major large-scale developments noted above have opened up new possibilities. Through

---

[1] Its great cooling towers rise in parabolic curves to 300 feet in pairs at each end of the plant, with chimneys in pairs rising from the four cube-shaped reactors between.

the energy of the West Cumberland Development Board and sympathetic treatment accorded by the State, a considerable amount of new light industry has been established. Some of this has been accommodated in the Solway Estate at Maryport, but new factories are less concentrated in trading estates here than in the Northeast, and they also play a much greater rôle in the present economy. The new undertakings started under the Distribution of Industry Act provide for 16 per cent of the insured population as compared with 7 per cent in the Northeast.

If, as a result of the smaller extent of the west Cumberland coalfield, the lack of regional variation in the type of coal, and the high degree of similarity of economic development, fewer regional distinctions had emerged by the twentieth century than on the Northeast Coast, the most recent trends and developments have produced considerable differentiation of functions between its major centres. Maryport, no longer a very considerable port, is a mining town, equipped in addition with a variety of light industries that give it an unusually high ratio of female employment. Both Workington and Whitehaven are active ports as well as mining centres, but whereas the former is also especially a steel town, the latter has now emerged as a major centre of the chemical industry.

The three towns share the functions of service centres, their urban fields dividing the coalfield in rough correspondence with their basic hinterlands as ports. In the south, Egremont, with its old castle nucleus on the river Ehen in the narrow gap between the fells and the sea, is an old market centre, enlarged by industrial accretions, that has developed modern service functions. In the north, Cockermouth (Pl. 26), another old-established market town that grew up round a castle at the point where the Derwent emerges from the mountains, although it lies off the mining field, is within easy reach for some colliery settlements. No other places have anything approaching a full range of urban services, but Aspatria and Cleator Moor have limited auxiliary functions. Cleator Moor has lost its administrative status as an Urban District and Aspatria never achieved that status.

For more centralised services Carlisle is within effective range. Its influence is naturally greatest in the north, where Maryport especially feels its competition, as well as that of Cockermouth. These considerations, together with the smaller size of Maryport and the less intensive mining settlement in its surroundings, account for its smaller importance as compared with Workington and Whitehaven. But neither space relations nor the relative size and equipment of the major urban centres allow any one among them to assume a primacy and extend its field at any level of function to embrace that of its neighbours. Only Carlisle, twenty-eight miles northeast of Maryport, clearly attains a higher rank. For primary urban functions the coalfield towns are relatively independent and share the territory in close correspondence with the principle of equidistant margins. Each commands the area that lies nearer to it than to any of its rivals.

CHAPTER 14

THE NORTHUMBRIAN AND CUMBRIAN LOWLANDS

The Northumbrian lowland

BETWEEN the dales of the Border hills and the Northumberland coast, the coastal plain narrows northwards and becomes severely constricted north of the Aln. Here the grit moorlands that surround the Cheviot and enclose Glendale closely approach the coast, and the moorland edge, which often lies below 500 feet, is within three miles of the seashore north of Belford. The main railway line, using this narrow gateway from England to Tweedside and Scotland, runs in places within sight of the sea. To the south, where the hills recede from the coast, the Wansbeck and Pont-Blyth flow coastwards across rather featureless drift country from moorlands of flaggy grits that form the secondary watershed across the middle of the county. On these uplands, east of the watershed, are some of the reservoirs that supply the boroughs of north Tyneside (Fig. 59).

In the Cheviot gate, north of the Aln, the cuesta features of the limestone measures, which include the Whin Sill, are not everywhere completely buried by glacial drift. Rock outcrops protrude as scarped hills above undulating tracts of boulder-clay. The northernmost outcrop of the Whin Sill (Fig. 58), crossing the lowland by Belford to the coast at Bamburgh, lay directly athwart the line of ice movement and suffered severe erosion, which has produced craggy features. It forms the rocky islets of Farne, and between its promontories, along the coast from Bamburgh to Dunstanburgh resistant limestones are responsible for other rocky features. Inshore fishing for crab and lobster was once the mainstay of a few villages, such as Craster, along this fretted coastline, but its attractiveness for summer visitors is now a more important resource, especially at Seahouses and Bamburgh. The uninhabited Farne Islands are the breeding grounds of vast colonies of sea birds, and large numbers of waders periodically visit the extensive tidal mudflats that all but join Lindisfarne (Holy Island) to the mainland. The limestones and the accompanying Whin Sill strike inland again before the mouth of the Aln is reached, and the coast farther south, formed in the upper Carboniferous rocks, has fewer headlands between more sweeping bays. From the mouth of the Coquet at Amble the coalfield begins, but north of Ashington pits and colliery settlements are sporadic and the landscape has generally retained its rural character. Not so south of the Wansbeck. Here the Great North Road for some miles south of Morpeth separates contrasted landscapes of coalfield to the east and rural farmland to the west.

Except for the coalfield in the southeast of the county and the Tyne valley farther west, all the Northumbrian lowland remains profoundly rural, an agricultural countryside that has acquired few new lineaments since the nineteenth century and earlier. Extractive industries are unimportant, even less so than formerly when the limestone outcrops were extensively quarried and the associated thin seams of coal were worked for lime burning and local landsale. Modern operations, on a larger scale, have been practically confined to Shilbottle colliery (Fig. 58) south of Alnwick, where a seam in the Middle Limestone Group is locally developed as an excellent household coal.

Throughout these lowlands rather heavy, boulder-clay soils prevail, with only restricted cappings of lighter fluvio-glacial material. The fields are often strongly striped with ridge and furrow that dates from or was emphasised by tile drainage about the middle of last century. Since then much of the former ploughland on these heavy soils has been laid down to grass, but at the same time the clay grassland has been greatly improved by the introduction of wild white clover and use of basic slag. The experimental work carried out at Cockle Park, north of Morpeth, since 1896, has shown how such grassland can be upgraded and the results have been widely applied. Thus on the large farms in the Cheviot gate, once mainly ploughed for wheat, beans, and clover, grass-fattening on long leys has taken the place of corn farming. In 1870 more than one-third of the land was in corn, but the proportion is now less than 10 per cent. Here most farms are more than 300 acres in extent, and have substantial buildings round open yards. At some of the farmsteads the surviving chimney-stacks of their old steam-engines are still conspicuous, but the upstanding concrete silos are now more general landmarks that pick out the farmsteads in the country-side. In the coastal belt between the Aln and the Wansbeck such large farms are less prevalent, but throughout the coastal strip that lies east of the Great North Road and north of the Wansbeck between Morpeth and Alnwick and beyond in the Cheviot gate the farming is now strongly directed to fattening, both of cross-bred lambs and Irish cattle. Where sand and gravel patches allow farms to have substantial areas of lighter soils, arable land retains greater importance, and these farms, with more winter fodder, carry more stock at that season.

Towards the west the grassland deteriorates in quality, and fields are often rush-infested. Farms are smaller, and the poorer grazing does not allow fattening of livestock. This is rearing country, concerned

17

north of the Wansbeck more with sheep than with cattle. But between the Wansbeck and Tynedale there is somewhat better grassland where cross-bred lambs and, especially, Irish cattle are fattened in summer. This country, rising gradually from 200 to 700 feet, presents extremely monotonous expanses of grass fields, bounded by thorn hedges. Plough-land has been reduced from about 30 per cent in 1870 to less than 10 per cent. The bleak landscape is dotted with occasional small conifer plantations. Broken escarpments of limestone and whinstone give rather more diversity farther west, but in the east rock outcrops are limited to low sandstone knolls. The margins of the rock-exposures share with the sand and gravel patches the sites of many of the villages (Fig. 22b).

This zone of country across Northumberland, flanking the Border dales which were the fastness of raiders, is close-set with relics of its turbulent history in the form of castles, bastle-houses, and peles (Fig. 23). To these grim buildings the peace of the last two centuries has added several country mansions and numerous substantially-built stone farm-steads among their fields. But new buildings erected since the begin-ning of this century are few. The continued and widespread decrease in the agricultural population during the past hundred years has especially depleted the grouped settlements and the personnel of the large one-time 'factory' farms of the north of the county, on which large forces of hired workers were formerly housed in barrack-like annexes.

A few urban service centres, notably Alnwick, Morpeth, and Hexham, have grown. Accession of service functions and extension and strengthening of their influence over the surrounding countryside have more than offset decline of their old handicraft industries. But Belford, whose development in the eighteenth century so impressed Arthur Young, has little importance as a service centre today. It lies in the marginal zone between the urban fields of Alnwick and Berwick that runs across the Cheviot gate. Besides serving a portion of the coastal plain, Alnwick is an important centre for the inhabitants of the dale to the west, but Rothbury on the Coquet is primarily a dale centre, with only a limited range eastwards down the valley. Amble, at the mouth of the Coquet, has never been more than a mining settlement and coal port, and the Coquet, without any developed urban centre itself, marks the approximate limit between the fields of Alnwick and Morpeth. The latter, an old-established market centre, has especially profited from centralisation to develop as the service centre both for extensive rural areas and for neighbouring colliery settlements. The rural tract between the Wansbeck and Tynedale is shared among the urban fields of Morpeth, Hexham, and Newcastle, with the last-named exercising a special pull by virtue of both its higher urban status and the accessibility given it by the main road that runs northwest from it towards Carter Bar. Stagshaw Bank fair, north of Corbridge, has long been dead, and the auction mart that sprang up at the lonely railway junction at Scots Gap, near the edge of the fells, has declined since motor transport has made it possible for livestock to be collected for and distributed from the great markets of the marginal towns. Along the Carter Bar road, seven miles from Newcastle and just off the edge of the coalfield, Ponteland has grown as a residential settlement, but otherwise there has been little influx of townsfolk seeking country residence. Indeed, continuing relative remoteness from urban services, dearth of piped and cabled services and the expense of providing them to such a thin and scattered population, and the marginal quality of much land for farming present a serious combination of rural problems.

The Cumbrian lowlands

The prevailing surface forms and soil character of the lowlands on the western side of North England alike differ from those of the east. Although the rock basis is even more completely concealed by drift deposits, the coating of these is not usually as featureless as that on the eastern side, and it is also generally much more sandy. The margins of the lowlands, too, are different in character. Whereas the east coast is usually cliffed and rocky, that of Cumberland north of the cliffs of the coalfield has a low, shelving shoreline in the great re-entrant firth of Solway. At its head the mouths of the Eden and Esk are separated by a low tongue of land that forms Rockcliffe Marsh (Fig. 56). Farther west, the Wampool and Waver discharge into Moricambe Bay. Beyond these river mouths, sinuous channels extend across great expanses of tidal flats. Hadrian's Wall was built along the edge of the firm land as far west as Bowness, to carry it beyond the extreme fords of the estuary. Here the firth narrows opposite Annan. Between the marshes of Solway head and Moricambe Bay low promontories of land are smoothly outlined seaward by dune belts attached to the raised-beach gravels of old spits. Inland is terraced marine alluvium (warp), intersected by a regular pattern of deep drainage-ditches. From these flats protruding islands of drift stand out, sometimes with the whaleback form of drumlins. In the centre of the major saucer-like depressions between are extensive bogs such as Bowness and Wedholme Flows. Such are the features of this distinctive coast.

The framing highlands pass down dip-slopes gradually into the lowlands of the eastern side of North England, except where the Cleveland escarpment rises boldly above the vale of Tees and Northallerton gate, but the inland margin of the western lowlands over a long stretch is the imposing wall of the great Pennine escarpment,[1] one of the sharpest geographical boundaries in England (Pl. 1). Elsewhere the inland limit is less well defined. North of the Tyne Corridor the ground rises gradually to the Border hills. From the vale of Eden and the Solway plain it rises somewhat more steeply towards the margins of the Lake

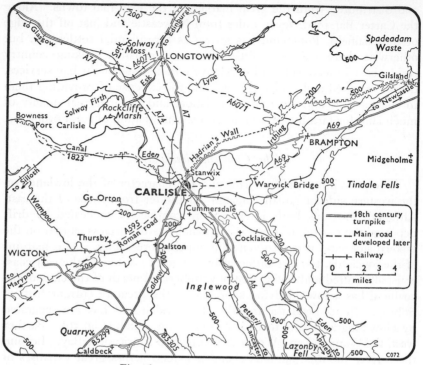

Fig. 56 THE SITUATION OF CARLISLE.

District, but here, too, the passage from Permo-Triassic to Carboniferous rocks shows no pronounced break of slope and is concealed beneath drift. The real margin of the Cumbrian massif is the sharp junction that characteristically corresponds with the edge of the pre-Carboniferous rocks as they rise steeply from the longitudinal groove in front of the infacing escarpment of the engirdling outcrop of the Carboniferous Limestone (Fig. 8). The crest of this limestone ridge is often above 1,000 feet, and lies above the margins both of the glacial drift and the enclosed farmland. The dip-slope as it descends to the lowlands is stepped by erosion surfaces, but the precise relations between surface facets and the irregular margins of drift-cover and farmland await complete investigation.

[1] In the south conical hills of Ordovician rocks stand up prominently immediately in front of the main escarpment.

The lowlands that surround the Solway present no strong relief, and the 200-foot contour is often not reached for 10 miles inland. The whole of this area was covered by the re-advance of the Scottish ice-sheet (Fig. 9). Apart from the post-glacial warplands of the coastal zone, however, the surface is softly undulating rather than flat. The ground-moraine that constitutes most of the area is strongly drumlinised, giving a predominance of convex forms (Fig. 10). Flatter tracts mark portions of the floors of pro-glacial lakes, as near Carlisle. There is an especially hummocky tract, with sharper and more irregular features, near the mouth of the Tyne Corridor, where the Brampton kame-belt is a medley of fluvio-glacial deposits. Winding esker-ridges and delta-fans form conspicuous mounds, and among erosion features there are notable sequences of spillways, such as those south of the railway between Wigton and Thursby, and those in Inglewood south of Carlisle. Everywhere exposures of solid rock are rare, confined to valleys where rivers have cut through the drift to engage in rock. A fragment of Lias rocks forms a low platform at about 200 feet round Great Orton, but is drift coated.

An important line of WSW–ENE faulting forms a significant boundary between the Solway plain and the open mouth of the vale of Eden to the southeast, and approximately corresponds with the limit of the last re-advance of the ice-sheet. To the southeast, in the vale of Eden, resistant sandstones form cuesta features with scarps facing west towards the Cumbrian dome (Fig. 8). The Petteril flows in front of the Penrith Sandstone escarpment, the Eden in front of that of the St Bees Sandstone farther east. Both rivers are in places quite deeply entrenched. Except on its western flank, on the dip-slope of the Carboniferous Limestone, the vale north of the Eamont shows less pronounced drumlin graining, but southeast from Penrith the upper portion of the vale in Westmorland, right up to 1,000 feet, has the 'basket of eggs' character of drumlin country *par excellence*. The grain is SSE–NNW, but beyond the position of an ice-shed that extended from Dufton Fell to Crosby Ravensworth Fell, crossing the vale near the site of Appleby, the drumlins are aligned towards the Stainmore funnel by which the ice escaped eastwards (Fig. 10). This tract of drumlinised lowland at the head of the vale of Eden (Pl. 1), hemmed in by high moorlands, is the 'Bottom' of Westmorland, nucleus of the ancient barony which became joined with the Barony of Kendal to form the county. The cultural affinities of dialects, customs, and traditions of the Barony of Kendal are very different, as reflects its orientation, and there is every justification for grouping it geographically with Lancastria.

Most of the ground-moraine material in these western lowlands is of light texture. T. V. Holmes aptly described that of the Carlisle–Silloth area as ' earthy gravel ',[1] and little of it gives really clayey soils. Sandy loam or medium loam would describe the character of much of the soil, and some of it is extremely sandy, as in the Brampton kame-belt (Fig. 12) and on some of the thin drift overlying the sandstone ridges. Altogether the soils are much lighter than in the eastern lowlands, and in spite of a moister climate more arable land has been preserved, though the reduction in the amount since about 1870 has been great. The coastal marshes, the haughs along the strips of valley-alluvium, and the laminated clays of lake-flats are essentially grass areas, as are marshy bottoms among the drumlins or in the compartments of intersecting esker and kame deposits. The really sandy tracts are sometimes patches of woodland, too poor for cultivation ; but where cultivated they are arable rather than grass. Generally, however, there is much variety of soil texture and drainage conditions within the compass of individual farms.

Mixed farming, with a heavy density of livestock both in summer and winter, is general. Farms of medium size, between 100 and 200 acres, are most characteristic, worked as family farms with little hired labour nowadays. They are prosperous and highly capitalised, equipped with electricity, piped water-supply, and machinery. Their stone buildings are substantial, though fairly old, and their byre accommodation is a prominent feature. Modernisation of the byres to conform to the standard required for tuberculin-tested milk production has often involved, among other things, incorporating the hay-loft above.

Arable land normally represents about one-third of the farm area, though it amounts to half or more in some sandy tracts and falls to considerably less in moister, less well-drained areas. The basis of management is grass-ley, retained for two or more years after a succession of oats, roots, and oats. Turnips or swedes are widely grown, and potatoes are sold off the farms to some extent, though they are less widely cultivated than the suitable nature of the soil might suggest. The farmer's income is derived essentially from a variety of livestock products, but although poultry and pig-keeping are often considerably more important than is usual for North England, liquid milk and fat stock, both cattle and lambs, are generally the mainstays. The Solway plain was till recently an important breeding area for Clydesdale farm-horses, but the general adoption of tractors has naturally affected this enterprise. Dual-purpose Shorthorns have been the chief type of cattle, but with increasing emphasis on milk production other dairy breeds have also become important in recent years. Butter making, until recently a notable feature of farm activity in the Cumbrian

[1] *Geological Survey Sheet Memoir : Carlisle, Longtown, and Silloth* (1899).

lowlands, has declined in favour of the sale of fluid milk, collected for large central dairies that have been established at various places. The fat lambs that are marketed in large numbers are produced from half-bred ewes with rams of Suffolk or some other large lowland breed ; others are bought in from Scotland in spring and grazed during the summer months on grass, their fattening being completed with swedes in winter. In the vale of Eden there is less emphasis on fattening cattle, but the rearing of Shorthorn cattle and both the rearing and fattening of cross-bred lambs are important. In the upper portion of the vale, in Westmorland, where most of the farmland lies between 500 and 1,000 feet, there is a marked diminution in the proportion of arable land, and this is rearing country.

On some of the most sandy tracts, on the heaths of the exposed high ground of the sandstone outcrops, in the Brampton kame-belt, and on spreads of coarse fluvio-glacial material elsewhere, plantations of conifers have been established, but in the old farmlands woodland is not very extensive. The countryside has a well-timbered appearance nevertheless, for trees are everywhere abundant in hedgerows and also occur commonly as strips of woodland along stream-courses, especially where these occupy incised valleys. The small fields of this long-enclosed countryside make an irregular pattern between winding lanes, and although farmsteads are numerous among the fields, considerable survivals of grouped settlement are evident (Fig. 24). The 'green' type of village (Pl. 21), with buildings grouped around an open green, is no less well represented than on the other side of the Pennines in Durham, though its study here has attracted much less attention. Thorough mapping of the occurrence of the type as a prelude to sound interpretation of its derivation is desirable. The characteristic building material, alike of parish churches and farmsteads, is red sandstone, usually the St Bees Sandstone, which provides the best local stone for building. Although this building material predominates in the existing settlements it is no longer quarried, and it is now very difficult to obtain stonemasons in Cumberland to carry out repairs to the stone buildings. The only sandstone quarries in operation are on Lazonby Fell, where the Penrith Sandstone is worked for paving setts.

Beyond the old farmlands there are fringing zones that represent the extensions of farmland and settlement brought about by systematic enclosure of commons under Acts of Parliament during the century preceding 1850. The intakes or allotments at the higher levels are enclosed by dry-stone walls and form a regular pattern of larger fields between straight country roads. Apart from scattered shelter-belts of conifers and small groups of trees that shelter the essentially scattered farmsteads, the landscape is bare and open. These upland farms, often

with poor, acid soils, are concerned with rearing, not fattening, livestock, and milk production is becoming increasingly important. On
the Carboniferous Limestone tracts old lime-kilns are a reminder of a
means by which sour, ill-drained soils were formerly improved, though
lack of local coal limited the practice as compared with the areas of
Yoredale rocks in the Pennine dales and in north Northumberland.

North of Brampton are some extensive lowland bogs in ill-drained
depressions of the drift surface. The land then rises gradually north-
eastwards towards Bewcastle Fells. The heavy, acid, drift soils of this
bleak, exposed countryside, which lies open to drenching rain from the
west, were greatly improved by drainage measures during the early
part of the nineteenth century, but drains have been sadly neglected
in the inter-war period. Although the boundary between improved
land and rough grazings is reached in many places below 600 feet,
much of the farmland considerably below this altitude is very marginal
in character. The grassland is poor and rush-infested, and the farming
is entirely concerned with rearing hardy types of livestock. Black
Galloway cattle are crossed with Shorthorns to produce blue-grey
calves to be sold as stores, and Blackface or mule sheep are bred. The
sport of coursing has a long tradition in the Border country, and since
its development as a form of mass entertainment for townsmen the
rearing of greyhounds has become a source of income of some importance on smallholdings in this part of Cumberland.

Along the Solway coastal belt are some distinctive forms of land-
use. The marshes of Solway head and round Moricambe Bay are
stinted grazings where fell sheep and hoggs are brought from the
northern part of the Lake District fells to winter, as others are sent
from the southern side to the shores of the Duddon estuary and
Morecambe Bay. Most of the farmland near the coast consists of
reclaimed warp—flat lowlying tracts intersected by the regular lines of
deep ditches. Owing to their low level, drainage is a continuing
problem and, at times of conjunction of high tides with strong onshore
winds, ponding back of the outfall subjects them to flooding. According to the height of the water-table and the nature of the topsoil that
overlies the heavy clay subsoil, the fields are used for arable or grass.
During the last twenty years, however, much land has been appropriated for airfields, and these tracts, where not occupied by hangars or
laid down as runways, are kept under grass. The wonderful close turf
of fine grass on the warpland finds a wide market over the country for
lawns and sports grounds, while some of the peat mosses are systematically exploited for moss litter.

The framing limestone hills that rise from the lowlands towards
the Lake District are still quarried at a number of places. The

principal quarries are north of Cockermouth near Papcastle, at Faulds near Caldbeck, west of Penrith, north of Shap, and at Hartley near Kirkby Stephen. At Shap the local granite is quarried, and, near the intersecting faults that mark the northwest corner of the North Pennine massif, coal mining has been active for at least two centuries in the district east of Brampton, near the mouth of the Tyne Corridor (Fig. 63). Nowadays few pits are left working either the Coal Measures of the Midgeholme coalfield at the foot of Tindale Fells or the Little Limestone coal farther west and north ; but this district is considerably scarred by the widespread activity of the past.

Now that local sandstone is no longer quarried for buildings, the only mineral provided by the Triassic rocks that form the basis of the lowland, as distinct from the marginal Carboniferous outcrops, is gypsum. It occurs near the base of the St Bees shales in lenses, but not as continuous deposits. These are worked at places along the Midland Railway line, chiefly near Kirkby Thore and Cocklakes. The railway follows the Eden valley, which in turn corresponds with the unresistant outcrop of shales. The gypsum was already being worked before the railway was built and was then conveyed to Carlisle by carts. At first the workings were open at the surface, but gypsum is now being mined. All the present operations are controlled by the British Plaster-board Company.

Since the first edition of the Ordnance Survey map was published a century ago, successive editions have had few changes to record in the lowlands of Cumberland, apart from completion of the railway system. There have been no substantial changes in the settlement pattern, although the numbers of the rural population have been substantially reduced, now that farming needs less labour and rural handicrafts are no longer pursued. Between 1851 and 1901 the population of most parishes declined in numbers by from one-sixth to one-fifth, and a further drop has taken place since. The handloom weaving and stocking knitting that earlier engaged the inhabitants of rural areas as well as market towns have died out altogether, and in the absence of mining or manufacturing development few parishes have increased in population during the past hundred years.

The growth of Carlisle during this same period is the more striking by contrast. The establishment of the city in the middle of last century as a great railway node [1] was followed by a remarkable expansion of its livestock markets, and its market status has been further strengthened by motor transport. No less significant has been its associated development as a service centre, emphasised by the multiplication of

[1] By 1876 the Citadel Station was a terminus for no less than seven railway companies.

modern administrative functions that have gathered in it as the county centre. Besides railway work, a considerable measure of industrial expansion has contributed especially to the local concentration of population, now nearly 70,000, and this in turn has played a part in enhancing

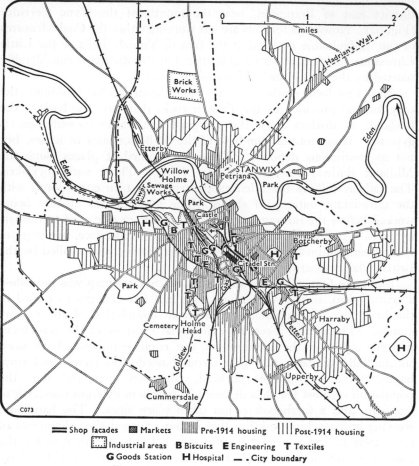

Fig. 57   CARLISLE: THE MODERN CITY.

the service status of the city. An exceptional feature in this part of the country, manufacturing industry is but one expression of the development of the city that has been made possible by modern communications.

The main shopping centre has grown along English Street between the old market place and the railway station established outside the south gate, and has spread beyond along Botchergate (Fig. 57). Alongside Botchergate also are the main livestock auction-marts.

254

Shops and offices have steadily ousted residence from the area that once lay within the walls. It is significant that the population within the walls attained its maximum in 1841, when only the first railway (from Newcastle) had reached Carlisle. Even before the coming of the railways the doubling of the population between the 1801 and 1841 Censuses, largely as a result of expansion of textile manufacturing, had produced considerable extensions outside the old gates. But there was still plenty of space available for the railways alongside the urban kernel, the old walled city. From the north the railways made use of the approach along the alluvial flats of the Caldew below the west wall, the earlier extension of housing outside Caldewgate having kept to the higher ground farther west (Pl. 45).

Beginning in the north, where Carr's biscuit works have expanded from their nucleus outside the Caldewgate, established in 1831 alongside the terminus of the early nineteenth-century canal,[1] an industrial belt extends south along the Caldew valley on the west side of the walled city (Fig. 57). Even before the railway period textile mills were ranged along the watercourses in the valley floor (cf. Pl. 45), and the railways, taking advantage of the valley line, confirmed its character as an industrial tract. Multi-storeyed woollen and cotton mills, with some very prominent chimneys, intermingled with mean housing, are characteristic features. Other industries, including engineering works and a large factory making and printing metal boxes, have also gathered here and beside the railway plexus that extends farther east, where large tracts of land on the south side of the city are occupied by railway works and sidings, laid out along and between the converging lines from east and south. The textile factories and the biscuit works offer employment for women to offset the predominantly male employment in railway work and in engineering, and Carlisle's occupation structure is remarkably well balanced.

As a textile manufacturing centre, Carlisle is especially interesting. It is one of the few outliers of cotton manufacture that have survived the modern concentration of the cotton industry in Lancastria, and its largest unit, the Holme Head works, is an example, unusual in Britain, of an integrated concern that deals with all processes from raw material to finished fabric. There are still a few mills well outside the urban area, along streams in rural settings.

Compact masses of terrace housing occupy the drift-covered plain across the Caldew valley and also stretch east of the city core as far as the Petteril valley north of the railways. In recent decades rapid

---

[1] This canal, the only one in North England, had been built in 1819–23 to the Solway at Port Carlisle. It did not last for long, for it was superseded by a railway, and Port Carlisle by Silloth. The canal bed became a railway track.

extension of the urban area has taken place along and between the radiating roads, especially across the Caldew to the southwest, and also on the south side between the converging railway lines in the Currock and Upperby district. The flat holms of the Eden, where the meandering river is extensively embanked, have been shunned by building, and open space, used for a market, parks, and sewage works, is here maintained immediately north of the city core. Across the Eden bridge, however, the old village of Stanwix has been swallowed up by suburban sprawl.

The Victoria Viaduct, opened in 1877, has strengthened connections between the city centre and the residential areas across the Caldew valley to the southwest, but although the various sectors of the outer residential zone are linked with the city centre, they are broken up and isolated from each other to a remarkable degree by the barrier effect of the streams and railway tracks.

On the Solway coast, 22 miles from Carlisle, Silloth is also exceptional in being a product of development within the past century. After its initial establishment, exactly a century ago,[1] as a small, regularly planned town beside the new port created at the terminus of the railway that superseded Port Carlisle and the Solway canal, it has not grown much either as a port or as a town, though it has become the principal seaside resort for the inhabitants of Carlisle and rural Cumberland. Grain is imported for the flour mills at the dockside, but the chief trade is in store cattle from Ireland.

Brampton, Longtown, and Wigton are all situated within about 10 miles of Carlisle, and have suffered from this proximity. They are decayed market-towns, their functions suppressed by the centralising power of Carlisle. None of them shows the fully representative range of services that is today characteristic of active towns in Britain. Penrith, however, lies eighteen miles south of Carlisle, far enough away to retain considerable independent status as a service centre. Situated about midway along the length of the vale of Eden, and commanding two routes westwards into the heart of the Lake District, it has become a considerable livestock market and well-developed service centre, with a population of 10,000. In the upper part of the vale, in Westmorland, Appleby and Kirkby Stephen have little importance as markets or as shopping centres, but in default of larger towns, they are centres for social services and administration. Brough, however, has lapsed into a mere village. Although it is situated at the road junction at the foot of Stainmore, it lay off the railway lines and had succumbed before it could be saved by motor transport.

---

[1] The railway was opened in 1856, Silloth dock in 1859.

THE DALES

CHAPTER 15

THE BORDER DALES

THE highland backbone of North England is a belt of country between twenty and thirty miles wide where opportunities for farming are severely restricted to the valley lands. In each river basin the settled zone is usually considerably less than half the total area, set among extensive tracts of deserted moorland. The strip of farmland tapers up the main valley and likewise up its tributary valleys, and the occupied area is thus fragmented among the prevailing waste country (Fig. 13 and Pl. 7). As a setting of human life, the typical dale is isolated from its neighbours on each side and is a cul-de-sac. Clear-cut definition by the moorland edge is lacking only down-dale, where the occupied strip along the valley widens and eventually opens out into the external lowlands. The high moorland watersheds, which completely interrupt the continuity of settlement, present considerable barriers to effective contacts between each dale and its neighbours. With few exceptions the railways that penetrate the dales are branch lines which stop short at railheads situated at varying distances up the dale-floors.

The outward orientation of the dales, which springs from the essential nature of their geography, has been emphasised by the development of modern communications, which has strengthened the functions of towns near or beyond the margins of the highland country at the expense of centres within the dales. In recent decades motor collection and delivery of livestock has powerfully contributed to market centralisation, motor transport and bus services have increasingly drawn the dalesfolk to the external towns for shopping and entertainment, and motor delivery-vans bring goods from outside right to the scattered farmsteads of the dales. The developed urban centres that now serve the dales lie in the lowlands outside and with few exceptions the dales are without fully developed towns. Indeed, Hexham and Haltwhistle in the Tyne Corridor and Barnard Castle in lower Teesdale are the only concentrations of more than 2,000 inhabitants.

The length of many of the dales means, however, that their economic and social life cannot be integrated entirely by external urban centres, even under modern transport conditions. There must be service centres of lower order within the dales, subsidiary knotting points in the texture of settlement, ranged in descending order of size and service-provision as the settled farmlands become more and more attenuated. But the degree of duplication of services that the distances involved make socially desirable is not economically practicable in view of the small population living within effective range. The well-known problems associated with rural service-provision in sparsely populated areas are encountered here in special degree. In the remoter upper parts of the dales not only do medical and educational services leave much to be desired, the inhabitants also must needs forego some of the urban amenities that most people in England have now come to regard as essential.

North Tynedale and, in its upper portion above Haltwhistle, South Tynedale are in these respects true dales, but the rest of Tynedale presents dale features in much less degree. It is a narrow valley lowland, confined for at least part of its length between moorland country to north and south. But it stretches over the main watershed into the Solway basin, so that the farmlands of Northumberland and Cumberland are here continuous through the highland country. From earliest times it has provided a passage between opposite sides of the country, the easiest and historically most important in central Britain. In modern times its rôle as a corridor has been emphasised by the construction of one of the earliest railways, as well as by road improvement. A special endowment of mineral resources in proximity to the through route that has fostered their exploitation helps to explain a degree of economic development and growth of population quite exceptional among the dales during the past century.

The dales of Northumberland that lie north of the Tyne Corridor are in many respects different from those of the North Pennines to the south. These differences are in part physical, but in part they derive from the different situations. In recognition of their most distinctive characteristics it seems appropriate to designate the two groups the ' Border dales ' and the ' Lead dales '. The troubled political history of the Border country has been as fundamental for the economic development and settlement history in the northern group as has the long history of lead mining in the southern group, though there are other important differences, notably of altitude, which must not be overlooked. Among the southern group lower Teesdale, outside the lead-mining field and with more lowland characteristics, is distinctive, while in the extreme north the fact that the physique is dominated by the belted arrangement of outcrops girdling the Cheviot massif is responsible for important modifications in the character of the northernmost dales. We shall consider in this chapter the Border dales, and in subsequent chapters the Lead dales and the Tyne Corridor.

In north Northumberland the tripartite arrangment of the geological outcrops (Figs. 3, 58) dominates the composition of the landscape and the distribution of farmland, though it does not entirely control either the drainage pattern or the human groupings that reflect its outward dispersal.

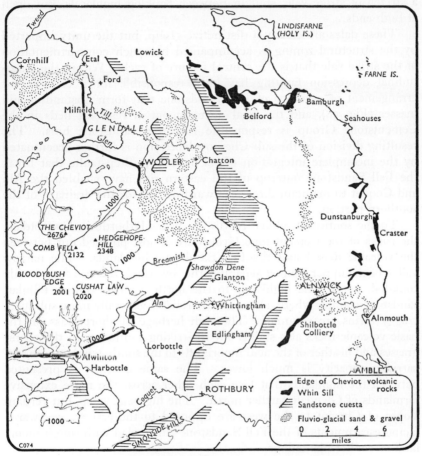

Fig. 58 NORTH NORTHUMBERLAND : PHYSICAL FEATURES.

Each drainage basin, however, shows the same three components – a strike vale, flanked by highlands of contrasting character (Fig. 8). The essential feature, so far as the human occupation is concerned, is the lowland into which the Cheviot glens open and which in turn is separated from the coastal lowland by sandstone moorlands. Along this sub-Cheviot depression, farmlands are continuous from the Coquet valley in the south across successive watersheds into the Aln and Breamish basins and thence by the Till lowlands to the Tweed. As dales, therefore, Coquetdale and Alndale are anomalous in that cultivation and settlement are continuous laterally across their flanking watersheds, while downstream, instead of opening progressively like funnels, their valleys are constricted like bottlenecks as they cross the sandstone ridge. Glendale is exceptional among the dales in being essentially a stretch of strike vale, shut in between flanking highlands, but open at both ends.

These dales are clearly a distinctive group, but the unity imparted by the structural zoning is accompanied by much compartmentation of the strike vale that is the central feature of each. Within the longitudinal depression faulting has been responsible for a complicated arrangement of outcrops of Fell Sandstone that form upstanding hill masses (Fig. 58), and the local development of resistant beds in the Cementstone Group is responsible for other sandstone hills. The resulting division of the sub-Cheviot depression is further accentuated by the incomplete integration of its drainage. Step-faults that break the Fell Sandstone outcrop of the eastern rim have enabled the Aln and Coquet to maintain direct eastward outlets for the drainage of the southern portion.

To the southwest, above Alwinton, near Harbottle in Coquetdale, the rocks of the Cementstone Group are almost pinched out between the volcanic massif and the Fell Sandstone highlands. The narrow valley of the upper Coquet separates the toweringly steep, yet smoothly rounded, porphyritic highlands to the north from the lower, tabular, sandstone country where, although the relief is generally more subdued, craggy forms are common. The rich herbage of short grass on the basic volcanic rocks also stands out in striking contrast with the coarse grasses and heather of the acid moorlands to the south, where the sheep-carrying capacity is much lower. The same contrast is presented between the highlands that face each other across the more extensive farmlands of Glendale farther north. The high and steep, but verdant slopes of Cheviot to the west are opposed to the craggy, westward-facing escarpments of the Fell Sandstone ridge, clad with rough moorland or conifer plantations.

Below Alwinton the Coquet keeps close to the Fell Sandstone outcrop, and most of the farmland is on its left bank, where the sub-Cheviot depression stretches away across the watershed into the Aln basin. Much of the undulating floor of this southern portion of the lowlands (Pl. 3) lies between 400 and 600 feet above sea level. Farther north there are extensive tracts at lower altitudes, and in Glendale the Milfield plain (Fig. 58), below 200 feet, is the flat floor of a lake-basin some twelve square miles in extent. The lake was impounded between the surrounding high ground and either the retreating ice-front in the

Tweed valley or the Cornhill kettle-moraine that had been deposited across the pre-glacial Till valley. When the lake was drained it was by a new channel that cut the deep ravine between Ford and Etal. In the southern portion of the plain, sheets of coarse gravel have been spread out by the Cheviot torrents on top of the deep, laminated clay of the lake bed, but farther north there are extensive tracts of alluvial flats that are still liable to flooding.

In the eastern compartments of Glendale, traversed by the Breamish, sand and gravel are also very extensive, though the surface is more irregular and hummocky. Most of the area west of the Breamish is a tract of kettle-moraine country, a medley of gravel mounds enclosing ill-drained hollows, where a mass of stagnant ice that was trapped in this basin dumped its load on melting.

Throughout these northern dales the farming emphasis is upon livestock. But the low altitude and the dryness of this rainshadow area, combined with the extensive spreads of light, gravelly soils, account for a much higher proportion of arable land than is elsewhere characteristic of dale farming. Both in this respect and in the prevalence of large farms, many of them comprising more than 300 acres of improved land, the sub-Cheviot depression resembles the coastal lowland rather than the other dales. The same applies to the rural settlement, with its high degree of representation of clusters in the form of hamlets and even considerable villages. Basically, it is a grouped form of settlement, characteristic of a long-occupied area of lowland farming that was colonised early by Anglian farmers, as the township names clearly indicate. As an area of old-established settlement, like the lowlands that lie immediately beyond the Border highlands, it was for centuries harried and impoverished by the ceaseless Border raiding. As some measure of protection those inhabitants who had sufficient means fortified their homes, and the district became as heavily studded with strong stone buildings as any part of the north country (Fig. 23). Among the dales, that is in the highland zone itself, only Tynedale can show a comparable density of such relics of the troubled past.

The substantial farm-buildings of modern times, set amidst a hedge-enclosed countryside, date from the agricultural revival of the eighteenth and early nineteenth centuries. The hired labour upon which the large farms relied was a feature quite untypical of the usual dale society, based elsewhere upon small family-farms, and the labourers lived in the grouped settlements that had come down from the Middle Ages. The lines of post and rail fencing between enclosures on the flat expanses of the Milfield plain, and the paucity of buildings, reflect the lateness of complete enclosure there. The Milfield plain is now a tamed, orderly, and productive countryside compared with the wilderness of gorse that existed in the eighteenth century, and only Kimmerston bog remains unreclaimed.

Even in the higher southern portion of the sub-Cheviot depression in Coquetdale the characteristics of lowland farming and settlement noted above are much more in evidence than in other dales, though less so than in Glendale. In Coquetdale, store cattle and sheep are the bases of the farming, whereas the lowland farms of Glendale also produce fat lambs. Arable land, which around 1870 amounted to about three-quarters of the farm area in Glendale, has decreased to less than half, and the primary function of ploughing is to renew grassland. Though most farms carry both cattle and sheep, near the Cheviot margin there is naturally more emphasis on sheep on farms that use the hill pastures. The peat-clad summits of the granite core are indeed barren, but the surrounding girdle of verdant, porphyry country provides rich sheep-grazing. The amount of lowland within the massif is negligible, however, and the V-shaped notches that are the glens are practically deserted. There are just a few lonely shepherds' cottages tucked away on the gravel haughs that are only slightly developed even at burn confluences (Pl. 2). The modern valley-settlements are far less numerous than the vestiges of prehistoric occupation that are to be found on every spur.

Sheep of the local Cheviot breed are still kept but so also are Blackface flocks, and these have been becoming increasingly popular. Production of pure-bred ewes for stocking lowland farms is a main concern, but half-bred lambs obtained by crossing with Border Leicester rams are also important. In recent decades understocking has allowed bracken to spread extensively on the hillsides and even to invade many of the higher fields in the enclosed lands. Sir George Stapledon considered that these bracken lands constitute ' the most improvable block of hill country in the whole of Britain '.

Scarped sandstone hills, carrying conifer plantations and patches of shaggy moorland, interrupt the farmlands of the sub-Cheviot depression, and to the east the continuous sombre wall of the sandstone ridge presents the same features, and isolates the dales from the coastal lowland.

Of all the dales, no others are so poorly endowed with mineral resources, for minerals of economic importance [1] are not associated with any of the three geological formations that constitute this group of dales. Lacking mining and quarrying to provide employment, and precluded by their remoteness from enjoying some other modern forms

[1] Except sandstone, quarried at a number of scattered localities in the past for building stone.

of economic development, the northern dales have remained profoundly rural and sparsely peopled. They have also experienced severe depopulation during the past century. This has been especially acute in Glendale, where conversion from arable to grass has taken place on a bigger scale and where there has been a drastic reduction in the amount of hired labour on the large farms. Among nearly 100 parishes only 9 have more inhabitants than a century ago, and the general loss has been of the order of 40 per cent. After slow growth during the first half of the nineteenth century had brought the total population in these northern dales to about 18,000, the number has since decreased to 11,000, of whom about 3,000 live in Wooler and Rothbury.

Rothbury, situated in the narrow gap by which the Coquet crosses the most imposing portion of the Fell Sandstone ridge, is the point most accessible from Tyneside, and has enhanced its functions as a livestock market and holiday resort since a railway reached it in the eighteen-sixties. Its population is still only 1,250, however, and elsewhere there has been little or nothing to offset the rural depopulation. Wooler, at the foot of the Cheviot and overlooking the Milfield plain, is centrally situated to be the natural focus of Glendale, but its population is now less than it was at the beginning of the nineteenth century. The more centralised urban functions have become increasingly concentrated in the external towns, Alnwick and Berwick, that are supported by more populous areas outside the dales. Their presence could not find justification within this secluded and thinly peopled region. Not more than 6,000 people live within the urban range of Wooler, and the population of Coquetdale above Rothbury is less than 2,000.

It is easy to exaggerate the importance of the natural passage-way formed by the continuous lowland along the sub-Cheviot groove. Practically its entire length was traversed by a Roman road, but this is so extraneous to the present-day pattern of communications that it is not even represented by country lanes until north of the river Breamish. Here the straight minor road approaching Lowick from the south follows its line, though the main road from Wooler to Berwick pursues a roughly parallel course farther west. The whole area is today a by-way, and although tourist traffic has recently increased along improved roads that offer scenically attractive alternative routes to motorists to and from Scotland through the north of Northumberland, the railway from Alnwick to Coldstream via Wooler was only a single-track line that was not built until 1887 and was closed again in 1930 because it was unprofitable. This railway and the first-class roads mentioned above traverse only the northern part of the depression. Above Rothbury, upper Coquetdale, in spite of its lateral connections with Redesdale and Alndale, is as isolated as any dale.

The remaining Border dales (Fig. 59) lie within the Tyne drainage basin. The western Cumbrian flank of the Border uplands is only a small portion of the total area and its dendritic drainage does not present clearly defined dales. The undulating upland surface descends gradually west and southwest without showing any sharp passage from moorland to farmland.

Geologically, the Border country is built of a great thickness of lower Carboniferous sediments (Fig. 3) laid down here before sedimentation began farther south in the North Pennines, where they are unrepresented. Among these rocks limestones form an almost insignificant fraction of the total thickness, and there are few resistant beds to grain the country, which slopes away with the dip of the strata from the Bewcastle and Cheviot domes. Northeast to southwest flexuring, combined with the lenticular development of massive grits, are responsible, however, for the higher ground in mid-Northumberland, behind which the drainage has been integrated so that the Rede flows into the North Tyne.

The altitude nowhere reaches 2,000 feet, and summit areas above 1,500 feet are not extensive. The relief is very subdued and, except for small, island-like protrusions of rock, most frequent in the east and southeast, the whole area north of the Roman Wall is coated with a homogeneous cover of boulder-clay. Drainage conditions almost everywhere are poor, and great areas are peat-clad. In spite of the considerable proportion of the surface that lies below 1,000 feet in these notably open dales, the farmland is no more extensive than in the much higher dales of the North Pennines (Fig. 13). In Redesdale and upper Tynedale above Bellingham there are less than 50 square miles of farmland in a total area of well over 300 square miles. Above Bellingham the enclosed land pushes a narrow tongue up North Tynedale as far as Falstone, and up the tributary valley of the Tarset burn to Waterhead, but beyond there are only discontinuous patches, chiefly on alluvial haughs, and the drift-covered valley-sides are often unenclosed even at 500 feet.

Enclosure of commons about the beginning of the nineteenth century added considerably to the area of farmland, but there has since been some reversion, and many of the enclosed fields are badly infested with rushes. Perhaps a quarter of the farmsteads are in the upland zone above 750 feet, but the enclosed area is only a small fraction of the total, amid deserted wastes, which until recently had changed little since the days when they were frequented by the moss-troopers. Such change as had taken place in their plant-cover had represented a deterioration in grazing value as a result of restriction to sheep. Much of the fell country has, in fact, become sheep-sick, drained of its never-

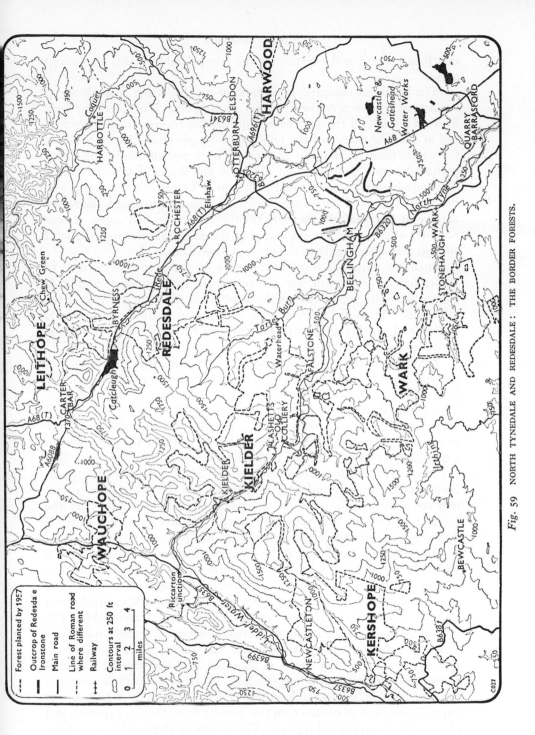

Fig. 59 NORTH TYNEDALE AND REDESDALE : THE BORDER FORESTS.

rich lime content and overrun by the less palatable plants that sheep avoid.

The hill farms comprise great areas of rough grazing, a single sheep needing often two acres or more for its support. The breeding flock lives on the fell all the year except during the severest winter weather and at lambing time, but the fells are no longer stocked with wethers, for which there is now no market. The breed of hardy hill-sheep preferred is the Blackface, and there are few flocks of Cheviot sheep. The pure-bred ewes are crossed with Border Leicester rams to produce mule and half-bred lambs for stocking lowland farms, and after they are five or six years old the ewes themselves are drafted away. Large numbers of cross-bred lambs reared in the dales pass through the local auction marts, especially at the great autumn sales.

Such few ploughed fields as there are on the farms are devoted to winter-fodder crops, but hay is everywhere the mainstay, and it is usually the only crop grown on the small areas of improved land of the hill farms. These fields are reserved for hay in summer, and provide shelter and grazing in winter for the less hardy sheep and for the breeding flock at lambing time.

Some of the marginal and rough land, especially in the Cumbrian portion, is used for outwintering hardy store cattle, but these are chiefly kept at the lower farms, where byres comprise most of the buildings. The dale farms that are mainly or entirely holdings of improved land combine cattle rearing with sheep. In winter, when the cattle are indoors, fields are available for sheep, but in summer they are used to graze cattle or to provide hay and other winter keep for the breeding animals. The hardier black Galloways, Shorthorns, or Shorthorn crosses are the most popular types of cattle, and the ' blue-grey ' calves that are sold in large numbers as stores at the local markets are the products of crossing Galloway heifers with a Shorthorn bull. There is little emphasis on dairying, and few of the cattle can be fattened locally.

The marginal farmlands of the Border country were already flecked with conifer plantations during the course of the nineteenth century as a result of the planting activity of private landowners. Since the Forestry Commission was set up after the First World War great tracts of the Border hills have been clothed with State forests (Fig. 59). The first plantings were made in the 'twenties, but the scale of operations has been greatly extended since 1945, and about 100,000 acres have now been planted. The limits of acquired land that can be regarded as plantable are now being approached. Most of the area lies beyond the low limit of improved land, but below 1,250 feet, which is the approximate limit of commercial tree growth here, though experimental planting has been carried higher. The forests lie in great blocks astride the watersheds (Pl. 4), with the highest summit areas standing out as islands of moorland. Several species of conifer have been introduced, but large-scale commercial planting is practically limited to two species of spruce (the Sitka spruce and the Norwegian spruce), established without a nurse crop on overturned turf after preliminary excavation of a system of deep drains. Mature timber will be available when the trees are between 60 and 80 years old. Since 1948 thinnings have been producing a valuable supply of poles, used especially for pit-props.

Most of the plantations have been established on land that was part of open sheep-runs, but there has been some encroachment on the in-by portions of holdings. By reducing these valuable wintering lands and by isolating parts of the summer grazings, forestry has tended to disrupt the older sheep-farming economy. Pasture corridors through the forests, however, provide access to the high grazings that crown the summits, and reduce fire risk, as does the maintenance of some smallholdings within the forest tracts. Forestry is a much more intensive form of land use, and when in mature management the forests will provide a living for ten times as many men as the same area did under hill grazing. Against the 10 per cent decline in the sheep flocks that has already taken place must be reckoned the benefits to the remaining farmlands of the shelter provided by the forests and of the improved communications along the new roads that have been built to give access to the forests.

Farming and forestry dominate the present-day economy, with mining and quarrying much less important, and manufacturing hardly represented at all. There is only a small woollen mill, at Otterburn, which produces blankets and rugs of high repute.

Although the rocks of the Carbonaceous and Limestone Groups of these dales have considerably greater mineral wealth than exists in the northernmost dales, mining has never been as important or as widespread as in the dales still farther south. North of the Roman Wall, which follows the Whin Sill escarpment, the lower Carboniferous rocks do not carry any workable veins of ore, and the whole area lies north of the Little Limestone coal. But thin coal seams at various lower horizons of the Limestone Group and in the Carbonaceous Group below have been worked fitfully by drifts. Most of these were to provide fuel for local domestic use, and for burning the thin limestones that were quarried locally from the same series. In two periods, about the middle of last century and again in the decades before the First World War, larger ventures were undertaken at Plashetts, towards the head of North Tynedale, and for forty years before 1878 the Redesdale ironstone was worked near the mouth of Redesdale, northeast of Bellingham (Fig. 59). Ore working was begun in 1839 by the ironmasters of the coalfield who were then desperately anxious to lay hold upon new sources of supply. Blast-furnaces were immediately established, and for a few years the local ironworks dealt with the ore, but later it was all sent to Tyneside for smelting. Ironstone has not been worked since 1878, and since the First World War quarrying, chiefly for roadstone from the Whin Sill and Great Limestone as they cross the lower part of North Tynedale, has been more important than coal mining, which does not employ more than 50 men at the few surviving drifts.

Except at Plashetts, the non-agricultural activities have chiefly been carried on in the lower parts of the dales, below Otterburn and Bellingham, and within or on the margin of the farmlands. But in 1957 there were over 500 men employed in forestry, and it was expected that the number would soon grow to about 2,000 ; and, since the forests lie for the most part beyond the farmlands, the accommodation of forest workers requires new settlements high up the dales. The Forestry Commission proposes ultimately to establish several new forest villages, and existing hamlets, such as Falstone, are to be extended. Three of the new villages, at Kielder (Pl. 4), Stonehaugh (in Wark Forest), and Byrness (in Redesdale Forest) are already being built (Fig. 59). They have been planned as nucleated settlements, each with central square or place, church, village hall, and shops, as well as colourwashed houses laid out in terraces or blocks.

Elsewhere the grey stone farmsteads stand as they did more than a century ago, with but few additions. Modest growth has taken place at Bellingham since the coming of the railway, and some development of service functions for the dale and mining ventures have left a few rows of brick terrace dwellings on the hillsides. These are the more conspicuous because they are so exotic in this countryside. On the other hand, there was little that has had a chance to survive from a still earlier period, before the seventeenth and eighteenth centuries, when the semi-nomadic herdsmen and cattle thieves settled down as farmers. Castles and pele-towers are fairly well represented only towards the eastern and southeastern margins (Fig. 23). They are plentiful in North Tynedale below Bellingham, but few are to be found in the upper dales, which were hardly extensions of the settled, civilised lowlands but rather the fastnesses of the Border clans who lived beyond the law. With little admixture from outside, the dales folk of today are their descendants, and the old clan names are highly represented among their modern surnames.

From these dales, where opportunities for an honest livelihood have been so restricted, there is a long tradition of exodus of surplus population, and at least in part they supplied the keelmen of Tyneside in

Elizabethan times. Over the past century the slight increase in population localised at Bellingham has not balanced the stready drain of people from the land, and the dale population has been considerably reduced. The grouped settlements, with some two-thirds of the present population, have suffered less than the dispersed farmsteads, and abandoned farm buildings are not uncommon. Depopulation, however, has been much less pronounced than in the dales farther north, where there was formerly more arable land and more hired labour. Railway and reservoir construction, as well as the shortlived mining ventures, brought temporary influxes into some parishes for periods during last century, but the new forest villages are indicative of something more lasting and significant.

As much by their inhabitants, who have been brought in from outside the dales, as by their novel layout and appearance, contrasted with and external to the older settlement pattern, these villages are signs of a new era. They represent the infusion of new life into a stagnating economy, just as the forests themselves have already given a new look to a landscape that had long experienced little significant change. Within a few decades forestry may support communities aggregating between 12,000 and 15,000 people in these dales. It is expected that by 1970 there will be 2,000 workers in Kielder Forest and another 500 each in Redesdale and Wark Forests. When allowance is made for people engaged in ancillary industries and in providing services for the primary population the above estimate does not seem unreasonable. Social problems much greater than the difficulty of recruiting labour will attend the provision for immigrant families and their assimilation into the dale communities. In the upper dales, above the confluence of the Rede and North Tyne, the newcomers will heavily outnumber the established inhabitants, who were only 4,000 in 1931.

These Border dales are isolated from populous areas and towns by sheer distance. For nearly a century before it was closed in 1956 a railway traversed the length of North Tynedale from Hexham to Riccarton Junction across the Border in Liddisdale, where it joined the Waverley line from Carlisle to Edinburgh. But only a trickle of through traffic used this route, and it was never doubled by a main road. Redesdale, with no railway, was not opened to through traffic till later, but it now enjoys more direct access to distant cities. A modern road (A 68), following the line of the Roman road (Dere Street) from Corbridge, converges at Elishaw in Redesdale with another main road (A 696) coming direct from Newcastle, and thence ascends the dale to pass over Carter Bar into Scotland. Its summit at 1,370 feet lies well below the Roman fort Ad Fines (Chew Green). By this road the inhabitants of Redesdale find urban services at Newcastle more accessible than anywhere else. Redesdale has also had another special association with Newcastle since the beginning of this century, when the Catcleugh reservoir was constructed to supplement the city's water supply. Other smaller, older reservoirs sited in the uplands of mid-Northumberland, on both sides of the watershed, also supply water to the Tyneside municipalities.

Upper North Tynedale, without a first-class road above Bellingham, is now more isolated than Redesdale. Bellingham, 17 miles down the dale from Kielder and at the mouth of Redesdale, can offer only a poor and incomplete range of urban services, and is no more than a service village, with a population of fewer than 700. The whole dale is clearly oriented towards Hexham, its nearest town although another 17 miles beyond Bellingham. A new secondary modern school at Bellingham serves the whole of North Tynedale above Wark, but Bellingham and all the rest of the dale still depend upon Hexham for grammar-school facilities. Farmers and livestock from the whole of the dale are drawn to the great marts at Hexham in the Tyne Corridor. From here the dale extends as a long attenuated strip of rural settlement stretching nearly 40 miles north to the Scottish Border. Between its farmsteads and the first ones on the Cumberland side of the fells to the west lies an area that is perhaps the most unfrequented in the whole of England and Wales. Many upland species of wild life that are now rare in Britain have here been able to live on undisturbed till our times. Now their sanctuary is threatened by the advancing forest that is transforming the habitat [1] as well as by falling missiles. Since Armstrong began to make guns at Elswick more than a century ago the wastes of Redesdale have been used as an artillery range, and in 1956 it was decided to use Spadeadam waste (Fig. 56), on the Cumbrian border north of the Tyne gap, for testing rockets.

To some degree, however, the protection of the wild Border country against many forms of spoliation has now been assured. Most of the area north of the Roman Wall that is here treated as comprising the Border dales was designated as National Parks in 1955. The land under the control of the Forestry Commission became a National Forest Park, and an even larger area adjacent to the east was designated by the National Parks Commission (Fig. 13). Only the farmlands of the sub-Cheviot depression, of Redesdale below Elishaw, and of North Tynedale below Bellingham, lie outside its bounds. Though traversed and skirted by tourist roads, the land included in these National Parks must rank as the loneliest, most secluded part of England. In spite of the anticipated influx of more forest workers it is likely to remain so.

---

[1] Thanks to the cover provided by the forest, however, roe deer are increasing in number again.

CHAPTER 16

THE LEAD DALES

THE dales of the North Pennines, south of the Tyne Corridor, form a group by reason of their distinctive similarity. The area is a structural and morphological unit, and from this springs the essential similarity of landscape and economy from dale to dale. But it is not a hydrographic unit, for the drainage lines diverge from the Cross Fell-Killhope Law node, and there is no grouping of the dalesfolk into a single unified community. In human terms the area consists not of one unit, but of several distinct units of similar type.

A rigid block has occupied the area of the North Pennines since before Carboniferous times, and from this remote geological past the area has acted as a structural unit. Its surface rocks are the upper series of the lower Carboniferous succession, which not only contain frequent, if thin, beds of limestone among the sandstones and shales, but were mineralised at the time of the Hercynian disturbances. Emphasised again as a structural unit by the Tertiary earth-movements, the area comprising these dales has throughout experienced the same sequence of stages of morphological development. During the Ice Age the main streams of moving ice from north and west skirted its margins and did not traverse its heart (Fig. 9). It was occupied by local ice and its drift has been derived from its own rocks rather than from outside areas.

The presence of numerous productive veins in the local Bernician strata has contributed more than anything else to give the dales of this group their distinctiveness : they are the Lead dales. Their distinctiveness in this respect, however, is reinforced by other physical circumstances, not least because they are higher. Except in the lower portion of Teesdale, which lies outside the mineralised area, only a very small proportion of their surface lies below 700 feet (Fig. 60). Cross Fell almost reaches 3,000 feet, and extensive tracts along the watersheds that splay out from this crown lie above 1,500 feet. The valleys, though mature and open, are deeply trenched in the moorland plateau, and their fairly steep sides are much less continuously coated with drift than in the Border dales.

The master drainage lines of these dales originated as dip-streams on the uplifted and somewhat domed surface of the block, and the upper dales now appear as inliers cut into the gently tilted sedimentary rocks. The outcrops of the harder strata, sandstones and limestones, can be traced as shelves along the dale sides. Down-dale these slope to-wards the valley floor till they are intersected by the river, and towards the dale heads they also approach the valley floor (Fig. 61). Thus the chief limestone bed, the Great Limestone, outcrops in the head valleys

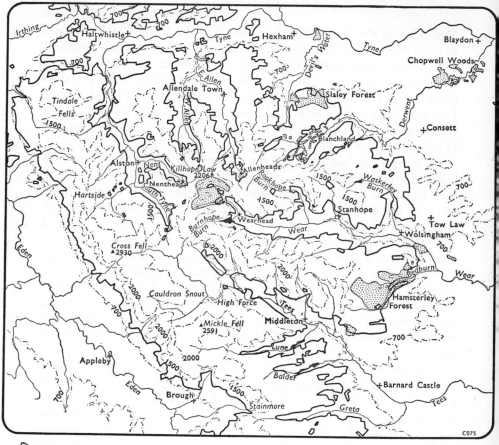

Fig. 60   THE LEAD DALES : RELIEF AND LAND USE.

of Weardale at nearly 2,000 feet, and appears again in the river bed at 530 feet near Frosterley. On the dale sides overlooking Stanhope, where it is extensively quarried, the level of its outcrops is about 900 feet. The uppermost of the limestone bands, the Fell Top lime-stone, appears about 400 feet above the Great Limestone. Above it is the massive coarse sandstone known as the Grindstone Sill, and on the summit ridges some cappings of Millstone Grit appear, especially in the direction of the dip. At a somewhat variable position among the lime-

stones below the Great Limestone is the Whin Sill. Its extensive outcrop in the floor of upper Teesdale is a conspicuous feature and gives
rise to waterfalls on the Tees at Cauldron Snout and High Force.
Whinstone is exposed more locally in Weardale, but does not appear
in the other dales. Usually below the outcrop of the Whin Sill along
the great western escarpment of the block is that of the Tynebottom

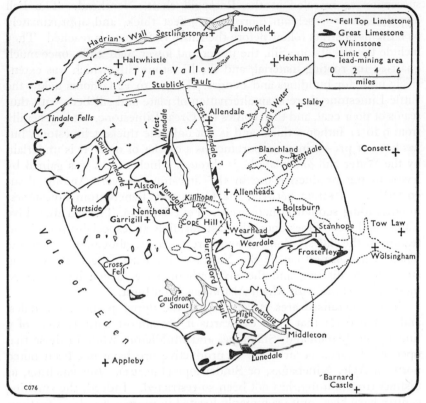

Fig. 61   THE LEAD DALES : GEOLOGY.

Limestone, the lowest limestone that appears in the dales, where it
outcrops in the bed of the Tyne above Garrigill and also in upper
Teesdale.

Though the Great Limestone has probably yielded more ore than
all the other strata together, the productive mineral-veins range over
about 1,000 feet of strata, which Sopwith called the Lead Measures.
There are only two important limestones above the Great Limestone,
but below it four other limestones are intercalated among the shales
and sandstones before the Tynebottom Limestone is reached. The
shale beds are known as ' plate ', while ' hazle ' and ' sill ' are local

terms for the sandstones. ' Sill ', however, is a name given to any persistent bed in the succession. The Whin Sill is one such, whence the derived use of the word in the standard terminology of geology to denote a concordant igneous intrusion.

The summary account of the rocks of the Lead Measures that follows is based especially upon Thomas Sopwith's description [1] and the succession as revealed at the Rampgill shaft, Nenthead. The Fell Top limestone is seldom more than 5 feet thick, and approximately 60 fathoms of strata follow before the Little Limestone is reached. They include the Whetstone Sill, the upper and lower Slate Sills, once much quarried for roofing material, and the Firestone Sill, which was extensively used for buildings and hedges. For 10 to 12 fathoms below the Little Limestone there is an alternation of plate and sill beds with thin seams of poor coal, and then comes the Great Limestone. It is generally from 9 to 11 fathoms thick, and is not only the thickest limestone, but has been of pre-eminent importance as a carrier of ore. It is underlain by the Water Sill and plate beds through which access was gained by levels to the productive ore in the limestone above. Among about 90 fathoms of strata between the Great and Tynebottom limestones, in descending sequence there are the Four Fathom, Three Yards, Five Yards, and Scar limestones, the last forming an especially prominent feature in the dales. Some distance respectively above and below the Three Yards limestone lie the Nattrass Gill hazle, the best building stone in the district, and the Six Fathom hazle, which has provided most of the stone with which Alston has been built.

The mineralised area is confined to the upper parts of the dales, and in the dales that open eastwards it lies almost entirely west of a line joining Blanchland, Stanhope, and Middleton, while in those that open northwards occurrences of productive ore have not been noted north of Ayle, Ninebanks, or Sinderhope (Fig. 61). But smelting, as distinct from mining, has not been so restricted. Indeed, the smelting centres have been quite commonly located in more accessible situations lower down the dales, beyond the actual mining field (Fig. 62).

The ores occur in veins of fissure-type, with local ' flats ' occasionally leading off horizontally from the sides of a vein. Most of the vein is occupied by gangue material (' rider ') in which strings of ore occur ; but the flats, which are the result of lateral spread of mineralised solutions from the veins, are much purer bodies of ore with little gangue material. The veins are usually thin and poor when they traverse shales,[2] probably because of the closing of the fault planes in

---

[1] T. Sopwith, *An Account of the Mining Districts of Alston Moor, etc.* (1833).
[2] The close-textured plate beds that overlie the Tynebottom Limestone, however, have carried productive veins.

these weaker rocks, but they are better developed in sandstones and especially in limestones, which lend themselves to the formation of wide, open fissures for ore deposition. 'Flat' deposits are confined to the limestone beds. The mining field is bisected from north to south

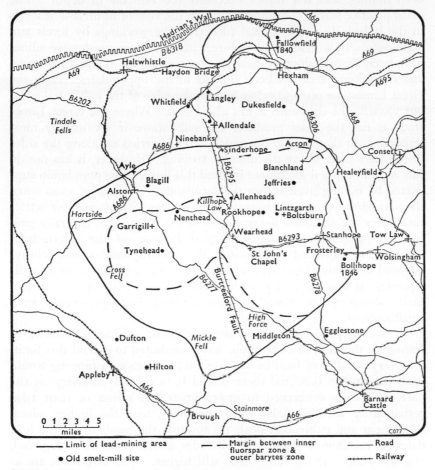

Fig. 62 THE LEAD DALES : MINING FIELD, SMELTING SITES AND COMMUNICATIONS. Most of the smelt-mills were established during the eighteenth century (see pp. 143-4 and 149).

by the Burtreeford dislocation, a faulted monocline which in places has a downthrow to the east of between 400 and 500 feet. It runs along the west side of East Allendale, across the upper end of Weardale, into Teesdale. Each half of the ore field shows a zonal arrangement of gangue materials, an inner zone of fluorspar being surrounded by an outer zone of barytes (Fig. 62).

275

Besides varying in productivity according to the country rock they traverse, the veins everywhere show rapid impoverishment with increasing depth. They are productive only near the surface, and this applies especially to their silver content. There has never been any deep mining, and few mines exceeded 100 fathoms in depth. The usual practice was to sink short shafts on the vein or to drive adit levels in the hillside to reach it, and to extend the workings by levels and cross-cuts. It is evident, therefore, that the most productive mines have been located along or near the outcrop of the Great Limestone, and the mining area has been limited to the upper dales. Here the Great Limestone often fits closely with the edge of the cultivated zone, but towards the daleheads it lies above this. Where the Great Limestone is not the chief producer the sills above it are usually most important, so that mining has tended to be carried on along the sides of the dales at or above the limit of farming. However, it has not on this account pushed settlement beyond this limit. The population supported by mining lived within the farmlands. The mines, even when they lay above this zone, were usually not far distant, and for settlement sites the sheltered lower slopes of the dales were naturally preferred. Moreover, no doubt in part because of the intermittent employment provided by mining, the miners were almost always engaged in farming in a small way, each keeping a few cows on a smallholding. It was the policy of the mine-owners of the eighteenth and early nineteenth centuries to provide their employees with such smallholdings.

It seems probable that mining, without causing settlement to transgress the limit of cultivation, has contributed to extend this limit. The very number of families seeking land to engage in farming would itself tend to do this, and there would be a natural tendency on the part of families concerned to approximate the scenes of their twin activities by wresting fields from the moor, near the higher mines. Settlement and cultivation push up towards the heads of all the lead dales as continuous tongues to altitudes above 1,500 feet (Fig. 60), and there are outlying farmsteads still higher. The farmlands are as large a proportion of the total area here as in the Border dales, although the general elevation is so much higher.

If this is in part attributable to the mining industry and its intimate association with farming, it must at the same time be recognised that physical conditions in the zone between 700 and 1,500 feet, in respect alike of shelter, soil, and drainage are generally much more favourable than in the Border dales. This zone is here below the summit plateau and includes the dale floors and sides (Fig. 60). In the Border dales the area of farmland is actually smaller than the area that lies below 700 feet.

Moorland below this height is more extensive than the area of improved land above. In the Lead dales on the other hand, in both Allendales, in upper South Tynedale, and in upper Teesdale, well over 90 per cent of the occupied zone lies above 700 feet, and even in Weardale and Derwentdale the proportion is still about two-thirds. In East Allendale the farmlands are as extensive as the area that lies below 1,250 feet, and in upper Teesdale nearly so.

Inevitably these high farms of the Lead dales are essentially pastoral, and within the old mining area of the upper dales hay is well-nigh the only crop (Pl. 5). Ploughed fields hardly appear until the dale floors pass into the zone below 700 feet. Almost three-quarters of the total area is moorland, which provides poor grazing only for hardy sheep; over much of its extent its value even for this purpose is confined to a short summer period. Within the farmlands cattle as well as sheep are reared. These are features common to dale farming everywhere, but in the Lead dales the pastoral farming practised is more intensive than usual. There are extensive hill-sheep farms, but practically all farmers keep some cows and the relative importance of cattle as compared with sheep is greater. Farming is organised to an exceptional degree in small units, these dales showing a remarkable predominance of holdings of less than 50 acres. The rearing of a few cattle was the natural type of farming carried on in the dales by small-holders engaged in lead mining, or in cartage in connection with the mining and smelting industries, and it has outlived the mining activity.

Over much of their extent the moorlands are grazed as stinted pastures, the grazing rights being attached to farm holdings and changing hands with them. For moorland-grazing hardy sheep must be used, and the Blackface breed is preferred to the Cheviot, of which there are few. In recent years the Swaledale variety has become increasingly popular. The pure-bred ewes are crossed with Border Leicester rams to produce lambs that are sold as stores, and on the better farmlands flocks of cross-bred ewes may be used with lowland breeds of ram (usually Oxford or Suffolk). Some of the lambs produced are fattened, but most are sold to farms outside the dales.

Most of the cattle are Shorthorns, and breeding of dairy Shorthorns became a special feature in some districts, such as Allendale. While sale of store cattle continues to be an important source of income for most farmers, an increasing proportion of them already get a regular cash income from sales of fluid milk, or are coming to rely upon this as their mainstay.

In some of the old farmlands there is an irregular pattern of small fields enclosed by thorn hedges, but the dry-stone walls that outline the patchwork of grass fields are the distinctive feature of the upper dales

19

(Pls. 5, 7). The enclosure of commons in the late eighteenth and early nineteenth centuries added large areas of new enclosed land, and the intakes dating from this period are invariably divided by stone walls. Below the framing moorlands that are sombre and brown for most of the year but colourful with purple heather in late summer, the valley farmlands present a detailed pattern in greys and greens. These tones dominate the landscape except in upper Teesdale, where the local estate practice of limewashing the buildings of tenants introduces a distinctive variant of white cottages. The landscape is remarkably bare of trees and offers sweeping views that are confined ultimately by even skylines. Clumps of sycamore and ash may give shelter to the farmsteads, and streaks of alder and willow scrub occur along the streams, but the voracious needs of mining and smelting operations long ago combined with grazing animals to denude the dales of their natural woodlands. During the nineteenth century local landowners introduced a number of conifer plantations, some of them extending to exceptionally high altitudes, but there is still little woodland in the heart of the area. Along the northern and eastern margins, towards the Tyne valley and the edge of the Durham coalfield, the Forestry Commission is carrying out extensive planting (Fig. 60). Higher up the dales, however, beyond the clearly delineated, though irregular, boundary wall of the farmlands (Pl. 7), open moors stretch across the watersheds. In place of the ragged pattern of forest and moorland that is now presented by the Border hills, moorland here reigns supreme. There is more ecological variety, however, in these moorlands than in those of the Border country. The altitudinal range over which they extend introduces a greater degree of zonation of vegetation, and a variety of treatment has contributed also to produce a much more complicated mosaic of moorland types (Fig. 14). Besides *nardus* and *molinia* grasslands, extensive areas have been developed as grouse moors where heather is dominant, but above about 2,000 feet heather gives way to bilberry, and on the boggy tracts of the summit plateau sedge moors are extensive, while Cross Fell presents special interest to the botanist by its association of sub-Arctic plants. Near their lower margins the rough grazings have been extensively colonised by bracken.

A century ago, when mining in these dales was at its peak, the ore field was producing yearly about 30,000 tons of galena, and the industry gave employment to more than 4,000 workmen. This old mining area, where the most accessible ore had been worked out and the law of diminishing returns was generally making itself felt, was quite unable, however, to face the fall in the price of lead that followed the development of new sources of supply overseas. During the 'seventies decline set in, at first slowly, but as the price of lead slumped it became catastrophic. One after another mines and smelt-mills closed down, and by the last decade of the century the industry was all but extinguished.

At Boltsburn in Weardale, where rich new flats of ore were discovered in 1892, and at Nenthead, where the great Belgian zinc concern, the Vieille Montagne Company, undertook the working of sphalerite (zinc-blende), which occurs there locally as a vein constituent, some revival took place. Even these enterprises were only shadows of the former activity in their dales, and in the other dales later fitful attempts to re-open mines have been of much less importance. With the exceptions just noted, ore production in the North Pennines this century has been largely incidental to the working of gangue materials, the waste products of former days for which modern industry offers new markets.

The gashes formed in the dale sides by ancient hushes, the great mine-dumps, derelict smelt-mills, reservoirs and water-wheels, and other residual features bear abundant testimony to the widespread presence and the former importance of the industry (Pl. 6). The stumps of chimneys, towards which long flues carried the poisonous, but also argentiferous, fumes from the smelt-mills, are still conspicuous landmarks on the fell tops. The mining activity of the past, however, has contributed a good deal more to the distinctiveness of these dales than is represented by such elements of the present-day landscape, numerous and conspicuous though they are. Just as real, if less obvious, are the lasting effects the industry has had upon the farming economy, upon settlement, and upon the social life of the people in these dales.

All the Lead dales have experienced serious depopulation. Its extent matches that experienced anywhere in North England, and the total population of this group of dales is now little more than half what it was a century ago. Where, in the Allendales, upper South Tynedale, and Derwentdale, the collapse of the mining industry has not been offset to any significant extent by quarrying activity, the population today is even less than it was in 1800. Even so, the population densities in all the dales of this group are relatively high and show a difference from those of the Border dales which is greater than can be accounted for by the employment provided in the non-agricultural occupations that now exist. It reflects a more intensive farming economy, which has survived the mining which produced it. The decline of lead mining caused an exodus from the dales, but it has not produced such whole-sale depopulation as must have taken place had the miners' families been entirely dependent upon this single source of livelihood. In many cases families remained to eke out a living on their smallholdings. Lead mining has left a strongly established tradition of part-time farming.

Dispersed farmsteads (Pl. 5) have always been the prevalent type of settlement in the Lead dales. Arable cultivation was never important in these high dales, where the agricultural colonisation was from the first essentially pastoral and to a considerable extent associated with the activities of miners. After the Norman Conquest large areas were hunting preserves, and no form of open-field system, with its accompanying village or hamlet settlement, was ever much represented except in the lower parts of the dales. Because of the scattered, shifting character of the mining and especially because of the association of mine work with cow keeping, the more modern development of mining has not changed this feature but rather has emphasised it. The parcelling out of the intakes created by the extensive parliamentary enclosures of commons contributed especially to the multiplication of scattered farmsteads on the new farmlands. Unlike coal mining in other parts of North England, lead mining in the dales, instead of concentrating workers in urban or pseudo-urban groups, has simply multiplied and extended scattered settlements over the dales. In this respect the modern limestone quarrying in lower Weardale exhibits a strong contrast. Organised by the iron and steel companies in large units which are highly localised, it has been responsible for urban growth at Stanhope. Grouped settlement, however, was also associated with some of the centres of the more concentrated operations of ore dressing and smelting in the dales, and naturally such clusters tended also to become service centres for the scattered dale population.

The lead-mining activity of the eighteenth and nineteenth centuries has contributed a profusion of buildings to the dale landscape, but few buildings from earlier times are represented. Indeed, fewer than usual date from the Middle Ages, a period when durable structures were erected in these dales to an even smaller extent than in most parts of North England. These dales lay outside the main lowland farming districts that attracted Border raiders and equally lay off the tracks of Scottish armies, so that they never had need of many castles or other fortified buildings. Nor were there many churches of medieval foundation. Some of the dale parishes, organised late from medieval forests, were very large indeed. When the great increase in population that accompanied the expansion of mining took place in the eighteenth and early nineteenth centuries, the religious needs of the miners, largely neglected by the Established Church, were met by the Methodist movement. From its inception Methodism has been strongly entrenched in the Lead dales. As in Wales and Cornwall, numerous small Nonconformist chapels are characteristic features of the countryside. They have played a most important rôle as centres of social life as well as of worship, and if it is now less vigorous than in earlier generations, the Methodist tradition remains a deep-rooted feature of the dale communities.

It has been shown that these dales owe some of the most distinctive characteristics of their geography directly or indirectly to the lead-mining activity of the past. Their designation as the Lead dales is amply justified. Other aspects of their distinctiveness are indicative of the greater extent to which the isolation that is so characteristic of the dale environment has here been broken down. In the main this is a simple result of the fact that most of these dales lie nearer the populous industrial area of northeast England, though in part it represents a further development of links that were forged in the prosperous mining era.

Lead mining brought turnpike roads in the early decades of last century, in place of the moorland tracks by which the dale ponies had previously transported the lead. Later it was lead mining again that was responsible for the construction of railways into these dales, though in most cases they penetrated only the lower parts to the smelting centres.

Since lead mining declined most of the dales have become largely dependent upon farming. Non-agricultural production is now chiefly concentrated in Weardale, which is therefore the most densely peopled among these dales. Its greater relative importance in part reflects its intrinsic endowment with minerals, but it is no less due to its relative accessibility. Only in Weardale have any important deposits of lead been discovered since the general decline of the industry set in ; but it is also significant that only Weardale has a railway (extended up the dale from Stanhope in 1895) that penetrates into the heart of the old mining area (Fig. 62). Transport difficulties have proved the great drawback in the way of renewed activity at lead mines for the production of gangue material, whether it is fluorspar or barytes, and in Weardale the spar resources have been most fully exploited.

Opening directly east towards the coalfield, Weardale has felt in special degree, moreover, the impact of a modern industrial development that has taken place there. From the eighteen-forties the iron-masters of the industrial area have sought raw materials in Weardale. At first it was the spathose ore (iron carbonate of about 40 per cent metal content) that was present, though very irregularly, as a constituent of the veins and flats in the lead mines. The blast-furnaces that were set up at Tow Law on the western edge of the coalfield in 1845 were located there with the specific intention of using this ore (Fig. 39). Ironworks also made their appearance in the dale at Stanhope. For a considerable period the spathose ores were worked, and in 1870 production exceeded 100,000 tons. Although it declined sharply soon afterwards, small quantities were still being produced at the beginning of this century, and were smelted at Tudhoe on the coalfield. On a much smaller scale, similar ore was also worked for a time near Alston and Nenthead, after the Alston branch railway had been built in 1856 from the Tyne Corridor ; this ore was sent to the coalfield for smelting.

Later, the iron companies undertook large-scale quarrying in Weardale to provide limestone flux for smelting. The points nearest and most accessible to the smelting centres where good stone occurs under easy working conditions are the easternmost outcrops of the Great Limestone on both sides of Weardale between Stanhope and Frosterley, and the largest quarries are here (Figs. 39, 61). Similarly, however, the Great Limestone is also quarried in lower Teesdale southeast of Barnard Castle, near Forcett.

Where the Whin Sill outcrops in upper Teesdale, near the railhead at Middleton, it is extensively worked for roadstone, and there are also some workings in the small exposures of whinstone that occur conveniently near the lines of transport in Weardale. Elsewhere, however, quarrying in the dales has been restricted to small-scale and intermittent, if widespread, working of limestone for roadstone.

The developed livestock-farming of the Lead dales, with its growing emphasis on milk production, is again something that has been made possible by the advantageous situation within range of large urban markets. It is a natural outgrowth under these favourable circumstances from an economy that has traditionally emphasised cattle rearing.

It was natural, too, that the North Pennines, lying in proximity to the growing colliery and industrial communities, should be called upon to play a part in providing them with water supplies. In modern times large reservoirs (Fig. 60), constructed by damming highland valleys, have been added to the older groups of small reservoirs that had been built to provide waterpower for ore-treating operations. The reservoirs are naturally located in the dales that have an eastward orientation towards the Durham coalfield and Tees-side. Except while they were being constructed, however, they have had no importance for local employment in the dales.

Although motor roads, unlike the railways, now form a network, albeit an open one, that provides inter-connections between the dales across the bounding moorland watersheds, the breaking down of the former isolation of the dales has increasingly emphasised their outward orientation. As the dales have become less self-contained, the small service centres that had grown up in them have lost importance to larger towns outside. Their markets have declined or lapsed altogether, and the newer forms of town-country relations have drawn the scattered dalesfolk into the developing fields of external towns such as Hexham, Consett, Bishop Auckland, and Darlington.

Although in economic terms it is little to set against the loss of prosperity that has followed local depopulation and the centralisation of service functions in these larger towns, the small dale-centres have enjoyed a modest development as resorts and residential settlements. Deprived of industry, they are the better able to assume this rôle. Thanks to their attractive settings, bracing air, and not least their situation within easy range of large urban populations, they are now frequented by summer visitors. A growing adventitious element of retired townsfolk has also been settling in the dales, notably for example at Allendale.

Under these influences the inbreeding and clannishness that sprang in the past from isolation are passing as the dalesfolk are becoming integrated into a much larger community. But the external associations of the inhabitants of each dale are mainly with those of the lowland into which it opens, rather than with those of neighbouring dales. The bus services that are playing such a major part in breaking down the isolation of the dale communities extend from the external towns high up the dales. It is significant, however, that bus services to inter-connect the dales across the watersheds remain undeveloped.

The typical progression of service centres of descending magnitude up the dale is well exemplified in all these dales. The service area of each centre extends up the dale and shows the lower part of the dale oriented away towards a more important centre down-dale. In the Weardale sequence from Bishop Auckland to Wearhead through Wolsingham, Stanhope, and St John's Chapel, the status of Stanhope is exceptional. Thanks to the local concentration of quarrying employment, it has become as large as Wolsingham, and, since it is better placed to serve the upper part of the dale and is less affected by the competition of Bishop Auckland, it has become the more important service centre, though Wolsingham retains the grammar school.

It remains to note the individuality of the lower part of Teesdale. Below Middleton, which grew up as the centre for the upper dale with its lead mines, the farmlands open out and extend across the watersheds. The farming country of the lower dale is not and never has been the scene of mining activity. As in the upper dale, the farming is still dominated by livestock enterprises, but it is of a more lowland character, less exclusively pastoral or concerned only with rearing. There is more arable land, the fields are enclosed by thorn hedges in place of stone walls, and no longer is there the close confinement of the farmlands by moorland. There are more scattered woods in the landscape, as well as hedgerow trees, and these richer farmlands show more evidence of an old, grouped settlement pattern. Among the texture of villages with ancient churches are not only the modern farmsteads but also several halls surrounded by parkland.

These characteristics become increasingly pronounced eastwards. To the west the valleys of the right-bank tributaries of the Tees are dale-like appendages from this lowland, hemmed in by moorlands. Lunedale and Baldersdale have been partly flooded by reservoirs that supply the Tees-side towns and they are elsewhere sparsely sprinkled with farmsteads. In all cases cultivation and settlement peter out westwards, and the Greta valley, although it is followed by a railway and main road that cross the main watershed, is no exception. Stainmore is not a gap, but only a saddle, and the farmlands on opposite sides are clearly separated by moorland. The railway has difficult gradients and a summit height of 1,378 feet.

In spite of its through routes much of lower Teesdale is a rural backwater. There has been a general, if slight, decline in the rural population, but localised increases brought about by limestone quarrying at Forcett have balanced this, and the total population of the district has been remarkably stable over the past century.

The old market town of Barnard Castle (population 4,400) is still the chief service centre of Teesdale. It has extended its influence up the dale at the expense of Middleton, although in turn it has itself suffered from the extending competition of larger, better equipped towns farther east. The old textile industries (stockings and carpets) that were so active in the early part of the nineteenth century [1] in and near the town have since died out. The last carpet factory closed in 1870, and only recently has industry reappeared, in the form of a pharmaceutical factory that is especially concerned with making penicillin.

---

[1] The 1831 Census recorded more than 400 men employed in manufacturing stuffs and carpeting at Barnard Castle.

CHAPTER 17

THE TYNE CORRIDOR

MANY of the features of a more lowland economy and landscape that have been noted in lower Teesdale are equally characteristic of the lower portion of Tynedale. The valley corridor that here lies between the North Pennine highlands and the wastes of the Border hills, however, is physically unique in the highland belt of North England. It makes a lowland breach below 500 feet and directly opposite the focal parts of the major lowlands on the western and eastern sides of the country.

Differences between this valley and the dales to north and south derive directly from the uniqueness of its physique and even more from the rôle as a route-way, which its nature and situation have destined it to play in the human geography of the north country. It has affinities both with the Border dales to the north and the Lead dales to the south, but even more with the lowlands to west and east that it connects. Its dale character is outweighed by its essential nature as a lowland thoroughfare, and Tyne Corridor seems to be a more significant designation than Tynedale for this middle portion of the Tyne valley and its westward continuation through the Haltwhistle–Gilsland gap into the basin of the Eden. The ill-defined watershed, below 500 feet, lies in the drift-encumbered floor of what was in glacial times a major passage by which western ice streamed east across the country (Fig. 9). Through this corridor the Romans drew the boundary of their empire, and from that time a road has traversed the country here. The modern rôle as western gateway for the industrial region on the coalfield was established right at the beginning of the railway age by the construction of the Newcastle and Carlisle Railway, which was opened in 1838. Earlier, more than one proposal had been made for a canal to connect east and west coasts through this lowland gate. The actual route had been surveyed on the ground when the success of the Stockton and Darlington Railway and the cheaper cost of railway construction caused the project to be abandoned in favour of the railway. The story is told in detail by W. W. Tomlinson in his *History of the North Eastern Railway*.

The Tyne Corridor, compared with the other dales, is physically distinctive as a strike-valley (Fig. 63) that corresponds with the axis of the synclinal trough between the North Pennine massif and the Bewcastle and Cheviot domes of the Border. The southern margin

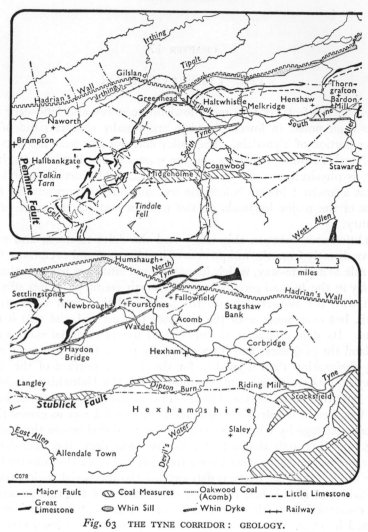

Fig. 63   THE TYNE CORRIDOR :   GEOLOGY.

of this structural feature, the system of east–west faults that delimits
the block, is not represented, however, by a great fault-escarpment as
is the western edge of the block.   North of the valley the strata rise
steeply northwards, and the rapid succession of limestone beds, among
shales and sandstones, with the Whin Sill intruded among them too,
forms a remarkable cuesta landscape.   Although the lines of these rock
escarpments protrude, there is generally a heavy mantle of drift, and
its western derivation is indicated by its reddish colour and the types of
boulder, in contrast with the local greyish drift of the North Pennine dales.

Along the valley, especially in the west towards the mouth of the corridor in Cumberland, the light sands and sandy loams provided by the extensive spreads of fluvio-glacial material and the gravelly haughs (Fig. 64 and Pl. 8) are suitable for arable cultivation. Elsewhere the boulder-clay gives rather stiff, heavy soils, and, as in the Border dales, the upper limit of improved land has been kept much lower than in the North Pennine dales (cf. Fig. 60). The high proportion of really low land nevertheless makes possible more extensive farmlands than are typical of the dales. In the east, both south of the main valley in Hexhamshire and on its north side, the farmlands are no longer restricted to a narrow valley strip confined between moorlands. East of Fourstones, moreover, the valley floor lies below 200 feet, and on the haughlands near Hexham market-gardening, an exceptional feature, makes a limited appearance, and the Forestry Commission now have nurseries here for stocking the Border forests. West of Hexham and the mouth of North Tynedale, however, the farmlands narrow. Above 700 or 800 feet there are flanking moorlands, but the cultivated strip is continuous across the main watershed, and, except for a short distance there, the farmlands maintain a width of over two miles, and there are extensive embayments where South Tynedale and Allendale open from the south (Fig. 64).

As in all the dales, the basis of the farming economy is an integration of cattle and sheep enterprises, but in these lowlying districts, and especially on the tracts of gravelly loams that Bailey described as ' turnip soils ', there is much more winter keep available. Whereas the breeding flocks of the higher dales are hardy, moorland types of sheep, here they are cross-bred ewes. These are crossed again with lowland breeds of ram, and some of the crop of lambs can be fattened for sale. Cattle, however, are specially important and account for most of the grazing units on the farms of Tynedale. The breeding of dairy Shorthorns is a special feature of this district, and Tynedale is still a great area of supply of high-quality dairy cattle. Butter making was formerly an important activity on the farms, but even before the Milk Marketing Board was set up many farmers were able to find a market for fluid milk. In the last twenty years milk production has increasingly become the mainstay of the local farming.

In the mixed farms of the east, near the industrial area, apart from the production of fat lambs, Irish and other store cattle, bought at Hexham market, are also fattened for the butcher. Away from the main valley, however, although the altitude is modest, conditions of soil, drainage, and climate make much of the land marginal for farming. During last century landowners introduced scattered conifer plantations, which, with their sombre colour and straight outlines, are

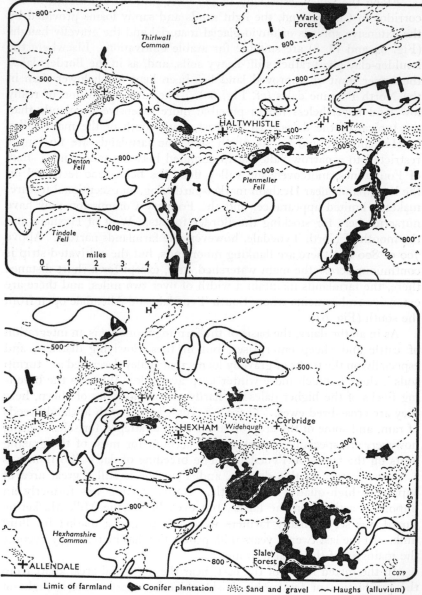

Fig. 64 THE TYNE CORRIDOR: PHYSICAL FEATURES AND LAND USE.

— Limit of farmland   Conifer plantation   Sand and gravel   Haughs (alluvium)

now a conspicuous element of the landscape (Pl. 8). Recently the Forestry Commission has undertaken considerable plantings in Hexhamshire, around Slaley (Fig. 64), where farmlands and large blocks of forest are now intermingled.

In a more striking fashion than with farming, the superior transport facilities available in the Tyne Corridor have greatly enhanced the opportunities for developing the mineral resources. These are intrinsically much greater than any possessed by the Border dales, and since the decline of lead mining they have given much more employment here than mining any longer provides in the dales farther south.

The Tyne valley lies north of the main lead-bearing field, but it has not been altogether without productive veins (Fig. 61). East of Haydon Bridge, in the tract between the Tyne and the Roman Wall to the north, lead has been extensively worked at a number of mines. There has been no production of lead since the Fallowfield mine closed fifty years ago, but Settlingstones mine, which ceased to raise lead in 1893, has subsequently been important as a source of witherite. This mineral (barium carbonate) is here the chief gangue constituent in place of the commoner barytes (barium sulphate).

The chief mineral wealth of the Tyne Corridor, however is coal. In the Lead dales there are only thin, poor seams of negligible importance, but in the Tyne Corridor productive seams in the limestone series combine with pockets of Coal Measures that are preserved on the northern, downthrow side of the southern boundary fault, to support numerous, if generally small-scale, workings. The largest of the Coal Measure pockets are found in the west, astride the South Tyne round Midgeholme and Coanwood, and the limestone coals are also best developed in the west (Fig. 63). The outcropping coals were worked at various places long before the construction of the railways, but the latter gave a great stimulus to new ventures. The two largest collieries, each of which employed several hundred men, were both near Haltwhistle, but at numerous other places the Little Limestone coals [1] and, lower, the Thirlwall seam have been worked from pits and drifts. Farther east a higher seam, the Oakwood, has also been productive, notably at Acomb. Most of the workings developed last century were situated on the railway or within easy reach of it by short sidings or aerial ropeways. In recent years, however, motor lorry transport has encouraged new activities in drift workings in more remote tracts along the northern outcrops.

Shortly after the building of the railway, blackband ironstone was worked for some years at Chesterwood [2] near Haydon Bridge, and lime-

[1] There are three seams, ranging over about 40 feet of strata below the limestone. Workable coal is usually the result of the union of two, or more rarely three, members.
[2] For a few years production was between 20,000 and 25,000 tons per annum, but by 1855 it had been worked out (Fig. 39).

stone quarrying was carried on farther east at Fourstones. This was on a larger, more concentrated scale than the earlier scattered operations for lime burning that have left their traces along the limestone outcrops north of the Tyne valley. The chief modern quarrying operations are also in the west, in the Haltwhistle district, along the broken, but imposing crags of the Whin Sill that carry the Roman Wall (Fig. 63). They present massive faces of hard stone, excellent for roadstone, and the Wall has already suffered some destruction from the quarrying operations.

The old textile and leather industries are dead, but manufacturing is still represented in the Tyne Corridor. Although not of great importance, its very presence is significant in view of its almost complete absence from the other dales. There is a local raw material at hand in the form of the fireclays that occur beneath the coal seams. Bricks, tiles, and drain-pipes were formerly manufactured extensively at Haltwhistle, and small works are still active at Bardon Mill, Corbridge, and Langley. An old paper mill, established in the eighteenth century, continues to operate alongside the railway at Warden, but the largest modern factory is at Haltwhistle, where paint is made. At the height of the inter-war depression, when both collieries had closed and most of the inhabitants of the town were unemployed, a local paint business was re-sited and expanded into a considerable enterprise that has grown successfully.

The opening of the railway was followed by some development of Gilsland on the Irthing as a spa, but this was never very considerable. More noteworthy developments have followed in the wake of modern communications in the eastern part of the corridor, which has been brought within the commuting range of Tyneside. Considerable residential expansion has taken place at Hexham, and nearer Newcastle at Corbridge and Stocksfield.

These modern developments in the Tyne Corridor, so foreign to the dales generally, are clearly reflected in the quite exceptional population history. In all the other dales the increase in population that took place in the earlier part of the nineteenth century was not maintained later. On the contrary, a sharp decline set in, so that today the population is less, and often much less, than it was a century ago. In this same period, however, the population of the Tyne Corridor has experienced considerable further increase, and growth was maintained until after the First World War. Since then the modest increase at Hexham and a few other places in the east has not been enough to balance a considerable emigration that has followed the decline in coal-mining activity farther west.

Thanks to its superior accessibility, which has been emphasised by modern communications, the Tyne Corridor has been able to show some industrial development, and more recently residential development, which, if modest in scale compared with what has taken place in some districts of North England, has been quite without parallel in the dales. The accompanying growth of population has naturally been concentrated along the main arteries. The road and railway closely follow the river and connect the villages and towns, which are sited on well-developed river terraces (Fig. 64). Most of the modern settlement has taken the form of extensions along the Newcastle-Carlisle road, especially near the railway stations. Thus Haltwhistle has extended westwards from its old cluster near the market square and church and has become a straggling, road town. Meanwhile villages that lie off this road have remained small and have retained their more compact form. An excellent illustration is provided by the extension of settlement along the road at Bardon Mill and to the west, with the old parish villages of Henshaw and Thorngrafton a little distance to the north. The military road that runs along the line of the Roman road behind Hadrian's Wall lies north of the Tyne valley and quite external to its settlement pattern, so that it provides a valuable fast route for through traffic, avoiding the towns and villages of the valley.

Much of the increase of population in the western districts is attributable, as we have seen, to coal mining. Ties with the west have been strengthened by the influx of considerable numbers of families from Cumberland into the Haltwhistle district, and much of the coal found its market westwards. The coal miners, unlike lead miners, rarely engaged in cow keeping, and gathered in grouped settlements near the mines rather than in scattered dwellings. The development of mining was therefore accompanied by a growth of village population, and several villages show a clear-cut distinction between the original cluster of stone cottages and the drab brick rows that have been added. Such terraces, however, are to be found, not merely as constituents of larger settlements, but sometimes, as in Cleveland, apart and isolated alongside derelict workings.

Although the modern extension of settlement has introduced new building forms and materials, which, in the absence of comparable expansion, are hardly represented in the other dales, the tradition of building in stone persisted longer here than usual, and it is more widely represented among modern buildings, at least until the First World War.

Away from the valley line, followed by road and railway, the settlement pattern has altered little since the beginning of last century, when extensive allotments of common land increased the farmland and added new farmsteads. Throughout Tynedale many of the present farmhouses and the substantial byres were renewed on old sites about this time. The good farmlands of Tynedale, lying along one of the most frequented paths followed by invading armies and raiders, are studded with the remains of fortified buildings, both peles and larger castles (Fig. 23 and Pls. 18, 20). To these the gentry added several new halls during the nineteenth century.

The Tyne Corridor is exceptional among the dales not only in the degree to which urban forms of settlement are represented in it. The central services that are of the very essence of townhood have gathered at Hexham to a degree quite unparalleled anywhere within the dales. Situated just below the confluence of the North Tyne and the South Tyne, near the eastern mouth of the Tyne Corridor, Hexham is endowed with a high degree of nodality. In this respect it is unrivalled among dale towns. The convergence of railway lines, but still more the development of motor transport and bus services, have strengthened its command over the surrounding farming districts, and have extended the range of its effectiveness as a service centre. In extent its primary urban field must be one of the largest in the country. For several urban services the inhabitants at the head of North Tynedale or at Allenheads can find no nearer centre. Bellingham and Allendale Town have largely succumbed to its centralising power. Their markets and retail trade have lost importance, and increasingly the Allendales and North Tynedale have been drawn within the field of Hexham. The Tyne Corridor itself, west to beyond Haydon Bridge, and the rural backwater of Hexhamshire to the south, are closely integrated with it. To the east, however, the competition of Newcastle is soon apparent, and the urban field of Hexham is severely restricted on this side.

Serving such an extensive area where farming is concerned mainly with livestock rearing, and handling also large numbers of store cattle moving from the west through the Tyne Corridor to farms in the eastern lowland districts, Hexham ranks as one of the major livestock markets of the country. Although it is near enough to Newcastle to have become in some degree a residential outlier of Tyneside, its importance is first and foremost as a market and rural-service centre. Since its glove-making industry died out, it has no longer any importance for manufacturing, and the local concentration of population numbers only about 9,000. This figure might give an altogether misleading impression of its urban stature, for most of the population, probably approaching 30,000, served by its shops and institutions live outside the Urban District.

In the west Haltwhistle is independent in most respects, though not all, and functions as service centre for the farming and mining population of a more restricted area. Its population at the beginning of the nineteenth century was less than 500, and its service status, although rooted in its long-established function as a local market centre, has been enhanced largely as a result of the local concentration of population that accompanied colliery development. Both to the west and east the range of its urban field is confined by the greater pull exerted by Carlisle and Hexham. Nor does its influence extend strongly far up South Tynedale. The upper dale is in Cumberland, and this historic association, while no doubt contributing to maintain economic and social ties with the county centre, is not out of harmony with the natural orientation. The Tyne flows north to Haltwhistle and there turns east, but, although there is a branch railway up the dale from Haltwhistle to Alston, road connection across the Tyne is poor and there is no regular bus service from Haltwhistle up the dale. On the other hand, there is an easy lateral route westwards from the dale on the north side of Tindale Fells. This is followed by a main road which turns the external relations of the upper dale away from Haltwhistle towards Carlisle. By this route, moveover, Alston is only 25 miles from Carlisle, whereas by the most direct connection Newcastle is 44 miles distant.

CHAPTER 18

THE LAKE DISTRICT

OF all the constituent parts of North England none is as generally recognised as a distinctive region as the Lake District. A highland area, with watersheds reaching 2,000 feet over considerable stretches and culminating in summits above 3,000 feet, the human associations of its radiating valleys, like the drainage, are dispersed. But such is its physical individuality, transcending alike a rich internal variety of scenery and the scattering of its external relations, that it is in the popular mind essentially one region. Although it consists of parts of the counties of Cumberland, Westmorland, and Lancashire it is in common parlance first and foremost the Lake District. Its special character and essential unity have now been given official recognition by its constitution as a Planning Area, and under the National Parks Act (1947) it was one of the first areas scheduled for reservation (Fig. 66).

The southern part turns its back upon the north behind a high watershed that is crossed by few routes. Furness is historically part of Lancashire, and the southwest of Westmorland, focusing upon Kendal, is isolated by high moorlands from the heart of the county at the head of the vale of Eden. But, although the Lake District does not lie entirely within North England as this is strictly delimited, its unity must be respected, and for separate regional consideration it must be treated as a whole.

The essential factor creating this unity of the Lake District is its distinctive physical character, whence derive both its inherent poverty as farming country and its wealth of attraction as a tourist area. For this latter rôle the intrinsic beauty of the scenery is made the more valuable by its relatively accessible situation for the inhabitants of this highly urbanised country.

The highlands composing the Lake District have a central core of very distinctive structure, where the ancient pre-Carboniferous rocks have been folded along northeast–southwest lines in a ' Caledonian ' grain, and this is surrounded by a broken girdle of limestone (Fig. 2). The limestone hills that fringe the massif as a transition belt of inter-mediate altitude are missing, however, from the southwest, where, between Egremont and Millom, Triassic rocks abut directly against rocks of the core. To the east the limestone highlands attach the Lake District massif to the Pennines and form a major watershed between the Eden and Lune drainage.

Mountains and lakes, rock and water, are ubiquitous elements of a richly varied scenic composition (Pls. 9–15). Both the individuality of the whole and the variety within it spring in part from the special features of the constituent rocks and structure, but more especially from the distinctive glacial history. Most of the present features of rock sculpture date from the later phases of the Ice Age when, after the major glaciation, the ice-sheets had fallen back from the massif and the district was occupied by shrinking valley-glaciers. These seemed to have advanced again from their cirque heads during a phase of deterioration of climate (cf. the post-Alleröd phase in Scandinavia) before their final retreat. The cragginess, the rock basins that contain tarns and lakes, the cliff buttresses and their great aprons of frost-shattered scree débris, are all attributable to this later glacial history. The degree of plucking and consequent cragginess, of over-deepening that has produced wall-like valley sides and hanging tributary valleys, and of valley-floor excavation that has been responsible for their stepped profile, all depended upon the type of country rock. Similarly the degree of later modification, such as lake-silting, has varied. The scenic variety that is dependent upon rock-type has already been discussed in Chapter 3, but it may be emphasised again that not only were the forms of the pre-glacial landscape more youthful in the volcanic tract than in the slate country to the north and south, but also that the erosional forms imparted by ice sculpture are most pronounced and most freshly preserved there.

Among all the distinctive assemblage of landforms, the association of mountains and lakes stands out as the criterion by which the region may best be defined. If a centre is taken on the central watershed at High Raise (Fig. 65), which lies somewhat east of its highest point, Scafell Pike (3,210 feet), the circumference of a circle of six miles radius marks approximately the positions down the radiating valleys where the main valley lakes, as distinct from small valley-head tarns, begin; and a circle of fifteen miles radius is seen to include every lake or tarn, with the single exception of the outlying Over Water on the north flank of Skiddaw, as well as almost all the land above 1,000 feet. The radial symmetry of the hydrography, however, is not perfect. Apart from the fact that the doming that initiated the drainage was slightly elliptical, with the area of maximum uplift elongated eastward to the Howgill–Kirkby Lonsdale fells, considerable modification of the valley lines has taken place by adjustment to the structure of the old rock-surface that had been concealed beneath a younger cover. Once the latter was stripped away from the central area, the hydrographic pattern super-imposed from it upon the old rocks beneath began to conform to lines of weakness and more rapid erosion therein. The NE–SW grain of outcrops is only feebly reflected in the drainage pattern, but the mosaic of fault-bounded blocks has been brought out in the relief. Belts of shattered rock that correspond with the tear-faults, which have strongly affected the old rocks, provided easily eroded zones along which streams cut back rapidly, effecting captures and leaving high-level gaps in the divides. That the spoke-like valleys of the Lake District are not more

┼─┼ Railway	⌒⌒ 1000 ft Contour	The circles show the areas within
▬▬ Main (A class) road		6 and 15 miles of High Raise

Fig. 65 THE LAKE DISTRICT: PHYSICAL FEATURES AND COMMUNICATIONS.

completely isolated from each other at their heads is due to the passes thus provided. The head of Matterdale, Sty Head, Honister, and others correspond in position to shatter-belts, the importance of which was emphasised by Marr.[1] A major shatter-belt runs ENE–WSW for fifteen miles, up Langdale, over Wrynose Pass, across the Duddon valley, and over Hardknott into and along upper Eskdale, then over into Miterdale. From this shatter-belt in Langdale another runs northwards by Red Bank into Grasmere and up the valley to

[1] J. E. Marr, ' The influence of the geological structure of the English Lakeland upon its present features ', *Quart. Journ. Geol. Soc.* **62** (1906), 66–129.

Dunmail Raise and so to Thirlmere, and is probably continued by the line of the Naddle valley to the Glenderaterra valley which separates Skiddaw from Saddleback. The main north to south road traverses the Lake District by the route over Dunmail Raise, which follows this shatter-belt that detaches the Helvellyn mountains from the Scafell group. Radial drainage is best developed round the latter. East of Dunmail Raise the pattern is dominated by the west–east divide which sheds drainage northwards and southwards. In the extreme north the drainage of the isolated Skiddaw massif itself shows quite a well-developed radial pattern.

Many straight valley-reaches, corresponding to shatter-belts, were already in existence before the Ice Age. They are characteristic of the Lake District and are to be attributed primarily to the structure and not to the peculiarities of glacial sculpture, though straightenings that show the triangular facets of truncated spurs do occur. There are noteworthy examples on the south side of Saddleback.

Within fifteen miles of High Raise low ground is very restricted in extent. Most of the area is high moorland, and valley land is further greatly reduced by the extent of the lake water surfaces, which often almost completely occupy considerable lengths of valley trench between high bounding walls. In consequence, the valley farmlands at the dale heads in the Lake District are detached and isolated from lowland farming areas outside in a way that does not apply in a normal dale. Lakes in several places extend right to the mouths of the mountain valleys, but where they do not the portion below the lake partakes of the essential character of the external lowlands, separated from the distinctive Lake District dale-head. Some valleys, for example Eskdale and Duddondale, although once tenanted by lakes, have been completely silted ; these, with the sheaf of dales north of Keswick, are much more similar in the nature of their human relations to the other dales of North England.

The highlands comprise a great central block of rough, heather and grass ' fell country ', with an outer fringe of mixed heather and grass moor. Irregular wedges of farmland extend up the foothills from the surrounding lowlands into the moorland (Fig. 13), and tongues of farmland penetrate the valleys where their mouths are not completely occupied by lakes. Attenuated and interrupted strips often fringe the lakes, especially on deltas and valleyside fans, and more poor farmland is found in the upper dales above the lakes (Pls. 12, 14). These dale heads, shut off from the outer world but intercommunicating across the watersheds by high passes, are the heart of the Lake District, where the characteristics that are responsible for its human distinctiveness were most developed and have lingered longest. For if the individuality of the Lake District derives clearly from its peculiar physical endowment it is not confined to this. To a special degree its people and their traditions stem from the Norse settlers who first effectively colonised its secluded, forested valleys. The place-names are throughout predominantly Norse, and both Anglian and Celtic names are much less represented than in the surrounding lowlands. Clearance for farmland, and especially the encroachment of grazing land upon the higher woodlands, continued throughout the Middle Ages, fostered by the activities of the Cistercian monasteries. The monks of Furness and Calder held extensive lands and had 'granges' in the heart as well as on the fringes of the Lake District. Their territories extended over the main watershed into Borrowdale, and the tracks over the passes that are now used by hikers once provided the links between their holdings. The flocks of the monks were let out to the local inhabitants, the 'herds', and so became known as 'herdwicks'. From Elizabethan times mining brought immigrants, some of them German, to swell the population in some localities and to modify the landscape substantially, especially because of the heavy timber requirements for mining and smelting.

As late as the nineteenth century the sparse population consisted of independent farmers, small owner-cultivators known as 'statesmen', who occupied the land by customary tenure. They wrung a poor living in this difficult country of rain and stones, for their methods were backward and their livestock poor. Since then Shorthorns and other improved breeds have completely displaced the longhorned cattle, and although flocks of local Herdwick sheep still roam the fells they are giving way to Blackface and Swaledale breeds. Much of the valley land is difficult to drain, and the wet climate is far from suitable for corn. There is very little arable land. Over the Lake District as a whole it amounts to less than 2 per cent even of improved land. Hay is the essential crop, although it is won often with the greatest difficulty. Cattle are grazed on enclosed pastures in summer, and the sheep are brought on to this 'inby' land during winter storms. Some are still sent to the Solway and Duddon marshes for winter.[1] Holdings are often large, but the greater part of their area consists of rough fell grazing. Others are small valley-farms that have stints, or rights of pasturage, on the fell, much of which is still held in common. The farm income is derived from sales of store cattle, store lambs, draft ewes, and, to an increasing extent, milk that is supplied to nearby towns and to the summer visitors. The farmhouses and byres (Pls. 11, 24) are usually old buildings of substantial, if simple structure, built

[1] T. H. Bainbridge, 'A note on transhumance in Cumbria', *Geography* **25** (1940), 35–6, and 'Observations on transhumance in southern Cumbria', *ibid.* **29** (1944), 22–3.

of grey stone with slate roofs ; but in Eskdale the local granite gives the farm buildings a distinctive pinkish colour.

The Lake District, however, is no longer only an area of poor farming. Since its natural beauty was discovered, appreciated, and publicised to the outer world by artists, poets, and other writers in the eighteenth and early nineteenth centuries, its attractions have been opened to the enjoyment of a larger public. From the time when it was visited and frequented by artistic coteries and their disciples, its importance as a tourist area has grown, greatly stimulated by the coming of railways and still more by recent transport developments on the roads. The increasing ability of townsfolk to reach and penetrate the Lake District has corresponded with a growing urge to escape from towns and an increasing appreciation of unspoilt natural beauty. The modern vogue for cycling and hiking, as well as for motoring, and the development of organisations such as the Youth Hostels Association to facilitate the satisfaction of these appetites, have affected no part of Britain more than the Lake District. The mountain country is now reached and even crossed by motor roads, from which networks of footpaths spread over the hills and take walkers where no motor vehicle can intrude. Public access to a large part of the area is now assured by the transfer of large tracts to the control of the National Trust, and elsewhere it is widely tolerated by other holders of land. Indeed, although tourists present farmers with some problems, their appearance in ever-increasing numbers has proved a boon to the local inhabitants. Without the market that visitors provide for milk and eggs, and the summer income derived from catering for their needs of food, lodging, and camping sites, the farm population could scarcely gain a livelihood. If the tourist industry counteracts the general tendency towards rural depopulation, its positive effects upon the settlement pattern are more restricted. The chief centres of the tourist industry, partaking of urban character, are the rail-heads in the Lake District— Keswick, Windermere and its lake-side annexe Bowness, and Coniston —while external towns on the routes of approach—Kendal, Penrith, and Carlisle—have undoubtedly also felt the benefits of tourist traffic. Hotels have also sprung up alongside main roads, especially where earlier nuclei existed, as at Ambleside, Grasmere, Glenridding, and Patterdale, or at points of special tourist attraction such as Lodore, Dungeon Ghyll, and Waterhead.

Within the Lake District, Keswick, Ambleside, and Bowness-Windermere have grown as service centres as well as tourist centres ; but the service functions for the valleys that open west are discharged with increasing effectiveness by the coastal towns and Cockermouth. Other external centres, notably Kendal, Penrith, and even Carlisle, have also extended the range and scope of their influence in parts of the Lake District. While their functions as tourist and service centres have been enhanced, Keswick and Cockermouth have witnessed the decline of the industries that were their mainstay a century ago. But, although the woollen industry of Kendal has similarly declined, an important footwear industry has risen in its place.

The most frequented traverses are through the district between north and south (Fig. 65). From the south the usual approach is by Kendal and Windermere and thence to Ambleside, Grasmere, and on to Keswick over Dunmail Raise (782 feet), or over Kirkstone Pass (1,489 feet) to Ullswater and so to Keswick or Penrith. A lowland valley, followed by railway as well as road between Penrith and Cockermouth through Keswick, separates the Skiddaw massif from the main block of highland. There is a network of motor roads in the relatively low-lying and negotiable Furness portion of the Lake District, but the western valleys are hardly penetrated by motorable roads, still less by railways, except for the line that was built for ore traffic from Boot in Eskdale. A large tract in the centre, about Scafell, with the grandest scenery, remains essentially walkers' country, and here, too, is the centre for rock climbing. Between the main roads over Shap and Kirkstone Pass there lies in the east a stretch of relatively tame hill country, with lakeless dales (Long Sleddale) that lie off the beaten tracks. Skiddaw massif, apart from its southern face with the ascent to the summit from Keswick, is also a secluded fastness.

If local farming and the tourist industry have been readily integrated and are mutually helpful, it is otherwise with some of the other interests that have been attracted by the opportunities offered them in the Lake District. The mining activities of the past, carried on intermittently for centuries, have left some scars, and those of the most recent major phase, about the middle of last century, are still fresh and unhealed. Mining has now petered out, its lingering survivals into the twentieth century represented chiefly in the Keswick district and at Greenside (Fig. 28). Some quarries are still working, but they are mostly small, and the only extensive operations are in granite, at Shap and Threlkeld. As a reminder of the once-famous graphite mine of Borrowdale, there is still a pencil factory at Keswick, though all the graphite is now imported.

The claims upon the Lake District for urban water supply and for forestry have come to the fore more recently. Urban and industrial development on the west coast of Cumberland naturally looked to the lakes in the wet highlands behind to meet its increasing needs of water. Workington, as well as Cockermouth, obtains supplies from Crummock Water, and Whitehaven from Ennerdale Water. But the far more distant city of Manchester has also been supplied from the Lake District since 1894, when it acquired Thirlmere, nearly one hundred miles away. This supply has since been augmented by the addition of Hawes Water in 1936.

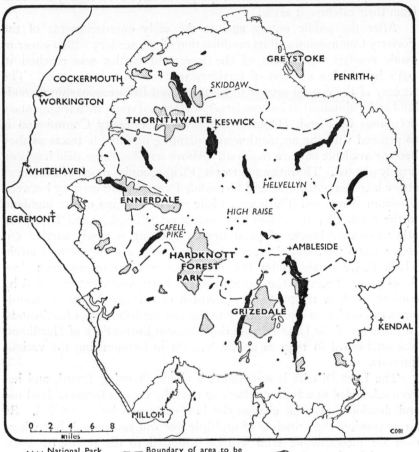

Fig. 66 THE LAKE DISTRICT NATIONAL PARK AND STATE FORESTS.

Woods were planted extensively in the catchment area of Thirlmere, but elsewhere large-scale afforestation is more recent, dating from the First World War and the setting up of the Forestry Commission in 1919. While there is natural harmony of interest between water-supply authorities and foresters, both modify the landscape, and neither interest is easily reconciled with the maintenance of traditional sheep-farming practice or with freedom of access by the public. Both Thirlmere and

Hawes Water have been considerably altered by the enlargement of their water-bodies, which in the latter case submerged the hamlet and church of Mardale, and by the control of outflow and the creation of a fluctuating and often unsightly shoreline. Except that through traffic on single valley roads is tolerated, the public have been rigidly excluded from their catchment areas.

After the public outcry against the early encroachments of the Forestry Commission and its modification of the scenery with a cover of exotic conifers, agreement of the interested parties was reached in 1936, by which a division of territory was recognised (Fig. 66). The scenery of the central area is to be preserved from encroaching woodland and maintained in its now largely deforested state, with fragmentary deciduous woodland. Outside this area the Forestry Commission is to proceed with the acquisition and planting of suitable tracts as they become available and are required. Above its lake, Ennerdale has been largely planted. Thornthwaite forest (Pl. 9) occupies much of the slopes above lake Bassenthwaite, and Grizedale forest the hill country between Coniston Water and Thirlmere, while on the margins of the highland to the northeast (Greystoke) and southwest (Blingdale and Irton) are other extensive blocks of plantations. Planting is rarely carried out above 1,200 feet, and the most favoured trees are spruce and larch, which thrive better under the prevailing wet conditions than does Scots pine. Recently the agreement has been somewhat modified by consent to allow temporary replacement of existing deciduous woodlands by conifers as a preliminary to the re-establishment of hardwoods. In the heart of the Lake District the National Forest Park of Hardknott was established in 1943 as an experiment in harmonising the various interests.

The Lake District is now under a single Planning Board, and has been scheduled as a National Park so that the various forms of land use and developments that change the landscape will be controlled. So far as possible the principle of multiple use will be applied, but where uses are incompatible land will be allocated to the respective uses, with an over-riding control in the interests of preservation of natural amenity. Meantime the acquisition of land by the National Trust proceeds, and in no part of the country is there such a density and extent of dedicated properties. The Trust now owns nearly 50 square miles in the area, and a further 30 square miles are protected by restrictive covenants. It owns nearly 50 farms and more than 100 cottages. Increasingly the Lake District is conforming to its principal function as a National Park.

SELECTED REFERENCES

PART I

CHAPTER 2

T. Eastwood's *Northern England* (2nd edition, 1946), in the Geological Survey series *British Regional Geology*, summarises the geology of an area almost co-extensive with that treated here, but Cleveland is excluded. It contains a catalogue of the published geological maps, and a comprehensive bibliography. The special district memoirs of the Geological Survey that relate to sheets of the 1-inch-to-1-mile maps contain detailed descriptions of the areas covered, but large portions of North England, including the Northumberland and Durham coalfield, have not yet been described in sheet memoirs. Two of the more recent memoirs, however, cover the area of the West Cumberland coalfield : T. Eastwood, *The Geology of the Maryport District* (Sheet 22) (1930) ; *The Geology of the Whitehaven and Workington District* (Sheet 28) (1931).

The *Transactions of the North of England Institution of Mining Engineers* from 1852 contain a wealth of detailed information about the geology of the coalfields and the other mineral resources of North England. From 1889 they are incorporated in the *Transactions of the Federated Institution of Mining Engineers*. The special reports of the Geological Survey on the mineral resources of Great Britain also contain much valuable material. Additional and more up-to-date data concerning some of these resources was provided in war-time pamphlets. Pamphlet 23 (1942), by Dr W. Anderson, on the Jurassic Iron Ores of the Cleveland District, merits special mention, and the new material relating to the Northern Pennines contained in other war-time pamphlets has been brought together in a post-war memoir : K. C. Dunham, *The Geology of the Northern Pennine Ore Field* (1948). Authoritative summaries of the economic geology are also to be found in two post-war surveys of industrial facilities : *The North East Coast* (North-eastern Industrial and Development Association, Newcastle upon Tyne, 1949), and *Cumberland* (Cumberland Development Council, Whitehaven, 1951).

The 1/625,000 Planning Maps of Great Britain in two sheets, published by the Ordnance Survey, include maps of Solid Geology, Coal and Iron, and Limestone. North England appears on the northern sheet, with Scotland.

Special attention should be drawn to the *Proceedings of the Geologists' Association*, **42** (1931) in which Part 3 (pp. 217–96) is entirely devoted to contributions to the geology of Northumberland and Durham. Among other works, the following deserve individual reference :

Barrow, G. *The Geology of North Cleveland* (1888)
Fox-Strangways, C. *The Jurassic Rocks of Great Britain*, vol. i (1892)
Marr, J. E. *The Geology of the Lake District* (1916)
Hollingworth, S. E. 'The Geology of the Lake District' *Proc. Geol. Ass.* **65** (1951), 385-402. Reviews the progress of later research and re-survey since Marr's Work and gives a detailed bibliography.
Postlethwaite, J. *Mines and Mining in the Lake District* (1913)
Trotter, F. M. and Hollingworth, S. E. 'The Alston Block' *Geol. Mag.* **65** (1928), 433–48
Woolacott, D. 'The Magnesian Limestone of Durham' *Geol. Mag.* **56** (1919), 452–65 and 485–98

CHAPTER 3

Hollingworth, S. E. 'High-level erosional platforms in Cumberland and Furness' *Proc. Yorks. Geol. Soc.* **23** (1936), 159–77
— 'The recognition and correlation of high-level erosion surfaces in Britain : a statistical study' *Quart. Journ. Geol. Soc.* **94** (1938), 55–84
Common, R. 'The geomorphology of the east Cheviot area' *Scottish Geog. Mag.* **70** (1954), 124–38
Linton, D. L. 'The origin of the Tweed drainage system' *Scottish Geog. Mag.* **49** (1933), 162–75
— 'Problems of Scottish scenery' *Scottish Geog. Mag.* **67** (1951), 65–84
Sissons, J. B. 'The origin of the drainage systems of southern Scotland and northern England'. Unpub. paper read to Inst. of Brit. Geographers, 1957
Trotter, F. M. 'The Tertiary uplift and resultant drainage of the Alston Block and adjacent areas' *Proc. Yorks. Geol. Soc.* **21** (1929), 161–80
Hollingworth, S. E. 'The evolution of the Eden drainage in the south and west' *Proc. Geol. Ass.* **40** (1929), 115–38
Marr, J. E. 'The superimposed drainage of the English Lake District' *Geol. Mag.*, Decade 3, Vol. 6 (1889), 150–5
Woolacott, D. 'The superficial deposits and pre-glacial valleys of the Northumberland and Durham coalfield' *Quart. Journ. Geol. Soc.* **61** (1905), 64–96
— 'The origin and influence of the chief physical features of Northumberland and Durham' *Geog. Journ.* **30** (1907), 36–62
Raistrick, A. 'The glaciation of Northumberland and Durham' *Proc. Geol. Ass.* **42** (1931), 281–91
Woolacott, D. 'The interglacial problem and the glacial and post-glacial sequence in Northumberland and Durham' *Geol. Mag.* **58** (1921), 21–32, 60–9
Trechmann, C. T. 'Scandinavian drift on the Durham coast' *Quart. Journ. Geol. Soc.* **71** (1915), 53–82
— 'On a deposit of interglacial loess and some transported preglacial fresh-water clays on the Durham coast' *Quart. Journ. Geol. Soc.* **75** (1919), 173–201
Carruthers, R. G. 'The northern glacial drifts ; some peculiarities and their significance' *Quart. Journ. Geol. Soc.* **98** (1942), 241–53
Radge, G. W. 'The glaciation of north Cleveland' *Proc. Yorks. Geol. Soc.* **24** (1939), 180–205
Hollingworth, S. E. 'The glaciation of western Edenside and adjacent areas and the drumlins of Edenside and the Solway basin' *Quart. Journ. Geol. Soc.* **87** (1931), 281–359
Trotter, F. M. 'The glaciation of eastern Edenside, the Alston Block, and the Carlisle plain' *Quart. Journ. Geol. Soc.* **85** (1929), 558–612
Hollingworth, S. E. 'The influence of glaciation on the topography of the Lake District' *Journ. Inst. of Water Engineers* **5** (1951), 485–96
Pearsall, W. H. 'The development of vegetation in the English Lakes, considered in relation to the general evolution of glacial lakes and rock basins' *Proc. Royal Soc.* B, **92** (1921), 259–84
Smith, B. 'The origin of the St Bees-Whitehaven gap' *Geol. Survey Summary of Progress for 1929*, iii, 37–41
Kendall, P. F. 'A system of glacier lakes in the Cleveland Hills' *Quart. Journ. Geol. Soc.* **58** (1902), 471–571
Smith, B. 'The glacier lakes of Eskdale, etc.' *Quart. Journ. Geol. Soc.* **88** (1932), 57–83
Dwerryhouse, A. R. 'The glaciation of Teesdale, Weardale, the Tyne valley, and their tributary valleys' *Quart. Journ. Geol. Soc.* **58** (1902), 572–608
Anderson, W. 'Buried valleys and late-glacial drainage systems in northwest Durham' *Proc. Geol. Ass.* **51** (1940), 274–81
Peel, R. F. 'A study of two Northumbrian spillways' *Trans. Inst. Brit. Geographers* **15** (1949), 73–89

Peel, R .F. 'The profiles of glacial drainage channels' *Geog. Journ.* **122** (1956), 483-7

Woolacott, D. 'The pre-glacial " wash " of the Northumberland and Durham coalfield' *Proc. Univ. Durham Phil. Soc.* **2** (1906), 205-13

Maling, D. H. 'The shape and nature of the pre-glacial Wear valley between Cocken and Chester-le-Street' *Proc. Univ. Durham Phil. Soc.* **12** (1954), 14-28

— 'The geomorphology of the Wear valley' Unpublished Ph.D. thesis, University of Durham

Woolacott, D. 'The superficial deposits and pre-glacial valleys of the Northumberland and Durham coalfield' *Quart. Journ. Geol. Soc.* **61** (1905), 64-96

Marr, J. E. 'The influence of the geological structure of the English Lakeland upon its present features' *Quart. Journ. Geol. Soc.* **62** (1906), 66-128

Raistrick, A. 'The glaciation of Borrowdale' *Proc. Yorks. Geol. Soc.* **20** (1925), 155-81

Gresswell, R. K. 'The glacial geomorphology of the southeastern part of the Lake District' *Liverpool and Manchester Geol. Journ.* **1** (1952), 57-70

Hay, T. 'Glaciology of the Ullswater area' *Geog. Journ.* **84** (1934), 136-48
A number of other papers by T. Hay on physiographic features of the Lake District appear in later volumes of the *Geographical Journal* between **90** (1937) and **103** (1944).

CHAPTER 4

Climate

The county reports of the Land Utilisation Survey for the four northern counties contain valuable chapters on climate by Professor Gordon Manley. Particular aspects of climate have also been treated by Professor Manley in the following papers :

'The effective rate of altitudinal change in temperate Atlantic climates' *American Geog. Rev.* **35** (1945), 408-17

'Some notes on the climate of northeast England' *Quart. Journ. Royal Met. Soc.* **61** (1935), 405-10

'The climate of the Northern Pennines' *ibid.* **62** (1936), 103-13

'Further climatological averages for the Northern Pennines' *ibid.* **69** (1943), 251-61

'Durham meteorological record, 1847-1940' *ibid.* **67** (1941), 363-80

'The occurrence of snow-cover in Great Britain' *ibid.* **65** (1939), 2-27

'Topographic features and the climate of Britain' *Geog. Journ.* **103** (1944), No. 6, 241-62

Soils

Trotter, F. M. and Hollingworth, S. E. *The geology of the Brampton district* (Memoir of Geological Survey, Sheet 18, 1932)

Bainbridge, T. H. 'The soils of Cumbria ; a preliminary study' *Empire Journ. Experimental Agric.* **7** (1939), 175-83

Vegetation

Harrison, H. H. and Temperley, G. W. 'The flora of the three northern counties' in *The Three Northern Counties of England*, ed. C. Headlam (1939)

Pearsall, W. H. and Pennington, W. 'The ecological history of the English Lake District' *Journ. of Ecology* **34** (1947), 137-49

Pearsall, W. H. *Mountains and Moorlands* (1950)

— 'The botany of the Lake District' in *British Association Scientific Survey of the Blackpool District* (1938), 134-8

Franks, J. W.   'Pollen analysis' *Agric. History Rev.* **5** (1957), Part I, 2–10
Blackburn, K. B.   'A long pollen diagram from Northumberland' *Trans. Northern Naturalists' Union* **2** (1953), 40–3
Raistrick, A. and Blackburn, K. B.   'The late-glacial and post-glacial periods in the northern Pennines' *Trans. Northern Naturalists' Union* (1931–2) 16–36, 79–103
Elgee, F.   *The Moorlands of Northeast Yorkshire; their Natural History and Origin* (1912)
Stapledon, R. G.   *The Land : Now and Tomorrow* (1935)
Ellison, W.   *Marginal Land in Britain* (1953)
Ordnance Survey 1/625,000 Planning Maps.   Vegetation (1945)
Lewis, F. J.   'The geographical distribution of vegetation in the basins of the Eden, Tees, Wear, and Tyne' *Geog. Journ.* **23** and **24** (1904), 313–31
Forestry Commission :
   National Forest Park Guides.   Hardknott (1949), *The Border* (1958)
   Census of Woodlands, 1947–9.   *Census Report No. 1* (1952)
House, J. W.   'Afforestation in Britain.   The Anglo-Scottish Borderlands' *Tydschrift voor economische en sociale geografie* **47**, No. 11 (1956), 265–76

PART II

CHAPTER 5

Details about prehistoric and Roman remains found in North England are recorded chiefly in *Archaeologia Aeliana* (1855–), the journal of the Society of Antiquaries of Newcastle upon Tyne, and in the *Transactions* (1874–) of the Cumberland and Westmorland Antiquarian and Archaeological Society.

For the prehistoric period see especially :

Raistrick, A.   'The Bronze Age settlement of the north of England' *Arch. Ael.*, 4th series, **8** (1931), 149–65
Collingwood, R. G.   'An introduction to the prehistory of Cumberland, Westmorland, and Lancashire north of the Sands' *Trans. C. and W. Antiq. and Archaeol. Soc.*, New series **33** (1933), 163–200
   (The same volume also contains Collingwood's paper on the prehistoric settlements near Crosby Ravensworth), 201–26
Elgee, F.   *Early Man in Northeast Yorkshire* (1930)
Hogg, A. H. A.   'Native settlements of Northumberland' *Antiquity* **17** (1943), 136–47
County History of Northumberland, vol. 14 (1935)

For the Roman period see :

Ordnance Survey map of *Roman Britain,* 3rd edition (1956)
Collingwood, R. G.   *Roman Britain* (1924)
— *The Archaeology of Roman Britain* (1930)
— and Myres, J. N. L.   *Roman Britain and the English Settlements* (1936)
Richmond, I. A.   *Roman Britain* (1947)
— *Roman Britain* (Pelican Books 1955)
— 'The Romans in Redesdale' *County History of Northumberland,* vol. 15, 63–159
The standard work on Hadrian's Wall is J. Collingwood Bruce, *Handbook to the Roman Wall,* 10th edition, revised by I. A. Richmond (1947).   See also E. Birley, *The Centenary Pilgrimage of Hadrian's Wall* (1949), and I. A. Richmond, 'Hadrian's Wall, 1939–49' *Journal of Roman Studies* **40** (1950), 43–56

CHAPTER 6

The *Victoria County History*, an essential work of reference for the other counties, does not exist for Northumberland. Instead there is the monumental *County History of Northumberland*, edited by M. H. Dodds. This is still incomplete, but since 1893 fifteen volumes, each dealing with a group of parishes, have been published. They carry on the work begun by John Hodgson, whose uncompleted *History of Northumberland* appeared in seven volumes between 1820 and 1858.

Among earlier county histories for North England, those by William Hutchinson (*Northumberland*, 2 vols. (1778), *Durham*, 3 vols. (1785-94), and *Cumberland*, 2 vols. (1794)) are especially noteworthy, and provided the basis for many other nineteenth-century volumes of county history.

The Anglian and Norse colonisation

O.S. 1:1 million map of Britain in the Dark Ages (1935)
Collingwood, W. G.   'The first English in Northumberland' *Vasculum* **11** (1925), 34-9
Collingwood, W. G. and Myres, J. N. L.   *Roman Britain and the English Settlements* (1936)
Myres, J. N. L.   'The Teutonic settlement of northern England' *History* **20**, 75 (1935), 250-62
Collingwood, W. G.   *Scandinavian Britain* (1908)
— *Northumbrian Crosses of pre-Norman Age* (1927)
Baldwin Brown, G.   *The Arts in Early England* (1903-27)
Mawer, A. and Stenton, F. M.   *Introduction to the Survey of English Place-names* (1924)
Mawer, A.   *The Place-names of Northumberland and Durham* (1920)
— 'Early Northumbrian history in the light of its place-names' *Arch. Ael.*, 3rd series, **18** (1921), 1-18
Sedgefield, W. G.   *The Place-names of Cumberland and Westmorland* (1915)
English Place-Name Society :
    Vol. 5   Smith, A. H.   *Place-names of North Riding* (1928)
    Vol. 22   Armstrong, A. M., Mawer, A., Stenton, F. M. and Dickins, B. *Place-names of Cumberland* (1952)
    Vols. 25 and 26   Smith, A. H.   *English Place-name Elements* (1956)
Ekwall, E.   *Place-names in ' -ing '* (Lund, 1923)
    Scandinavians and Celts in the Northwest of England (Lund, 1918)
Lindkvist, H.   *Middle English Place-names of Scandinavian Origin* (Upsala, 1912)

The period after 1066

The Boldon Book, 1183, ed. W. Greenwell, Surtees Soc. Pub. 25 (1852). (A translation, with critical commentary, also appears in *V.C.H., Durham*, vol. 1)
Gray, H. L.   *English Field Systems* (1915)
Jolliffe, J. E. A.   'Northumbrian Institutions' *Eng. Hist. Rev.* **41** (1926), 1-42
Bazeley, M. L.   'The extent of English forest in the thirteenth century' *Trans. Roy. Hist. Soc.*, 4th series, **4** (1921), 140-72
Graham, T. H. B.   'Englewood' *Trans. Cumb. and West. Antiq. and Arch. Soc.*, New series, **33** (1933), 15-23.   (Contains perambulations of forests of Englewood and Allerdale, 1300)
Hedley, W. P.   'The medieval forests of Northumberland' *Arch. Ael.*, 4th series **28** (1950), 96-104
Percy Bailiffs' Rolls of the Fifteenth Century, ed. J. C. Hodgson, Surtees Soc. Pub. 134 (1921)
Survey of the Palatinate of Durham Compiled during the Episcopate of Thomas Hatfield, 1345-82, ed. W. Greenwell, Surtees Soc. Pub. 32 (1857)

Nall, W. 'The Alston Mines' Trans. North of England Inst. of Mining
    Engineers 53 (1902–3) 40–52
Cooke, A. M. 'The settlement of the Cistercians in England' Eng. Hist.
    Rev. 8 (1893), 625–76
Bradshaw, F. 'Northumberland at the end of the thirteenth century—The
    Lay Subsidy Roll of 1296' Arch. Ael., 3rd series, 13 (1916)
Ridpath, G. The Border History of England and Scotland (1848)
Hunter Blair, C. 'Wardens and deputy wardens of the Marches of England
    towards Scotland in Northumberland' Arch. Ael., 4th series, 28 (1950), 18–33
Curwen, J. F. 'Castles and fortified towers of Cumberland, Westmorland
    and Lancashire north of the Sands' Trans. Cumb. and West. Antiq. and
    Arch. Soc., Extra series, 13 (1913)
Bates, C. J. 'The Border Holds of Northumberland' Arch. Ael., New series,
    14 (1891)
Graham, T. H. B. 'The townfields of Cumberland' Trans. Cumb. and West.
    Antiq. and Arch. Soc., New series, 13 (1913), 1–30
Thorpe, H. 'The green villages of County Durham' Trans. Inst. Brit.
    Geographers, 15 (1949), 155–80
Charlton, E. Memorials of North Tynedale (1871)
Tomlinson, W. W. Life in Northumberland in the Sixteenth Century (1898)
Beresford, M. The Lost Villages of England (1954)
— 'The lost villages of northern England' in Studies in Architectural History
    (York, 1954), 115–37

CHAPTER 7

General

Pirenne, H. 'L'origine des constitutions urbaines du Moyen Age' Rev.
    Hist. 53 (1893) and 57 (1895)
Stephenson, C. Borough and Town. A study of urban origins in England (1933)
Tait, J. The Medieval English Borough (1936)
Stenton, F. W. Anglo-Saxon England (1947)

Carlisle

Jefferson, S. History of Carlisle (1838)
Ferguson, R. S. History of Carlisle (1889)
    Victoria History of the County of Cumberland (1901–05)

Durham

Hutchinson, W. History and Antiquities of the County Palatine of Durham,
    Vol. 2 (1787)
    Victoria History of the County of Durham (1905–28)

Newcastle upon Tyne

Gray, W. Chorographia : a Survey of Newcastle-upon-Tyne (1649)
Bourne, H. History of Newcastle (1736)
Brand, J. History and Antiquities of Newcastle, 2 vols. (1789)
Welford, R. History of Newcastle and Gateshead, 3 vols. (1884–7)
Charleton, R. J. Newcastle Town (1885)
Records of the Company of Merchant Adventurers of Newcastle, ed. J. W. Boyle
    and F. W. Dendy, Surtees Soc. Pubs. 93 (1898) and 101 (1899)
Records of Newcastle Hostmen's Company, ed. F. W. Dendy, Surtees Soc. Pubs.
    105 (1901)
Hearnshaw, F. J. C. Newcastle upon Tyne (1924)

Among much relevant material in publications of the local learned societies,
attention is drawn especially to two important papers in Archaeologia Aeliana :

Hinde, J. H.   'The original site and progressive extension of Newcastle'
   Arch. Ael., New series, **3** (1859), 53–64
Dodds, M. H.   'The Bishop's Boroughs' *Arch. Ael.*, 3rd series, **12** (1915), 81–185

The last-named paper, the *Victoria County Histories*, the *County History of Northumberland*, and the earlier county histories and topographies by Hutchinson, Mackenzie, Hodgson, and others contain valuable material on other towns. See also :

Garbutt, G.   *History of Monkwearmouth, Bishopwearmouth, and Sunderland* (1819)
Sharpe, C.   *History of Hartlepool* (1815)
Brewster, J.   *History and Antiquities of Stockton-upon-Tees* (1796)
Tate, G.   *History of Alnwick*, 2 vols. (1866–9)

The edition of Leland's *Itinerary* quoted is :

Leland, John   *Itinerary circ.* 1535–43, ed. L. Toulmin-Smith (1906–10), vols. 1 and 5

CHAPTER 8

General

Smailes, A. E.   ' Early industrial settlement in northeast England ' *Advancement of Science* **6** (1950), 325–31
Nef, J. U.   ' The progress of technology and the growth of large-scale industry in Great Britain, 1540–1640 ' *Econ. Hist. Rev.*, Series I, Vol. 5 (1934), No. 1, 3–24
Levy, H.   *Monopolies, Cartels, and Trusts in British Industry* (1927),
Hughes, E. *North Country Life in the Eighteenth Century*, (1952)
Clow, A. and N.   *The Chemical Revolution* (1952)

Mining and smelting in the northern Pennines and Lake District

Nall, W.   ' The Alston mines ' *Trans. North of England Inst. of Mining Engineers* **53** (1902–3) 40–52
Wallace, W.   *Alston Moor ; its Pastoral People, its Mines and Miners* (1890)
Smith, S.   ' Lead and zinc ores of Northumberland and Alston Moor ' *Special Reports on the mineral resources of Great Britain* **25** (1923)
Carruthers, R. G.   ' Lead and zinc ores of Durham, etc.' *ibid.* **26** (1923)
Eastwood, T.   ' Lead and zinc ores of the Lake District ' *ibid.* **22** (1921)
Monkhouse, F. J.   ' Some features of the historical geography of Elizabethan mining enterprise in the Lakeland ' *Geography* **28** (1943), 107–13
Collingwood, W. G.   *Elizabethan Keswick.* Cumberland and Westmorland Antiq. and Arch. Soc., Tract 8 (1912)
Postlethwaite, J.   *Mines and mining in the Lake District* (1913)
Raistrick, A.   ' The London Lead Company, 1692–1905 ' *Trans. Newcomen Soc.* **14** (1933–4), 119–48
—   *Two Centuries of Industrial Welfare : The London Lead Company* (1938)
—   ' Lead-smelting in the northern Pennines during the seventeenth and eighteenth centuries ' *Proc. Univ. of Durham Phil. Soc.* **9** (1935), 164–79

Coal mining and the coal trade

Galloway, R. L.   ' An account of some of the earliest records connected with the working of coal on the banks of the river Tyne ' *Arch. Ael.*, New series, **8** (1880), 167–97
—   *The Annals of Coal-Mining and the Coal-trade*, 2 vols. (1898 and 1904)
Green, W.   ' Chronicles and records of the northern coal-trade ' *Trans. North of England Inst. of Mining Engineers* **15** (1865–6), 175–265
Nef, J. U.   *The Rise of the British Coal-trade*, 2 vols. (1932)

Records of the Newcastle Hostmen's Company. Surtees Soc. Pub. **105** (1901)
Gardiner, Ralph *England's Grievance Discovered in Relation to the Coal-trade*
    (1655). For notes, with maps, see C. H. Spence in *Arch. Ael.*, New series,
    13 (1888), 285–302
Simpson, T. Y. 'Old mining records and plans' *Trans. Inst. of Mining
    Engineers* **81** (1930–1), 75–108
Raistrick, A. 'The steam-engine on Tyneside, 1715–78' *Trans. Newcomen
    Soc.* **17** (1937), 131–63
Forster, T. E. 'Historical notes on Wallsend colliery' *Trans. Inst. of Mining
    Engineers* **15** (1897–8), 77–86
Makey, W. H. 'The place of Whitehaven in the Irish coal-trade, 1600–1750'
    Unpublished M.A. thesis, University of London (1952)
Ford, P. 'Tobacco and coal ; a note on the economic history of Whitehaven'
    Economica **9** (1929), 192–6
Moore, R. W. 'An historical sketch of the Whitehaven collieries' *Trans.
    Inst. of Mining Engineers* **7** (1893–4), 613–42
Fletcher, Isaac 'The archaeology of the West Cumberland coal-trade'
    Trans. Cumberland and Westmorland Antiq. and Arch. Soc. **45** (1878–9)

Iron industry

Bell, W. Lothian 'On the manufacture of iron in connection with the
    Northumberland and Durham coalfield' *Trans. North of England Inst.
    of Mining Engineers* **13** (1863–4), 109–55
Fletcher, H. A. 'The archaeology of the West Cumberland iron trade'
    Trans. Cumberland and Westmorland Antiq. and Arch. Soc. **5** (1879–80),
    5–21

Other industries

McIntire, W. T. 'The salt-pans of the Solway' *Trans. Cumberland and
    Westmorland Antiq. and Arch. Soc.*, New series, **42** (1942), 1–12
Pilbin, P. 'A geographical analysis of the sea-salt industry of northeast
    England' *Scottish Geog. Mag.* **51** (1935), 22–8
— 'The influence of local geography on the glass industry of Tyneside'
    Journ. Tyneside Geog. Soc., New series, **1** (1936), 31–45
— 'The external relations of the Tyneside glass industry' *Econ. Geog.* **13**
    (1937), 301–14
Clephan, J. 'The manufacture of glass in England ; the rise of the art on the
    Tyne' *Arch. Ael.*, New series, **8** (1880), 108–26
Buckley, F. 'Potteries on the Tyne and other northern potteries during the
    eighteenth century' *Arch. Ael.*, 4th series, **4** (1927), 68–82
Tomlinson, W. W. 'Seaton Sluice' *Arch. Ael.*, New series **24** (1903), 229–43
Baldwin, C. E. *The History and Development of the Port of Blyth* (1929)

CHAPTER 9

The principal contemporary authorities are :

Young, Arthur *A Six Months' Tour through the North of England, 1770*, vol. ii,
    Letters 14 and 15 ; vol. iii, Letters 15 and 16

Special reports to the Board of Agriculture :

Pringle, A. *A General View of the Agriculture of Westmorland* (1793)
Bailey, J. *A General View of the Agriculture of Durham* (1794)
Bailey, J. and Culley, G. *A General View of the Agriculture of Northumberland*
    (1794)
— *A General View of the Agriculture of Cumberland* (1794)
Tuke, J. *A General View of the Agriculture of the North Riding* (1794)

Eden, F. M.   *The State of the Poor* (1797), vol. ii : Parochial reports
Brand, J.   *History and Antiquities of Newcastle upon Tyne* (1789)
Baillie, J.   *An Impartial History of Newcastle* (1801)
Gibson, J.   *Plan of the Collieries of the Rivers Tyne and Wear, with the Country Eleven Miles round Newcastle* (1787)
Casson, W.   *Plan of the Rivers Tyne and Wear* (1804)
Holmes, J. H.   *Treatise on the Coal-mines of Northumberland and Durham* (1816)
Garbutt, G.   *Historical and Descriptive View of Monkwearmouth, Bishopwearmouth and Sunderland* (1819)
Brewster, J.   *History and Antiquities of Stockton* (1796)
Donald, T.   *The County of Cumberland Surveyed, 1770–1* (1783)
Hutchinson, W.   *History and Antiquities of Northumberland*, 2 vols. (1778)
— *History and Antiquities of Northumberland*, 3 vols. (1785–94)
— *History and Antiquities of Cumberland*, 2 vols. (1794)
Graves, J.   *History of Cleveland* (1808)
Sharpe, C.   *History of Hartlepool* (1816)
West, R.   *Guide to the Lakes* (1778). By 1812 ten editions had appeared.
Wordsworth, W.   *A Guide through the District of the Lakes* (1835). Latest edition 1951. In somewhat different form this work first appeared in 1816. It is of exceptional interest to modern geographers to note the headings under which Wordsworth undertook his ' description of the scenery of the Lakes '. The first section is ' a view of the country as formed by nature ', and this is followed by ' the aspect of the country as affected by its inhabitants '.

Other authorities

Slater, G.   *The English Peasantry and the Enclosure of Common Fields* (1907)
Leonard, E. M.   ' Inclosure of Common Fields in the seventeenth century ' *Trans. Roy. Hist. Soc.* **19** (1905), 101–46
Bainbridge, T. H.   ' Eighteenth century agriculture in Cumbria ' *Trans. Cumb. and West. Antiq. and Arch. Soc.*, New series, **42** (1942), 56–66
Garnett, F. W.   *Westmorland Agriculture, 1800–1900* (1912)
Stroud, Dorothy   *Capability Brown, 1716–83* (1950)
Hussey, C.   ' Gibside, Co. Durham ' *Country Life* (8 February 1952), 354–7
Pevsner, N.   *The Buildings of England, Co. Durham* (1953)
— *The Buildings of England, Northumberland* (1957)
Hinde, J. H.   ' The Old North Road ' *Arch. Ael.*, New series, **3** (1858), 237
Jervoise, A.   *The Ancient Bridges of the North of England* (1931)
Nicholson, N.   *The Lakers* (1955)

CHAPTER 10

Smailes, A. E.   ' The development of the Northumberland and Durham coalfield ' *Scottish Geog. Mag.* **51** (1935), 201–14
— ' Population changes in the colliery districts of Northumberland and Durham ' *Geog. Journ.* **91** (1938), 220–32
House, J. W.   *North-eastern England. Population Movements and the Landscape since the Early Nineteenth Century* (King's College, Newcastle, 1954)
Tomlinson, W. W.   *The North-Eastern Railway: its Rise and Development* (1914)
Smiles, Samuel   *Lives of the Engineers. George and Robert Stephenson* (1904)
Redford, A.   *Labour Migration in England, 1800–50* (1926)
Fynes, R.   *The Miners of Northumberland and Durham* (1923)
Mackenzie, E.   *History of Northumberland* (1825)
Mackenzie, E. and Ross, M.   *History of Durham* (1834)
   Mackenzie's works contain detailed enumerations of the industrial establishments at each place.

Dunn, Matthias   *The Coal Trade of the North of England* (1844)
  A Treatise on the Winning and Working of Collieries (1848)
Fordyce, W.   *History of Coal and Coalfields* (1860)
Webb, S. and Webb, B.   *The Story of the Durham Miners, 1662–1921* (1921)
Hall, T. Y.   'The Northern Coalfield (with map and list of collieries)' *Trans.
  North of England Inst. of Mining Engineers* **2** (1853–4), 103–226
— 'Rivers, ports and harbours of the Northern Coalfield' (with plans),
  ibid. 10 (1861), 41–72
Reports of the Royal Commission on Coal, 1871
Industrial Resources of the Tyne, Wear and Tees (1864), ed. W. G. Armstrong
British Association : Report of the Meeting at Newcastle upon Tyne, 1863
Clapham, R. C.   *An Account of the Commencement of Soda Manufacture on
  the Tyne* (1869)
Meade, R.   *Coal and Iron Industries of the United Kingdom* (1882)
Handbook to the Industries of Newcastle and District (1889), ed. W. Richardson
Guthrie, J.   *The River Tyne, its History and Resources* (1880)
Johnson, R. W.   *The Making of the Tyne* (1895)
Richardson, W.   *History of Wallsend* (1923)
Dodd, J. J.   *History of Spennymoor* (1897)
Sharpe, C.   *History of Hartlepool* (1851); supplement to 1816 edition
Potts, T.   *History of Sunderland* (1892)
Baldwin, C. E.   *History and Development of the Port of Blyth* (1929)
Ord, J.   *History of Cleveland* (1846)
Marley, J.   'The Cleveland Ironstone' *Trans. N. of England Inst. of Mining
  Engineers* **5** (1856–7), 165–219
Gjers, J.   'Historical sketch of the rise and progress of the Cleveland iron
  trade' *Trans. Chesterfield Inst. Engineers* **3** (1875), 63–75
Head, J.   'Recent developments in the Cleveland iron and steel industry'
  Proc. Inst. Mech. Engineers **45** (1893), 224–77
Marley, J.   'The discovery of rock-salt at Middlesbrough' *Trans. N. of
  England Inst. of Mining Engineers* **13** (1863–4), 17–22
— 'The Cleveland and south Durham salt industry' *Trans. Inst. of Mining
  Engineers* **1** (1889–90), 339–73
Stuart, T. W.   'The Tees salt industry' *Trans. Inst. of Mining Engineers* **3**
  (1891–2), 632–3
Whelan, W.   *History and Topography of Cumberland and Westmorland* (1860)
Bainbridge, T. H.   'Barrow in Furness' *Econ. Geog.* **15** (1839), 379–83
— 'Cumberland population movements, 1871–81' *Geog. Journ.* **108** (1946),
  80–4
— 'Population changes over the West Cumberland coalfield' *Econ. Geog.*
  25 (1949), 128–33
Richardson, B. W.   *Thomas Sopwith* (1891)
Steavenson, A. L.   'The Carboniferous Limestone quarries of Weardale'
  Trans. Inst. of Mining Engineers **22** (1901–2), 115–23

PART III

CHAPTERS 11–18

Most references have already been given under the several aspects dealt with
in the chapters of Parts I and II. There follow here some additional references
which are more appropriately or conveniently related to the contemporary
regional geography treated in Part III.

General

Fawcett, C. B.   'North-East England' in *Great Britain. Essays in regional
  geography*, ed. A. G. Ogilvie (1930), 332–48
Campbell, F. J.   'Cumbria' *ibid.*, 349–67

Daysh, G. H. J. and Caesar, A. A. L.   'The North-East Region of England' in *Studies in Regional Planning*, ed. G. H. J. Daysh (1951)
Daysh, G. H. J.   'Cumberland' ibid.
Hanley, J. A., Boyd, A. L., and Williamson, W.   *An Agricultural Survey of the Northern Province* (1936).   Deals with the four northernmost counties of England.
Sykes, E. Clucas   'The agricultural geography of Northumberland' *Geography* **18** (1933), 269–80.   A valuable summary.
The Three Northern Counties of England, ed. C. Headlam (1939)
The Land of Britain, ed. L. Dudley Stamp.   The Report of the Land Utilisation Survey of Britain.   Part 47, County Durham (1941); Part 49, Cumberland (1943); Part 50, Westmorland (1943); Part 51, Yorkshire, North Riding (1945); Part 52, Northumberland (1945).

The industrial areas (*chapters* 11–13)

'A scientific survey of North-Eastern England.'   British Association, Newcastle upon Tyne (1949)
Publications of the North East Industrial and Development Association :
    A Physical Land-Classification of Northumberland, Durham and the North Riding (1950)
    The North-East Coast; A Survey of Industrial Facilities (1949).   Compare the earlier industrial surveys made for the Board of Trade (1932) and the North-East Development Board (1936)
    The Northern Region.   Reviews of Employment 1946, 1947, 1950, 1952, 1954, 1956, 1958
    Migration—a Study of Movement of Population and its Effects on the North-east (1950)
    West Durham—a Problem Area, by G. H. J. Daysh and J. S. Symonds (1953)
Ministry of Labour Reports of investigations into industrial conditions in certain depressed areas, No. 2, *Durham and Tyneside* (1934)
Ministry of Fuel and Power.   Regional Survey Reports :
    The Durham Coalfield (1945)
    The Northumberland and Cumberland Coalfields (1945)
Uhlig, H.   *Die Kulturlandschaft.   Methoden der Forschung und das Beispiel. Nordostenengland* (Köln, 1956).
Hedley, A. M.   *A Mineral Survey of Coal-mines in Southwest Durham* (1936)
Sharp, T.   *A Derelict Area ; the Southwest Durham Coalfield* (1935)
Temple, A.   'The derelict mining villages of southwest Durham'.   Unpublished M. Litt. thesis, University of Durham (1940)
Beaver, S. H.   'Coke manufacture in Great Britain' *Trans. Inst. Brit. Geographers* **17** (1951), 133–48
Manley, G.   'The City of Durham' *Geography* **23** (1938), 147–55
Sylvester, D.   'Durham City' *Sociological Review* **36** (1944), 67–75
Sharp, T.   *Cathedral City—a Plan for Durham* (1945)
Edwards, K. C.   'The New Towns of Britain' *Nottingham University Survey* **6** (1956), 7–19
Wilkinson, Ellen   *The Town that was Murdered.   Jarrow* (1939)
Mess, H. A.   *Industrial Tyneside, a Social Survey* (1928)
Middlebrook, S.   *Newcastle upon Tyne, its Growth and Achievement* (1950)
Johnson, R. W. and Aughton, R.   *The River Tyne*.   Official handbook (1930)
Middlesbrough Survey and Plan, ed. M. Lock (1947).   See especially A. E. Smailes, 'The geographical setting', 63–81, and 'The economic structure and development of Tees-side and Cleveland', 81–105
The social background of a plan (*Middlesbrough*), ed. Ruth Glass (1948)
Lock, M.   *The Hartlepools.   A Survey and Plan* (1949)
Daysh, G. H. J. and Watson, E.   *Cumberland, a survey of industrial facilities* (Cumberland Development Council, 1951).   Compare the earlier survey of West Cumberland, 1938

313

The rural areas (chapters 14–18)

Bainbridge, T. H.   ' Carlisle, a geographical analysis ' *Journ. Tyneside Geog. Soc.*, New Series **1** (1937) 102–11

Houston, H.   ' The Till Valley : A study of a Border Area ' *Scottish Geog. Soc. Mag.* **43** (1927), 78–91

The Border.   National Forest Park Guide (H.M.S.O. 1958)

Sharp, T.   ' Forest villages in Northumberland ' *Town Planning Rev.* **26** (1955), 165–70

House, J. W.   *Bellingham and Wark, a Comparative Survey* (North Tyne Survey Committee, 1951)

— *Population Structure and Employment Conditions* (North Tyne Survey Committee, 1952)

House, J. W. and Dow, R.   *The West Tyne Rural Problem* (North Tyne Survey Committee, 1954)

Smailes, A. E.   ' The Lead Dales of the Northern Pennines ' *Geography* **21** (1936), 120–9

' The dales of Northeast England '.   Unpublished M.A. thesis, University of London (1933)

Collingwood, W. G.   *The Lake Counties* (1932)

Symonds, H. H.   *Afforestation in the Lake District* (1936)

PLATES

Plate 1 (*top*) THE PENNINE ESCARPMENT and the ' Bottom ' of Westmorland at the head of the vale of Eden. In the foreground, drumlin country, a patchwork of farmlands enclosed by stone walls. (See Fig. 10.)

Plate 2 (*bottom*) THE CHEVIOT. View up the Harthope burn glen into the heart of the Cheviot massif. (See Fig. 58.) Note the ragged pattern of bracken and grass clothing the gravel-strewn valley floor, the steep valley-sides, and the smoothly rounded summits.

Plate 3 (*top*) THE COQUET VALLEY AND THE SIMONSIDE HILLS. View southeast across the southern part of the sub-Cheviot depression towards the Fell Sandstone escarpment. The hamlet of Harbottle, on the Coquet, appears in the middle of the picture ; undulating grasslands at about 500 feet, interspersed with fragments of woodland. (See Fig. 58.)

Plate 4 (*bottom*) KIELDER FOREST, NORTH TYNEDALE. Kielder 'Castle' (at 650 feet) in the foreground, with the new forestry settlement near by on the dale-floor, and plantation blocks covering the dale-side above. (See Fig. 59.)

Plate 5 (*top*) ALLENDALE. View across a side valley near Allendale Town. The incised valley of the Shield burn is marked by the strip of woodland across the picture ; and on the even skyline (above 1,000 feet) there is a conifer plantation. In the foreground, typical stone buildings (Forster-stead, above 800 feet), and other scattered farmsteads on the hillside opposite. Pastures enclosed by stone-walls, with mown hay drying in ' pikes ' in some fields on the right.

Plate 6 (*bottom*) NENTHEAD. View down Nentdale from near its head, showing the old smelt-mill above the village of Nenthead (about 1,500 feet). Note the even skyline of the Pennine summit-plateau. (See Figs. 60–2.)

Plate 7 (*top*) THE HEAD OF WEARDALE. View from Killhope Law looking down Weardale. Note the open, partly drift-filled valley cut below the smooth summit-plateau surface. The enclosed farmlands, framed by moorlands, begin in the middle of the picture. (See Figs. 14 and 60.)

Plate 8 (*bottom*) THE TYNE CORRIDOR AT HALTWHISTLE. In the foreground, Haltwhistle, sited on a river terrace, and on the right the bridge of the Alston Branch railway. Beyond the haughs of the South Tyne are the terrace margins on the south side of the valley ; and below the smooth skyline of Plenmeller Fell are extensive conifer plantations. (See Figs. 63 and 64.)

Plate 9 (*top*) GRISEDALE PIKE AND THORNTHWAITE FOREST. View south from the Whinlatter road towards Grisedale Pike (2,593 feet), a typical summit in the Skiddaw slate country. The conifer plantations are part of Thornthwaite Forest, one of the State forests of the periphery of the Lake District. (See Fig. 66.)

Plate 10 (*bottom*) DERWENTWATER AND SKIDDAW. View looking north from Ashness (packhorse bridge) across Derwentwater to Skiddaw, with Keswick lying at the end of the lake beneath the steep, but smooth, slopes of Skiddaw. In the middle distance, on the right, Falcon Crag (Borrowdale Volcanic rocks).

Plate 11 (*top*) WATENDLATH. An isolated Lakeland hamlet, at about 850 feet, by the tarn in the Watendlath valley above Derwentwater. The craggy hillside opposite, typical of the volcanic country, is Grange Fell, with a track leading over towards Borrowdale. Note the 'inby' pastures, enclosed by stone walls.

Plate 12 (*bottom*) BUTTERMERE. Air-view southeast showing the farmlands of the dale-head in Warnscale Bottom, enclosed by mountains in the heart of the Lake District. In the foreground, the alluvial flats that now separate Crummock Water from Buttermere; other delta flats jut out into the lake. Note the hanging side-valleys between rocky ridges.

Plate 13 (*top*) TROUTBECK, NEAR WINDERMERE. The hummocky moraine surface of the dale floor and the steep flanks are grass farmland, with occasional conifer plantations, and streaks of woodland along the beck and in side gills.

Plate 14 (*bottom*) WINDERMERE. Air-view south from near Bowness, with Belle Is. in the foreground. Note the softly rounded, well-wooded, Silurian hill country that is typical of the southern portion of the Lake District.

Plate 15 (*top*) KENTDALE, WESTMORLAND. The poor pastures on the ill-drained, drift-covered floor of the trough-like glaciated valley are rush infested. In the foreground, a herd of hardy, black Galloway cattle, a breed popular on upland farms in North England. On the craggy fellside note the reversion of enclosed land, with colonisation by bracken and scrub.

Plate 16 (*bottom*) RAVENSTONEDALE, WESTMORLAND. The limestone fells that join the Lake District mountains to the Pennines, with the valley of the Lune followed by the Darlington-Tebay railway. Below the moorland edge note the field pattern, sharply brought out under snow cover by the lines of the stone walls that enclose the pastures.

Plate 17 (*top*) HADRIAN'S WALL, near Housesteads, looking east. The wall here surmounts the crags of the Whin Sill escarpment on the north side of the Tyne Corridor, presenting the most impressive stretch of its course. To the north lie the wastes of the Border Fells. (See Figs. 18, 63, and 64.)

Plate 18 (*bottom*) WILLIMONTSWYKE, a pele tower in the Tyne Corridor opposite Bardon Mill. The present farm-buildings incorporate the tower that was the home of the Ridleys and reputed birthplace of the martyr Bishop.

Plate 19 (*above*) BAMBURGH CASTLE. The Norman castle (restored in the nineteenth century), successor to the Anglian ' burh ' of Dinguardi, occupies a rocky headland of the Whin Sill on the Northumbrian coast opposite the Farne Is. (See Figs. 20 and 58.)

Plate 20 (*below*) PRUDHOE ON TYNE. The medieval castle, on the south side of the Tyne valley near the western edge of the coalfield, overlooks the haughs that are now occupied by modern chemical works alongside the Newcastle–Carlisle railway.

Plates 21 and 22 'GREEN' VILLAGES ON OPPOSITE SIDES OF THE PENNINES. (*above*) Milburn, north of Appleby, lies at the foot of the Pennine escarpment. (*below*) Heighington, northwest of Darlington, is situated on the limestone plateau of Durham. Whereas at Heighington the church occupies a site within the green, at Milburn the church is one of the buildings that enclose the elongated green.

Plates 23 *and* 24 TRADITIONAL BUILDING FORMS IN NORTH ENGLAND. (*top*) An old cottage at Kirk Merrington (Co. Durham) typical of the coalfield and coastal lowland of Northeast England. The walls are of roughly-dressed freestone, with a roof of pantiles. (*bottom*) Farm-buildings at Cracoe, near the lower end of Ullswater—byres (both walls and roof of stone) with hay-loft, and attached gin-house, features typical of North England farmsteads within the altitudinal zone of cattle-keeping and corn-growing.

Plate 25 (*top*) ALNWICK. Beneath the castle of the Percies, the market-town has grown up on the south side of the river Aln. In the background, across the river, is North Demesne, the deer park.

Plate 26 (*bottom*) COCKERMOUTH. The market-town (birthplace of Wordsworth) has grown alongside the medieval castle, which occupies the fork site at the confluence of the rivers Cocker and Derwent. Note the widening of the axial street as a market-place.

Plate 27 (*above*) WHITEHAVEN. The artificial harbour within breakwaters, and the core of the town, showing the regular layout of Lowther's new town of the seventeenth century.

Plates 28, 29, *and* 30 MINING SETTLEMENT IN NORTHEAST ENGLAND.

Plate 28 (*below*) ASHINGTON, NORTHUMBERLAND. A colliery 'town' typical of modern large-scale mining operations, with mass housing in terraces to accommodate workers employed at the large colliery alongside. (See Fig. 42c.)

Plate 29 (*above*)   OLD MINERS' ROW AT SEATON DELAVAL, NORTHUMBERLAND, with kitchen-gardens dotted with untidy sheds ('crees'), alongside the colliery wagonways and overshadowed by pitheaps.

Plate 30 (*below*)   NINETEENTH-CENTURY TERRACE-HOUSING in brick, with slate roofs. Note the ranks of terrace-housing on the hillside, the backyards, the access roads that are mere dirt tracks, and, in the foreground, the 'crees'. The scene is at Skinningrove, in the Cleveland orefield (see Fig. 54), but the features noted are equally characteristic of colliery settlements.

Plate 31 (*top*) AN OLD PRINT showing a colliers' row at Longbenton (southeast Northumberland). Note the typical features of terrace-housing with pantile roofs, outhouses across a back-lane, and pithead in proximity.

Plate 32 (*bottom*) AN EIGHTEENTH-CENTURY PRINT showing wagonway (operated by horse and gravity), wooden staith, and keel on the river Tyne.

Plates 33, 34, 35, *and* 36 SOME FEATURES OF THE INDUSTRIAL LANDSCAPES OF NORTH ENGLAND. (*top*) Shipyard at Walker on Tyne. View across the Tyne from Bill Quay to the Vickers-Armstrong shipyard. (See Fig. 45.) (*bottom*) Staiths on Tyneside. The picture shows collier vessels loading at staiths in Northumberland Dock on the north side of the Tyne below Wallsend. (See Fig. 45.)

Plate 35 (*top*) SKINNINGROVE IRON AND STEEL WORKS. This outlying smelting centre lies on the Cleveland orefield near the mouth of Kilton beck. The farmland of the drift-covered coastal plateau is seen in the foreground and on Warsett Hill behind. Note the distinctive silhouette of the blast furnaces and rolling mills, and the extensive spoilheaps. (See Fig. 54.)

Plate 36 (*bottom*) CALDER HALL AND WINDSCALE, CUMBERLAND. Here, on the Cumberland coastal plain, are the oldest and newest of man's contributions to the distinctive features of the landscape of North England. In the foreground is a prehistoric stone circle and, behind, are the giant structures of the Calder Hall nuclear power station (right) and the Windscale plutonium factory (left). (See pp. 236, 241.)

Plate 37 (*top*) SUNDERLAND. Air-view from the southwest towards the mouth of the Wear. In the foreground, Bishopwearmouth ; in the background, the modern breakwaters protecting the harbour entrance, and, on the right, coal-shipping docks. Note, farther up the estuary, shipyards and the bridges. (See Figs. 48 and 49.)

Plate 38 (*bottom*) TEES-SIDE. Air-view of the south side of the Tees estuary, the modern seat of the iron and steel industry. Below the great bend at Cargo Fleet extensive reclaimed tidal mud-flats are partly occupied by industry. In the foreground, North Ormesby in east Middlesbrough, just east of Middlesbrough Dock ; beyond, the steel works at Cargo Fleet ; the more distant steel towns, South Bank and Grangetown, are screened by the smoke pall. (See Figs. 51 and 53.)

Plate 39 (*above*) LOWER TYNESIDE. The shipbuilding towns of Hebburn (foreground) and Wallsend (across the river). The riverside works, with berths and fabricating sheds conspicuous, are immediately backed by terrace-housing. In the left foreground are ballast hills, prominent features of lower Tyneside, relics of the old days when returning colliers dumped their ballast on the river banks.

Plate 40 (*below*) DURHAM CITY. Compare with Plate 46 and Figure 44. The main features of these maps are clearly distinguishable on this air photograph. Note the steep wooded sides of the Wear valley in its great loop. At opposite ends of the weir below Prebends' Bridge (foreground) are the ruins of a corn mill and a fulling mill.

Gateshead Church | High Level Br. 1849 | Swing Br. 1876 | new Tyne Br. 1928 | Castle Keep | St. Nicholas' Cathedral | All Saints

Plate 41 (*above*) NEWCASTLE AND THE TYNE BRIDGES. View looking upstream from below Gateshead. Modern bridges span the valley high above the Quayside, but at the low level, on the site of the Old Tyne Bridge, is the Swing Bridge. Immediately behind the Castle Keep and All Saints Church are elevated railway tracks. Compare with Figures 25 and 26, and Plates 43 and 44.

Plate 42 (*below*) NEWCASTLE. View south from Grey's Monument (on the site of the old north wall) down Grey Street towards the river and Gateshead. The uniform, classical façades of Grey Street are typical of Grainger's reconstruction of the city centre in the eighteen-thirties. (See Fig. 26.) In the background note the cuesta formed by the hard sandstones that overlie the High Main coal.

All Saints | Gateshead Church | Tyne Bridge | G a t e s h e a d   F e l l | Castle Keep | St. Nicholas' Cathedral

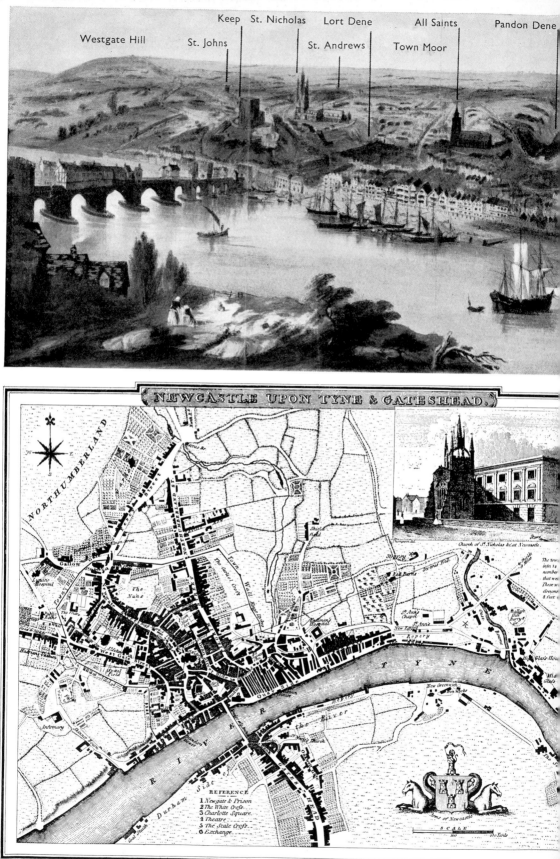

Westgate Hill   St. Johns   Keep   St. Nicholas   St. Andrews   Lort Dene   Town Moor   All Saints   Pandon Dene

NEWCASTLE UPON TYNE & GATESHEAD.

Church of St Nicholas &c. at Newcastle.

REFERENCE
1 Newgate & Prison
2 The White Cross
3 Charlotte Square
4 Theatre
5 The Scale Cross
6 Exchange

Arms of Newcastle.

SCALE

Engraved by J.Roper, from a Drawing by G.Cole.

London, Published for the Proprietors, by Vernor, Hood & Sharpe, Poultry, Feb.y 1.st 1808.

to accompany the th

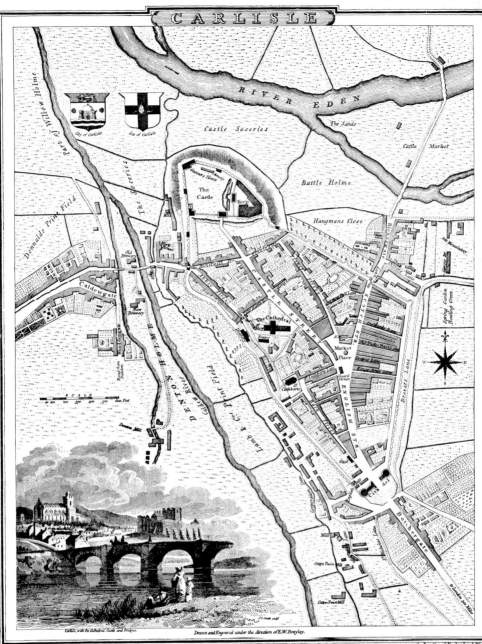

Plate 43 (*opposite, top*) NEWCASTLE at the end of the sixteenth century. This panorama, reproduced from an old picture, shows the hilly site, with deep denes, occupied by the walled city at the north end of the Old Tyne Bridge. Compare with Figures 25 and 26 and Plates 41 and 44.

Plate 44 (*opposite, bottom*) NEWCASTLE at the beginning of the nineteenth century. Extra-mural suburbs have begun to spread outside the gates, but within the walls there are still considerable open spaces. Note the persistence of the medieval skeletal plan (cf. Fig. 25), the crowded buildings in the 'chares' behind the Quayside, and the industrial works (especially glasshouses) downstream near the mouth of the Ouseburn. Compare Figure 26 and Plates 41 and 42 which show the modern city.

Plate 45 (*above*) CARLISLE at the beginning of the nineteenth century. The essential features of the walled medieval city (described in Ch. VII) persist, though suburbs are developing outside the gates. Note on the north the braided course of the river Eden across the holms, and the industrial works outside the city along the river Caldew. The inset view is from the northeast. Compare Figure 57 which shows the modern city.

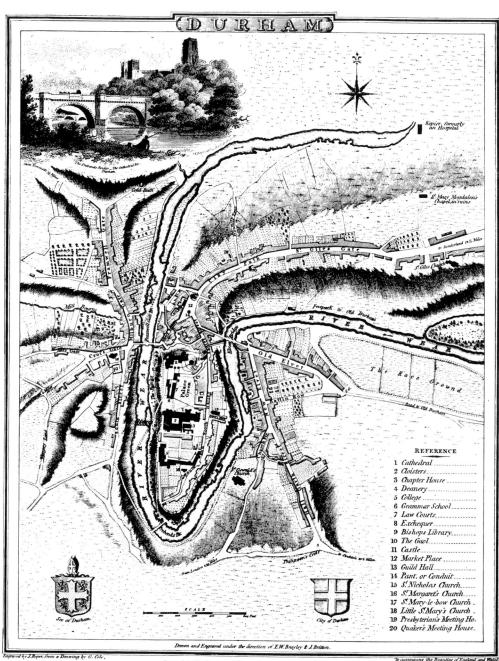

DURHAM

Engraved by J.Roper, from a Drawing by G.Cole.

London: Published for the Proprietors, by Vernor & Hood, Poultry, Dec.r 1.st 1803.

To accompany the Beauties of England and Wales.

REFERENCE

1 Cathedral
2 Cloisters
3 Chapter House
4 Deanery
5 College
6 Grammar School
7 Law Courts
8 Exchequer
9 Bishops Library
10 The Gaol
11 Castle
12 Market Place
13 Guild Hall
14 Pant, or Conduit
15 St Nicholas Church
16 St Margaret's Church
17 St Mary-le-bow Church
18 Little St Mary's Church
19 Presbyterian's Meeting Ho.
20 Quaker's Meeting House.

See of Durham

City of Durham

Drawn and Engraved under the direction of E.W.Brayley & J.Britton.

Plate 46 DURHAM at the beginning of the nineteenth century. The features of the medieval city described in Chapter VII are clearly distinguishable. The inset view is from the south, with Prebends' Bridge. The summit of the peninsula (Palace Green, 210 feet) lies more than one hundred feet above the river Wear. Compare the modern city as it appears on Plate 40 and in Figure 44.

INDEX

22